The Ham Radio Handbook

By

Donald L. Stoner, W6TNS

The National Amateur Radio Association
16541 Redmond Way, Suite 232
Redmond, WA 98052

For versions of this work customized for specific markets and applications, contact the publisher, The National Amateur Radio Association.

Single reprints of the Introduction Chapter are available at no cost. Quantity reprints of this material, for distribution by clubs, manufacturers and Amateur Radio dealers are available at nominal cost. Contact the publisher for more information.

Purchasers of this book may register as Associate Members in the National Amateur Radio Association at no charge. See page 200.

Second Printing 1991
Cover — Photos courtesy of Evelyn Garrison, WS7A, ICOM America, Inc.
        Composition — Patricia Meeks, KS7L.

9 8 7 6   5   4   3   2

Table of Contents

Foreword

I'm a pretty "upfront" sorta guy and I won't try to kid you. Earning an Amateur license may not be the easiest challenge you have ever faced. In the following chapters, you will be confronted with terms you have never heard before and concepts that may be totally alien. However, the rewards of earning an Amateur license far outweigh the value of the time you expend studying for the ham test.

Actually, without the Morse code hurdle, passing the Amateur test is relatively easy. In fact, you can do so simply by memorizing the answers to the questions you will find in the various chapters of this book. It's not cheating, but it will leave you feeling vaguely discontented each morning when you look in the mirror to shave or put on your makeup.

The new Technician class license, without a Morse requirement, appeals to people who are not technically inclined. Hopefully, The Ham Radio Handbook will also. I've tried to make the text understandable to the "non-techies" who constitute the average reader.

Who is the average reader of this book? It's anyone who is interested in obtaining a ham license. One could not conceive of a better hobby for young people. It doesn't matter who you are or what you look like. To someone on the other end of a radio communications circuit, you are just one of many interesting people that congregate on the Amateur bands. Want to make new friends? If so, ham radio is for you. And young ladies — want to meet young men? Get a ham license and you'll receive more attention than someone wearing a string bikini.

Are you a boater? No matter where your vessel is located, on the face of the globe, you can be in contact with an Amateur. Radio conditions may not be optimum to work a commercial shore station or the Coast Guard. But with a ham rig connected to your backstay, you are never out of radio contact with someone, somewhere in the world.

Ham radio is the most ideal hobby ever "invented" for retired persons. First, it is infinitely more reliable than CB in your camper or van. When you want help, you don't need whistles and static. With a FM two-way radio in your vehicle, you can have static-free contact with other hams virtually anywhere you travel in the U.S.

This book is dedicated to two people and an organization. It was my dad, K6HX, who convinced me to quit bootlegging and get my license almost 40 years ago. I miss you, Dad! I cannot forget Fred Maia, W5YI, who started the ball rolling toward a code-free Amateur license. He has forever changed the course of Amateur Radio. Finally, this book is dedicated to those hard working and underappreciated people at the FCC who gave our fraternity the most powerful tool since the invention of the vacuum tube.

Donald L. Stoner, W6TNS

Introduction

Amateur Radio — The King of Hobbies

To their non-Amateur friends, "hams" are slightly eccentric characters who live in a little world all their own. To their spouse, a ham is the "lunkhead" who gets solder on the carpet and is responsible for enormous electric bills. Neighbors sometimes consider them members of a vast organization dedicated to the violent overthrow of television. All will agree that hams seem to speak in a foreign tongue. But to their fellow hams, an Amateur is simply a person with the most interesting, unusual and rewarding hobby in the world.

Amateurs *are* special and participate in the only hobby, called the Amateur Service, regulated by the federal government and International law. Amateurs are given free access to radio frequencies which are worth literally billions of dollars to commercial interests.

Beyond question, the world of ham radio provides a thrill and excitement like no other leisure time activity. The only question is do you have the desire and persistence to earn the right to be called an Amateur?

Something For Everyone

Ham radio is actually a large group of sub-hobbies within a single hobby, all tied together by electromagnetic waves. It can be an escape from the humdrum of everyday life which allows you to talk with other hams all over the world. Amateurs are encouraged to experiment with their equipment and develop new techniques.

Amateurs have many methods of communication. Most use a microphone since it is the fastest way to convey your thoughts and comments to someone else. Many hams do their "talking" with computers. A few hardy souls even have their own TV stations. Some prefer to use Morse code, claiming it is more relaxing, reliable and the equipment is less expensive.

Astronaut Ron Parise, WA4SIR, flew in mission STS-35. (NASA Photo)

In all, there are more facets to the hobby than there are on the British Crown jewels! Did you know that Amateurs have their own satellites which support communication all over the world? We can even talk by Amateur radio to astronauts (both American and Russian) circling the earth in their space ships. The fastest growing segment of our hobby are the computer buffs who can communicate all over the world.

Who Does It?

Amateurs can be found in all walks of life. Well known political figures, such as Barry Goldwater (K7UGA) and His Majesty King Hussain of Jordan (JY1) are both Amateurs. Dick Rutan (KB7LQS) had an Amateur station aboard "Voyager" when he and Jeanna Yaeger made their famous flight.

Country western fans know the names of picker Chet Atkins and singer Ronnie Milsap (WA4CZD and WB4KCG respectively). Other famous hams include rock guitarist Joe Walsh. Donnie Osmond used to be KA7EVD and Marlon Brando is still FO0GJ (Tahiti). Some of the older readers will remember entertainers Andy Devine and Arthur Godfrey (K4LIB) as well as musicians Pee Wee Hunt and Alvino Rey (W6UK).

Barry Goldwater, K7UGA, is the elder stateman of Amateur Radio. (CQ Magazine Photo)

What Do Hams Talk About?

Let's look at a few activities that occupy the time of more than 450,000 Americans. Chatting, or "rag-chewing", is the most popular diversion. All hams love to talk! As soon as his feet hit the floor, Sam Ham will flick on his receiver and transmitter, even before turning on the coffee pot. Around the nation, other hams are doing the same thing. More often than not, a group of these "early birds" collect in a "round-table". A microphone is passed around via the air waves until it is time for various members to dash off to work. The scene is repeated after supper by some of the more avid members of the clan.

"What do you find to talk about?" hams are often asked. Sex, religion, and politics used to be avoided, but open discussion is quite commonplace these days. Generally, the conversation is less likely to be on technical things than on taking care of the house, car problems and critiquing the latest Steven Spielberg movie.

Hamming On The Highway

Sam Ham might also be interested in another phase of the hobby called mobile operation. If so, he probably has a miniature duplicate of his home station built into the family car. As Sam threads his way to the office, he can once again participate in the "round-table" from his rolling radio station. Or, should Sam elect to, he can switch the frequency of his equipment and join in the conversation with a similar group of hams clear across the country.

Public Service

Before you get the idea that Amateurs are just a bunch of chattering magpies, remember that it's called the Amateur Radio Service. The original intent was public service and the handling of messages. The majority of Amateurs carry on in the same tradition. Amateurs provide public service without pecuniary interest (compensation).

Ham radio is also a communication service for **self-training** and **technical experimentation**. We are allowed access to priceless radio spectrum on the assumption that Amateurs form a **valued pool of skilled communicators** in times of emergency. It is absolutely essential that we maintain this tradition if we are to retain our frequency allocations throughout the communications spectrum.

The Thrill Of DX'ing

The term **DX** means communicating long distance by radio. The DX-minded ham is an unusual variation of the typical Amateur. Like Sam Ham, our inveterate DX'er rises before dawn. He turns on the station and starts the coffee brewing almost at the same time. However, DX Dan does not jump into a round-table. Instead, he squashes a pair of headphones on his ears and intently tunes the receiver dial to and fro. Several days may come and go without so much as a peep out of DX Dan's powerful transmitter. Then one morning Dan flushes his quarry and a look of grim determination settles across his face. He is listening to the faint rolling dots and dashes of 9N1MM, Father Moran, operating from Katmandu, Nepal! Suddenly, as 9N1MM stands by, Dan's powerful "rig" springs to life and the needles on the transmitter measuring instruments swing to and fro. Less than one minute later, Dan pushes the telegraph key away and writes down this new contact in his log book.

Most amazing, perhaps, is that DX Dan probably heard many other rare and exotic stations while searching the band for 9N1MM. On a typical morning he may have heard most of the districts of the Soviet Union, Sarawak, Brunei, Mauritius, the Orkney Islands, Qatar, Trucial Oman, and of course the more common countries such as England, Japan, Australia, or New Zealand. But Dan ignored their CQ ("I'm looking for a contact") calls in favor of the more elusive Nepal Amateur. He had contacted these other stations long ago. As our inveterate DX'er prepared to dash off to work, he checked off the new conquest. Nepal was number 261 on his list of the more than 300 countries in the world.

To quote Dave Bell, W6AQ (who appeared in a video called *The New World of Amateur Radio*), "When you turn on your radio and get on the air, it's like going fishing. You never know exactly what you are going to catch. That's the thrill of DX."

Ham Radio "Wall Paper"

In addition to the thrill of having "hooked" a new one, Dan will get a material reward also. Hams exchange postcards, called **QSL**'s, which confirm their contacts. Each card carries details such as the date and time of contact, mode of transmission (voice or code), and a signal strength report. Thus, sometime after his contact, Dan will receive a card that he can proudly display on the wall of his ham station.

Ambassadors Of Goodwill

There's plenty of "wallpaper" in this Amateur's "hamshack."

An interesting variation of the DX-minded ham is Ambassador Al. Al "gets his kicks" by conversing with overseas Amateurs, mostly to gain friends and exchange ideas. Although he may never meet one of these hams, he is truly an ambassador of international goodwill. These electronic ambassadors can tell you what the temperature was yesterday in Kuala Lumpur, Malasia, or who is winning the tennis matches in Melbourne, Australia. Al has two or three favorites overseas and maintains weekly contact schedules with them. Often they exchange inexpensive gifts, and once in a while they have the opportunity of meeting each other.

Young people make excellent "ambassadors of the air waves" for the United States. By communicating with youth in other countries, they help dispel the myth of the "ugly American".

Radio Repeaters

Have you ever tried to communicate with someone using Citizens Band equipment? Not very effective is it? Ham radio has a couple of features not available to CB'ers. The first is Amateur Radio use of **FM (frequency modulation)** equipment. The reception is crystal clear and you only hear one station at a time. Another aspect of FM communications is the use of **repeaters**. These devices consist of a receiver and retransmitter. Neither FM or repeaters are allowed on the Citizens Band.

Repeaters are usually installed on mountain tops or on the roof of a tall building. The repeater picks up the signals from an Amateur's hand-held or mobile two-way radio and resends (or repeats) it at higher power levels on another frequency as much as 100 miles distant, and with perfect clarity.

There are more than 12,000 Amateur repeaters on the air in North America. You can drive from coast-to-coast and border-to-border and never be out of range of an Amateur repeater. In an emergency you can always contact someone for help with a two-way radio so tiny it will fit in your pocket or purse.

Repeaters are great for talking to friends in distant cities. For example, you can be driving around downtown Los Angeles and talk to another station motoring in San Diego. Repeaters also permit communication beyond mountains (which would normally shield or block the signals).

Some repeaters even have a telephone access so you can call your XYL and make up stories about why you'll be late for dinner. Many Amateur mobile and hand-held radios have a "Touch Tone" pad just like a regular telephone. This permits you to access the repeater telephone channel and dial a telephone number. Best of all, you don't need to pay money to the local cellular telephone system. There's no free lunch, however. Remember, you can't use the ham bands for business. If you want to call your broker and corner the stock market, you'll need a cellular telephone.

This tiny ICOM handheld transceiver can communicate for 100 miles or more via a repeater. (ICOM Photo)

What's An XYL?

For convenience, I have used the male gender in describing the various types of Amateurs. However, men certainly don't have a monopoly on the hobby. Female Amateurs are referred to as YL's or "young ladies". An XYL (not ex-YL) is a married young lady.

There is no accurate tabulation, but approximately one out of every thirty hams is female.

Think it's too difficult? Probably the first woman ham was Miss Cecil Powell, secretary to the co-founder of the American Radio Relay League, Hiram Percy Maxim. In 1915, she constructed her own station, learned the code, and became an active Amateur.

What do YL's talk about? Well, what do women talk about whenever they get together? There are DX'ers, public-service spark plugs and "ambassadresses" among the skirt and sweater brigade too.

Welcome CB'ers!

Since it began, ham radio has grown at a steady pace with more newcomers arriving each year than there were "silent keys" (a ham who has passed away). In the early 70's, the ham population began to expand at a much higher rate than previously. This was due to interest in the Citizens Band. People were introduced to the wonders of radio communications but wanted something better. Ham radio provided it. Hams talk worldwide, limited only by radio conditions. There are no distance restrictions as in CB. Amateurs use static-free FM radios for local contacts. They are also allowed up to 1500 watts output power using any mode of communication rather than just a few watts on AM or single sideband.

The problems of CB and the attraction of ham radio has brought many new members into our hobby. Today, probably 20 percent of the existing Amateurs are ex-CB'er's. Amateurs embrace CB "born again" communicators and encourage them to get a ham license.

How About You?

Think you'd like to be a ham? Want to join about three million others worldwide who experience the thrill of communications by ham radio? Anyone can become a licensed Amateur operator. You don't even have to be a U.S. citizen and there are no age restrictions. There are five year old Amateurs and senior citizen hams in their nineties.

It's really easy, and getting easier every day, to open that first door to the Amateur Service. You have to pass a simple test but, you don't need to be examined at an office of the Federal Communications Commission (FCC). Since 1984, the government has been completely out of the ham testing business. **Volunteer Examiners (VE's)**, holding senior Amateur licenses, now handle this function.

The New Technician Class

What do I mean by "really easy and getting easier?" Until recently, the regulations required that you be able to receive the Morse code to obtain an Amateur license. Actually communication by Morse is quite enjoyable and challenging but it was perceived by the public to be a difficult obstacle.

As a result of this perception, the FCC recently created a new entry level of Amateur license. The recipient of this license does not need to show a proficiency using Morse code. The license is called the new Technician Class. It was created by dropping the 5 word-per-minute Morse code test from the existing Technician Class license.

All prospective hams are tested by a VE (Volunteer Examiner) team. VE's examine entry-level applicants under two different testing programs. These programs are the Novice examination program and the VEC (for Volunteer Examiner Coordinator) System. Up until recently there was only one entry level Amateur license, the Novice. Now there are two: Novice and the new Technician. Novices are examined by a team of two amateurs holding General Class and higher level operator licenses. It takes three Volunteer Examiners under the more formal VEC System and they must hold either an Advanced or an Extra Class Amateur license.

Most Amateur examinations are administered under the VEC System since VE's are systematically accredited and provided Amateur testing information and materials by a VEC. A VEC is an organization established to act as the testing liaison between the VE and the Federal Communications Commission who issue the Amateur operator license. VE's are always happy to have newcomers to ham radio appear at their testing sessions. The new no-code Technician Class applicant must be examined under the VEC System and a small testing fee (approximately $5.00) is charged to defray the cost of the examining program. There is no charge to be administered the Novice examination.

VEC's now take the place of the FCC in the testing function. They develop all examinations and testing guidelines and make them available to the Amateur testing community. It is the VEC who now manages the Amateur operator testing function for the govern-

Céline Calvo, KB7LOY, who is from Bruz, France, passed her Novice exam during a short vist to Seattle, WA., in conjunction with the 1990 Goodwill Games.

ment. Practically every city of 50,000 or more has monthly VEC examinations conducted by volunteers.

The new Technician license is really a "beginners permit". To earn it, and prove you are qualified to be an Amateur, you still have to pass a test. Volunteer Examiner Coordinators have developed a large pool of multiple choice questions that apply to the things beginning hams should know. All of the questions, even the exact word-for-word multiple choice answers are known to the public and widely published. Copies of these exams, with the correct answers, are included in this book.

The new Technician question pool is a combination of the questions for the Novice Class license (called Element 2) and the questions from the previous Technician Class license (called Element 3A). The Volunteer Examiner simply administers 55 questions from the two pools according to a selection formula. This formula is stated by the government in the Part 97 Rules and Regulations for the Amateur Service. There are about 700 total questions in the Element 2 and 3(A) question pools from which the VE selects for your Technician examination. [Approximately 375 in Element 2 and 325 in Element 3(A)].

Your VE team will select 30 questions from the Element 2 pool and 25 from Element 3(A). Passing Element 2 requires that you answer 22 questions correctly. Element 3(A) requires 19 – a total of 41 correct. You need not pass both test elements at the same time. Instead you may take one element and the other later. If you fail one portion, you still receive credit for the test element passed. The VE team will give you a credit slip, called a **Certificate of Successful Completion of Examination (CSCE)**, good towards the remaining examination element which must be completed during the next 365 days. If you don't pass the remaining test element during the next year, you lose credit for the portion you passed. The process is very similar to the written test given to obtain an automobile driving license. You study the rules, procedures, questions and then pass the test.

The first step in obtaining a Technician license, is to submit an application, called an FCC Form 610, to your Volunteer Examiners. The FCC Form 610, called the **Application for Amateur Station and Operator License**, consists of three sections. Section I is completed by the applicant. The Section II Certification and the Administering VE's Report is completed by your examiners. You can obtain a copy of the 610 form by calling your local FCC office (listed under U.S. Gov.) or by requesting one from The National Amateur Radio Association if you use or lose the copy included with this book.

After you pass the test, your application will be immediately forwarded by the VE team to the VEC who coordinated the testing session. (A copy of your credit certificate must be attached to your application if you claim credit from a previously passed examination element.) The VEC verifies everything is correct, then forwards the material to the FCC. The application is returned to you if you fail the test. It is important to obtain a photocopy of your successful Novice application if you plan to upgrade to a higher class before your license arrives. The next VE team will require proof that you have already passed the examination before testing you further.

You can't go on-the-air until your license arrives. It takes about six weeks to two months to get your "diploma" from Uncle Sam. Then the fun begins. The first time you go on the air, your forehead will break out in a cold sweat! You'll forget all the rules of communications and your sentences will be punctuated with "er's" and "uh's." But after a few days of this "infection" from the ham radio "bug," you'll sound like an ole timer.

The new Technician Class license allows you full Amateur privileges on the very high frequency (VHF) and ultra-high (UHF) bands including six meters and above. Most of the satellite and computer communication occurs on these bands.

Once you earn your Technician Class license, don't stop there. The next step is the so-called "Technician Plus" (for Technician plus Morse code) level, followed by the General, Advanced and Extra Class. You no longer have the option of becoming a Novice class operator once you enter at the code-free Technician level. To advance to "Tech Plus" you must pass the Element 1(A) five words-per-minute telegraphy examination at a VEC System test session. You are not permitted to go back and take the 5 WPM code exam under the two VE Novice examination program. While considered an upgrade, no new operator license will be issued by the FCC to the "Tech Plus" operator. Instead your new privileges will be vested by the Certificate of Successful Completion given you by the examining team when you pass the code.

"Tech Plus" operators additionally obtain segments of the Amateur 80, 40, 15 and 10 meter band. Most of these bands are for telegraphy but you are permitted voice transmission in a portion of the ten meter band.

Continue to study and improve your knowledge. Remember, a Technician "ticket" is simply a key which opens the first door and allows you to enter a wondrous room with many more doors. There is no "free lunch" in this world. You get what you pay for whether the currency is sweat or dollars. The new Technician license is only the beginning, not the ultimate goal. Plan on learning the Morse code so you can access the other Amateur bands. You'll be glad you did!

The Novice Class

The Commission decided to retain the Novice Class operator license in order to provide an alternate entry level operator license opportunity to persons — especially youngsters — who can pass a telegraphy requirement in place of the more comprehensive written examination requirement for the codeless Technician Class operator license.

Novice privileges are not as desirable as those associated with the new code-free Technician. Novices obtain code spectrum on 80, 40, 15 and 10 meters and may operate in the voice mode on a segment of ten. In addition Novices obtain portions of the 222 and 1270 MHz ham bands.

To become a Novice you must pass Element 2 (30 questions) and Element 1(A), (to prove you can send and receive Morse at not less than five words-per-minute). This examination may be administered by two General or higher class Amateur operators who need not be accredited by a VEC. It is also frequently conducted at VEC sessions if the applicant requests the Novice instead of the Technician examinations. The only difference is that the 5 WPM code will be administered instead of what some people perceive is the harder Element 3(A). You may be administered the 5 WPM telegraphy test under the two VE Novice program only if you have never held the code-free Technician Class operator license. Once you hold the Technician license, you will be charged a test fee for administration of the five word-per-minute code test. This is because "Tech Plus" is considered an upgrade from the Technician Class license. All licensing above the Novice class must be conducted under the VEC system which carries a test fee. (2A12.1) (2A12.2)(2A12.3)

As a general rule, to engage in worldwide communications you need at least a Novice or Tech Plus class license (sometimes the six meter band transmissions travel great distances). With either license you can communicate by voice on the 10 meter Amateur band and by Morse code on other bands. The 10 meter band is capable of continent spanning range at various times of the year. The bands where you are permitted to use Morse have long distance capabilities at nearly any hour of the day and night.

Learning to receive the Morse code can best be done with a personal computer (using a program such as Super Morse, by listening to over-the-air code practice or with the audio training tapes available in the commercial marketplace. Morse code seems difficult, but in actual fact is quite easy. All it takes is a bit of practice. At examination time, you will be sent a minimum of five minutes of Morse at five words-per-minute.

You are specifically required to correctly answer 41 out of 55 written test questions extracted from two question pools to become a Technician. However, your examiners are allowed much more freedom to determine if you have passed the Morse code test. Their only guidelines are: (1) they must be convinced and certify that you can send and receive the International Morse code at five words per minute during a transmission of at least five minutes; and (2) the text transmitted must contain forty-three different characters. These are all the letters of the alphabet, all numerals 0-9, four punctuation marks (the period, comma, question mark, slant bar) and three operating procedure signs (AR,

BT and SK). While not required, most telegraphy examinations take the form of an actual telegraphy communication, between two amateurs. You probably will not be administered a telegraphy hand-sending test since the FCC has taken the position that operators who can transcribe Morse code can also send it.

Some examiners will ask you to correctly copy 25 characters in a row (punctuation, numerals and prosigns count as two characters) to determine if you can copy the code. Others might ask you to answer seven out of ten questions about the transmitted text or fill in missing words from the copy. Even a multiple choice or true/false code examination is legal. The format of the telegraphy test is left to the discretion of the VE.

Dan, N7NYQ, went from a non-ham to passing his General exam in only six months. Now he's working on his "Extra."

Helping Hams

In virtually every area of the country there are "Helping Hams" who want to assist you in joining our hobby. To paraphrase the Beatles, if you could "use a little help from your friends", let us know at The National Amateur Radio Association. Give us your ZIP code and we will tell you how to contact one or more "Helping Hams" who live near you. NARA also has a data base of information on Volunteer Examiners. These VE's can advise you of local ham radio classes and, when the time comes, provide your Amateur test. NARA will also help you locate Amateur clubs and other organizations which are interested in guiding you to become a ham radio operator. Just call or write for information.

Handicapped Hams

Volunteer examiners are permitted to utilize special provisions when administering examinations to handicapped applicants at the 5 WPM level. These accommodations may include pausing the telegraphy test after sentences, phrases, words or even individual letters. The examiners may require a physician's certification indicating the nature of the disability before determining which, if any, special procedures must be used. Even if you are sightless, have no hearing or do not have use or control of your limbs, there is a way to transmit and receive ham radio communications. If you have a handicap of some sort, don't be reluctant to contact the Courage-Handi Ham System in Minnesota. For more information on this organization, write Courage Center, 3915 Golden Valley Rd., Golden Valley, MN 55422 or call (612) 588-0811.

Other Resources

The premier national group representing radio Amateurs is The American Radio Relay League. Every Amateur should belong to this organization. Their address is:

American Radio Relay League
225 Main Street
Newington, CT 06111
Telephone (203) 666-1541

Membership is currently $30.00 per year and with it, you receive an automatic subscription to their monthly publication, *QST*. The League has an extraordinary array of literature of interest to newcomers. Their book, *How to Tune in the World* is excellent. They also produce other Novice course materials which are available at most Amateur Radio stores.

The National Amateur Radio Association is a special interest group. This non-profit organization was formed to:(a) publicize Amateur Radio to the general public:(b) bring young people into the hobby:(c) teach existing Amateurs how to be better Amateurs and (d) protect Amateur frequency allocations. NARA can be reached in a number of ways:

National Amateur Radio Assoc.
16541 Redmond Way, Suite #232
Redmond, WA 98052
Inquiries 1-800-GOT-2-HAM
Business Phone (206) 232-2579
MCI ID: 365-8035
CompuServe: 70371,111

A membership in NARA is $10.00 per year. Your membership includes a subscription to a monthly journal called *The Amateur Radio Communicator*. It also supports representation in Washington, educational programs such as exhibitions at The National Science Teachers Association meetings and at similar conferences.

Another special interest group is TAPR. If you are keen on computer communications via ham radio, you should contact:

Tucson Amateur Packet Radio
P.O. Box 12925
Tucson, AZ 85732
Telephone (602) 749-9479

They are the group which promoted and popularized packet radio communications via ham radio.

Last, but by no means least, is AMSAT which stands for the Amateur Satellite Corporation. This amazing group has parlayed memberships, donations and contributed labor into more than 20 communication satellites which have orbited the earth exclusively for Amateur use. If you would like to learn how you can transmit all over the world via satellite, these "orbital mechanics" can be contacted at:

AMSAT
850 Silgo Avenue
Silver Spring, MD 20910
Telephone (301) 589-6062

An excellent study device for Morse Code is the program mentioned earlier, called **Super Morse**. This program, written for MS-DOS computers, is available from The National Amateur Radio Association. It comes on a 5 1/4 inch disk and the price is only $3.00 to cover postage and handling. Super Morse is shareware (you owe the author a contribution if you use it).

Magazines are an excellent source of information no matter what field you are interested in. You can sometimes pick up copies of Amateur magazines on newsstands.

QST has something of interest for every ham with special emphasis on ARRL activities. Their address is ARRL, QST Magazine, 225 Main Street, Newington, CT 06111.

CQ's emphasis is on DX'ing, contesting and awards. They can be reached at CQ Magazine, 76 North Broadway, Hicksville, NY 11801.

73 is famed for its rich editorials by Wayne Green and for its emphasis on construction and articles for beginners. Write them at 73 Magazine, WGE Center, Hancock, NH 03449.

For those interested in Amateur television transmissions, there are two excellent publications on the subject. One is *Amateur Television Quarterly*, 540 Oakton St., Des Plaines, IL 60018-1950. Drop a line to Henry Ruh, KB9FO if you would like a sample copy.

USATVS Journal is published by Mike Donovan, KA0JAW. Mike has been reporting on ham TV for 22 years. They can be reached at USATVS, 1520 Cerro Dr., Dubuque, IA 52001.

An excellent publication for "homebrew artists" is called *Nuts & Volts* magazine. If you like to build things, or are interested in electronic parts and used equipment, you'll find what you are looking for between the covers of this publication. N&V covers not only ham things but television, test equipment and computer goodies. You can reach them by writing T & L Publications, Inc., P.O. Box 1111, Placentia, CA 92670. Tell them NARA sent you and watch for a sample copy in the mail.

If you would like to learn more about attaching your computer to an Amateur station, you will enjoy reading *Digital Digest*. It is the premier publication for the one's and zero's crowd and is only $16.00 per year. Digital Digest is published bimonthly by Arvo & Associates, 4063 Goldenrod Rd., Winter Park, FL 32792.

There are advertisements for a number of Amateur radio companies in these magazines. A letter to the advertiser requesting information will bring a quick response- usually a fat envelope full of literature.

These magazines provide an extraordinary amount of useful technical information. However Amateur news is usually 60-90 days after the fact due to publishing deadlines. For the best up-to-date information on what's happening in the ham radio world, you should subscribe to the popular newsletters.

The most famous is the *W5YI Report*. This 10 page document is published by Fred Maia (W5YI) every two weeks and contains news which is never more than a few days old. The W5YI Report costs $24.50 per year and can be obtained by writing: The W5YI Report, P.O. Box 565101, Dallas, TX 75356-5101. The telephone number is (817) 461-6443

The oldest newsletter is *The Westlink Report*. It is published 26 times per year. It covers general Amateur radio news, FCC actions, new equipment releases, industry news, DX reports and propagation forecasts. The price is $24.50 per year. It's available from: Westlink Report, 28221 Stanley Ct., Canyon Country, CA 91351, telephone 1-(800) HAM-7303 or (805) 251-5558 in California.

There's a free service that provides the latest information on ham radio each week. It is the *Amateur Radio Newsline*, produced by Bill Pasternak (WA6ITF) and is heard weekly on repeaters all over the country. Check with your local repeater operator for the time "Newsline" can be heard.

Let's Do It!

There's no shortage of information and there are no secrets. Come on and join us in this world of dits and dah's and ones and zeros. I can personally guarantee that your life will never again be the same. At the very least, you'll make new friends and have new experiences. Isn't that worth a few hours of your time?

73, DE Don Stoner, W6TNS
President
The National Amateur Radio Assoc.

Chapter

1

The Birth Of A Hobby

None of the questions in the Novice or Technician test relate to the traditions of Amateurs. I think some of them should. These traditions are one of the things which separate Amateur Radio from other less disciplined radio services.

Hertz, The First Ham

Although we consider ham radio a twentieth-century hobby, the birth of an infant called "wireless" took place long before the turn of this century. In 1887, the chief interest of the population was attending band concerts in the park. That year, Heinrich Hertz, a brilliant young German scientist was experimenting with the radiation of electricity. Hertz discovered that if he applied electricity to a loop of wire, he could cause a spark to jump the gap in another loop a short distance away — and with no connecting wires! This was the first form of radio communication.

Heinrich concluded correctly that electromagnetic waves traveled between the source gap and the spark gap at the speed of light. The source and the gap could be separated by only a few feet, otherwise the spark could not be detected. Heinrich Hertz could be called the world's first Amateur. In appreciation and respect for his contribution, we have renamed

Heinrich Hertz was the first person to generate radio waves

the familiar unit of frequency to honor Hertz. Today, instead of speaking of cycles, kilo-cycles or megacycles, we use the terms Hertz, kiloHertz and MegaHertz (Hz, KHz and MHz).

Morse Was an Artist

It's a little known fact but Samuel Finley Breese Morse first achieved distinction as an artist, particularly as a painter of miniatures. He was the son of a Calvinist minister who was educated at Yale College and who received his art training in Europe. It was during the return voyage from Europe in 1832 that he devised the now famous code bearing his name.

Although well known for devising this system, he also invented the telegraphic sounder and printer. Both devices employed electromagnets, a battery and a telegraph key. Often the key was located a long distance from the electromagnets and connected by wires. This was the first telegraph line.

Morse connected the armature (controlled by the electromagnet) to an ink pen which could print on paper moving through the device. This created a printed record of the code. Using this scheme, the various alphanumeric characters of a message could be represented by combinations of the two signal elements, the "dot" and the "dash". For example, a "dot" followed by a "dash" represents an "a" in the international Morse code.

After working with the "printing telegraph", Morse and his colleague, Alfred Vail, realized that the messages could also be understood by the sound of the clicking armature. Holding the key down for a short length of time created a short click or "dot" sound while depressing the key longer increased the time before the next click. This represented a "dash".

The Morse code was utilized when radio telegraphy was introduced in 1897. Even submarines used the code by employing magnetic fields. Ships communicated between themselves using a signaling lamp wherein a shutter was manually actuated to form "dots" and "dashes".

Marconi Made Wireless Practical

Guglielmo Marconi was the first to transmit signals across the Atlantic.

Apparently Hertz did not see the possibility of using electromagnetic waves for long distance communication. Guglielmo Marconi, an Italian genius, carried Hertz's simple experiment further by connecting one side of the "sending" spark gap to wires buried in the ground. The other side of the gap was connected to a "skywire" or antenna. Marconi utilized the telegraph code (devised by Samuel Morse for telegraph lines) with his new invention. Using this equipment, electromagnetic waves generated by the crackling spark traveled more than a mile to a remote receiving site. Transmitters, receivers and wireless communications had arrived on the scene; the year was 1895.

Marconi worked diligently to increase the range of communication. More sensitive devices were invented to reproduce the sound of the code. In time practical distances reached 200 miles. Government and commercial companies all over the world copied Marconi's experiments and his wireless equipment. By the Fall of 1901, using a mighty spark gap transmitter, Marconi was able to thrust his signals 1,800 miles across the Atlantic Ocean from Wales to Newfoundland.

Litz Wire and Shellac

Cascading events and technological advances created more public interest in wireless communications than had ever been known. Experimenters found that they could listen in on this eighth wonder-of-the-world. They wound coils, varnished baseboards and built their own receiving stations. Interest in sending Morse code surged with the general population and Amateur transmitting stations sprang up all over the nation. Folks at the English end of the transatlantic circuit exhibited a similar interest. Their Amateur experimenters were called "am's" and the name stuck for radio experimenters (it makes a good story, anyway!).

Keep in mind that there were no tubes, transistors, integrated circuits or even such basic items as capacitors, resistors or measuring meters. You couldn't go into a ham radio store and pick up a kit of parts. And there were no government regulations, frequency allocations, or organizations representing Amateurs. Anyone who wanted to experiment built the necessary parts and plunged into the construction of his or her Amateur station.

Snap, Crackle and Pop

Then the rotary spark gap was invented. Rather than use a fixed gap for the spark, this device used many gaps which rotated on a wheel at high speed. It produced pleasant sounding oscillations at the then fantastic rate of 50,000 cycles per second.

Even more important, the oscillations could be modified by the human voice! Reginald Aubrey Fessenden, a physicist, used speech to communicate with ships from his experimental station in Brant Rock, Mass. Many experimenters feared insanity when voices, rather than the whine of the rotary spark gap, leapt out of their headsets. But once again, Amateurs scrambled, this time to hurl their voices across space. The art of radiotelephone transmission had been created; the year was 1906.

Publications describing all kinds of devices for the experimenter were numerous. The papers described feats of distance and "heroism" by wireless stations almost daily. The tiny stream of fire created by Hertz and Marconi had become a tremendous blaze in the eyes of experimenters everywhere.

With the increased activity came an ever-rising tide of interference between stations. Amateur, commercial and government activities were intermingled. The calliope of sounds culminated in the Wireless Act of 1912. This was the beginning of the rules which provide the framework under which Amateurs operate today. Most important, the government was to control all wireless transmissions and all operators had to be licensed. The intrepid Amateurs, who sparked the imagination of commercial interests, were relegated to purgatory. Their operations had to be confined to wavelengths shorter than 200 meters (near the high end of the present broadcast band). Commercial and government stations were the only wireless stations allowed below this frequency, except by special permit.

The Amateur hobbyists protested violently, for they felt that this regulation effectively slashed the wrist of their sending hands. The new wavelengths were uninhabited and incapable of propagating energy across a small village, or so they thought. The more progressive experimenters soon discovered that their range had been increased, rather than decreased, and with no additional transmitting power! The better stations could communicate over distances in excess of 30 miles.

Formation Of The ARRL

In 1914 another great event occurred. The Radio Club of Hartford, Conn., formed a league of Amateur stations. This group, known as the American Radio Relay League, still represents it's members in all official matters. The purpose of the League was to band Amateurs together so they could relay messages from one point to another as commercial stations did.

An early network of Amateurs was attempted between Boston and Denver, with the eventual hope of spanning the continent. Soon, with the leadership of League co-founder Hiram Percy Maxim, messages were flying back and forth. By 1921, with improved equipment and techniques, a message and answer could make the round trip between coasts in six minutes!

Hiram Percy Maxim, co-founder of the American Radio Relay League. (ARRL Photo)

Although the League suffered severe financial troubles, it was able to publish the first issue of its official organ in December, 1915 — a magazine still known as "*QST*".

During the First World War, two-thirds of the 6,000 Amateurs trooped off to the battlefield, and all Amateur transmissions ceased. During the war, and with the help of Amateurs, the government discovered how valuable the wavelengths shorter than 200 meters were. These frequencies became the exclusive property of the Navy and after the shooting had died down, the Navy was hesitant to return them. Under the pressure of League president Maxim and secretary Warner, however, the government relented. In October of

1919, Amateur operation was restored. Call letters, consisting of a number and two letters, were again assigned, based on area, to Amateurs. (It was much later before the A, K, N and W prefixes were added).

The Magic Bottle

The war also made a commercial item out of a device that was once a laboratory curiosity. In 1905, Sir Ambrose Fleming invented the diode "valve". It consisted of a filament and plate inside an evacuated bulb. Current would only flow from filament to plate and not the other way around. Thus, it could be used to convert alternating into direct current.

In 1907, Dr. Lee DeForest installed a grid between the filament and the plate. He found that by varying the voltage on the grid, he could control the current flow between the filament and the plate. More important, only a small change of voltage on the grid would result in a large voltage change at the plate. This is called **amplification**. The device was patented as the "Audion" or triode vacuum tube.

Because of amplification, this "magic bottle" could be used to make receivers more sensitive. Even more important, the vacuum tube could be used to generate radio signals electronically, with no moving parts whatever. Suddenly, generating stable radio frequency energy became possible. Further, the human voice could now be transmitted over the airwaves in channels much narrower than with the spark gap.

The glow of the vacuum tube filament cast a shadow over the spark gap and helix coil which signaled the end of a great era. With a mighty whoosh of ozone, King Spark sputtered and died!

New Vistas

Armed with this new electronic invention, the ARRL sent Paul F. Godly, 2ZE, to Europe for transatlantic tests. During the experiments, thirty American Amateurs were heard on the continent. Finally, after many months of preparation, the first two-way Amateur contact flashed across the Atlantic.

In the course of these tests, it was discovered that the shorter wavelengths provided superior propagation of electromagnetic energy. Later it was found that the wavelengths between 40 and 10 meters were optimum for long distance contacts. A mass exodus to the "short wavelength" bands began which made the California Gold Rush seem like a school fire drill. Further, Amateurs found that their ability to communicate over long distances was affected by the time of year and a strange, new cycle which seemed to be influenced by the sun.

Radio station F8AB in France was the first to work an American Amateur Radio Station.

An American Inventor

The inventions of Major Edwin Armstrong will forever shape and influence ham radio. In 1918, he discovered the principal of heterodyning and invented the superheterodyne receiver.

Until Armstrong's invention, it was necessary to peak each amplifier stage in a radio receiver individually. The receivers were called tuned radio frequency or TRF receivers. This peaking was an awkward operation. Some designers tried to tie the knobs of the various stages together, but it was virtually impossible to obtain perfect tracking.

Major Armstrong discovered that the amplifying circuits of a radio could all be tuned to a single frequency. Using the heterodyne principal, the desired station could be converted to this single frequency for processing. All modern radios and television receivers employ this superheterodyne principal.

Equally important was Armstrong's invention of frequency modulation. Prior to 1937, voice was broadcast by varying the amplitude or strength of the electromagnetic waves radiated by the antenna. Armstrong discovered that voice information could also be conveyed by varying the frequency of the electromagnetic waves, rather than the amplitude. Since static and electrical interference varies in amplitude but not frequency, noise can be completely filtered out in a frequency modulation receiver. Thanks to Armstrong, you hear high fidelity, static free reception on the FM band, not to mention the VHF ham bands.

The Single Sideband Mode

As you might suspect, spark gap transmissions were not very efficient. Each transmitter consumed more radio spectrum "real estate" than does an entire Amateur band today! The vacuum tube made narrow channel amplitude modulation possible. But with the passage of time a new technology made AM obsolete. The technique was called single sideband, suppressed carrier or simply SSB.

Single sideband is not a recent invention. It has been around for longer than most people reading this book. The telephone company has used single sideband since the '30's in order to squeeze more channels into their telephone circuits.

It took the Strategic Air Command (SAC) and the "cold war" of the '50's to bring single sideband out of the closet. General "Butch Griswold" and Curtis LeMay, working in

conjunction with Arthur Collins of the Collins Radio Company, developed an extraordinary communications network using conventional Amateur single sideband equipment. The network permitted reliable communications with SAC sideband equipped airplanes and SAC bases all over the world at any time of the day or night.

Amateurs like Wes Schum and Herb Johnson adapted the SSB technique to popularly priced ham gear. When this happened, the mass exodus from "Ancient Mary" (Amplitude Modulation) to single sideband was underway on the ham bands.

The transition was not painless, however. "Sidebanders" huddled at one end of the 20 and 75 meter ham bands, while the "AM'ers" reigned supreme in the remainder of the bands. Slowly, but inexorably, the ranks of those operating SSB expanded. Invariably they interfered with diehard "AM'ers". The SSB "static" a ham heard on their AM receiver was very annoying. But the benefits afforded by SSB could not be denied. Over time, most "AM'ers" either died off or converted to SSB.

For communications, AM (like spark) is a relic of the past. It is still used on the Citizens Band. In commercial service, only the Aeronautical Service still uses AM for communication between planes and to the control tower at airports.

Not only is SSB an extremely efficient use of spectrum but it packs a lot of communication "punch" per watt of power. Want to see the hair on the neck of an ole time CW man stand straight out? Just make the statement, at your next club meeting, that SSB will "get through" anytime that CW can also be received! Most "sidebanders" believe that it will but the subject is always good for a lively debate.

Ham Radio — Out Of This World

Today, with modern technology, we think nothing of speaking with Amateurs on the other side of the globe - it happens daily! In fact, the Amateur Service has literally soared through the ionosphere and far out into space.

The introduction of satellite communication certainly ranks as one of the major accomplishments of Amateurs. In 1959, I suggested in the April CQ Magazine the possibility of putting an Amateur station in orbit. The concept was picked up by a group of Amateurs who worked for a major aerospace company. The idea grew to become the **OSCAR (Orbital Satellite Carrying Amateur Radio)** program.

Their initial effort culminated in a shoebox sized satellite which held a tiny transmitter and whip antenna. It was keyed electronically and beeped the Morse code letters for the Amateur greeting (HI) from space.

OSCAR One was launched on December 12, 1961. Amateurs around the world were thrilled to hear their representative "speaking" from the cosmos.

If you would like to hear what the first OSCAR satellite sounded like, the National Amateur Radio Association sells a tape called "The Flight of OSCAR One." It was recorded

The "DOVE" MICROSAT satellite (AMSAT Photo)

at Vandenberg AFB in 1961. Also captured are transmissions on the 40 meter OSCAR net along with reception of the HI beacon. The tape can be ordered from NARA and is priced at $4.95 postage paid.

Today, we Amateurs have sophisticated repeater satellites in elliptical orbits which are capable of worldwide communications. They can also store and forward digital messages. Ham satellites are all the more amazing when one considers that they were built with contributed labor and are launched through private enterprise without government assistance. The organization responsible for these technological miracles is called AMSAT, The Amateur Satellite Corporation (*see Introduction - Resources*).

Computer Communications

Another event which forever changed the face of ham radio was the introduction of computer packet communications. Until recently, clattering, oil spewing teletype machines were the closest thing hams had to digital communication.

The "sparkplug" of Amateur packet communications was Dr. John D. Mercado of the Canadian Department of Communications. In addition to introducing the Digital Certificate of Proficiency license in Canada, he inspired the Vancouver Amateur Digital Communications Group to develop packet radio. This is a fast and error-free method of communicating with computers. The Vancouver club developed a device called a Terminal Node Controller (TNC). It is similar to a computer modem but optimized for the one-way-at-a-time communications of ham radio.

In the early '80's, a group of Amateurs in Tucson, Arizona took the concept one step further. The Tucson Amateur Packet Radio (TAPR) organization "tweeked" and simplified the Vancouver design. They built kits and licensed the new TNC design to manufacturers. As a result, most packet TNC's sold today are based on this famous TAPR design (*see Introduction- Resources*).

Continue The Traditions

While this "thumb-nail" sketch is by no means complete, it should convey to you some of the important history and tradition behind our fantastic hobby. Those who join us are expected to respect the traditions of Amateurs, to appreciate the loan of valuable spectrum and to maintain our high standards. Now, let's get to work and study for the Technician examination.

Chapter

The FCC Rules and Regulations

This section of your test will include 10 questions from the Novice question pool of Subelement 2A and 5 questions from Subelement 3AA. At the end of various paragraphs, in this and following chapters, you will note mysterious characters in parenthesis. These refer to the question pool numbers. If you understand an explanation, you can mentally and visually skip over these numbers and go on to the next paragraph. If your understanding is a bit hazy, look up the question at the end of each chapter and try to answer it based on what you learned in the paragraph.

It's now time for the "main event!" The preceding two chapters were just the "prelims." In this corner, wearing the mauve trunks with the brocade trim is the Federal Communications Commission. And in the opposite corner, bouncing from foot-to-foot and throwing practice jabs, is "Prospective-Tech" (that's you). Proceed fearlessly, "Prospective-Tech," everyone is pulling for you to win this bout, including the FCC.

The Rules of the Road

There's not much exciting about rules and regulations unless you happen to break one! However, you'll need to know about the "rules of the road" in order to pass your Amateur Radio license test. About a third of the questions you'll be asked will involve rules.

Virtually all transmitting stations are regulated through rules established by the Federal Communications Commission (FCC). Amateurs operate under the **Amateur Service** in **Part 97 of title 47 CFR (Code of Federal Regulations)** of these rules. Amateur communication is defined as non-commercial communications between Amateur stations, for pleasure and not for compensation. The Amateur Service is a radio communications service for the purpose of self-training in communications and technical investigations.

The rules in Part 97 discuss such things as station operating standards, technical standards and emergency communications. (2A2.1)(2A2.2)(2A3.1)(2A3.2)

Who can earn an Amateur license and become a ham? Almost anyone of any age, size or shape, even if the they are not a citizen of this country. There are even Russians who hold a valid American Amateur Radio license. In fact, the only people who are specifically precluded from holding a U.S. Amateur license are representatives of a foreign government. (2A11.1)(2A11.2)

At the present time, Amateur rules and regulations are in a state of flux. In November, 1988, the FCC decided to reallocate a part of the Amateur 220-225 MHz band to commercial service. The "new" 220 band will now be from 222 to 225 MHz.

During 1989, the FCC released PR Docket No. 88-139 which reorganizes and further deregulates Part 97 of the FCC Rules and Regulations. Part 97 is the section which establishes the rules for the Amateur Service. There have been a few changes in the question pools as a result of this docket.

Another factor which affects the traditional order of things is the newly created Technician Class Amateur license which eliminates Morse code testing. The questions and answers in this book are up-to-date and include any revisions that result from the new code-free Technician license.

As we proceed through this decade, questions on the Amateur examinations will change. If you would like to study Part 97 in depth, a booklet containing the rules can be obtained from The National Amateur Radio Association for $5.00 postage paid.

But fear not, "slugger;" the dedicated Volunteer Examiners who conduct the testing for your Amateur license are also aware of the changes in the rules. It is highly unlikely that anyone would "flunk" you because of confusion due to changing law.

The Amateur FCC License

One of factors which distinguishes the Amateur Service from the Citizens Band is the **Amateur license**. This document, sometimes referred to as a "ticket" by hams, is issued by the Federal Communications Commission. Let's talk a bit about the ham license. You could be asked several questions based on it when you take the Technician test.

The FCC authorization really consists of two licenses on a single piece of paper. One part of the document conveys operator privileges. This is the **operator license** and, as the name implies, permits you to operate an Amateur station. (2A5.1) (2A6.1)

As a newly licensed Amateur, the document the government sends you also provides a **station license**. This portion permits you to have an Amateur station. An Amateur station consists of the apparatus necessary for carrying on radio communications. The address on your ham license is the current and accurate mailing address. This is where you

AMATEUR RADIO LICENSE — NOT TRANSFERABLE

EFFECTIVE DATE	EXPIRATION DATE	CALL SIGN	OPERATOR PRIVILEGES	STATION PRIVILEGES
09/09/83	09/09/88	K6HX	EXTRA	PRIMARY

NAME AND ADDRESS
LEWIS E STONER
334 HIDDEN PINES RD
DEL MAR   CA 92014

FIXED STATION OPERATION LOCATION
SAME AS MAILING ADDRESS

THIS LICENSE IS SUBJECT TO CONDITIONS OF GRANT ON REVERSE SIDE

UNITED STATES OF AMERICA
FEDERAL COMMUNICATIONS COMMISSION
GETTYSBURG, PA 17325

LICENSEE'S SIGNATURE

FCC FORM 660
JANUARY 1983

FEDERAL
COMMUNICATIONS
COMMISSION

receive correspondence and where the FCC can communicate with you, if they need to. (2A6.2)(2A7.1)(2A13.1)(2A14.1)

The Amateur operator named by the license has a written authorization to be the control operator of an Amateur station. He or she is held responsible for the correct operation of an Amateur station. Your Amateur license is *good for the period specified on the license*, which is currently **10 years** from the date of issue. If your license expires and you forget to renew it, you have a two year grace period to do so. Renewal or modification of your license is simply a matter of filling out an FCC Form 610 and sending it to the FCC in Gettysburg, PA. You can obtain a copy of Form 610 upon request at no charge from The National Amateur Radio Association. (2A4.1)(2A4.2)(2A5.2)(2A8.1)(2A8.2)(2A16.1)(3AA3.1)(3AA3.2)(3AA3.3)

Your Amateur Call Sign

There is a third component to the Amateur license. It is your **station identification**. When you are granted a license, you also receive a distinct set of alphanumeric characters which constitutes your **call letters** The call letters of US Amateur stations begin with the letters A, K, N or W. The group can be 2 by 1 (WX7S), 1 by 2 (K6DC), 1 by 3 (N7NQL), 2 by 2 (AC7XY) or 2 by 3 (KB7GIS). The digits can be any number, zero through nine. The numbers represent certain geographic areas of the country. For example all California or Hawaii licensees are issued number six designators. As a brand new Amateur, your call letters will be from the 1 by 3 (Group C) or 2 by 3 (Group D) variety. Novice operators are always issued Group D format callsigns. Technicians usually get Group C (1 by 3) call signs starting with the letter "N." Technicians receive Group D (2 by 3) callsigns when all of the "N" prefixed 1 by 3 callsigns are allocated in a specific radio district. (2A15.1)(2A15.2)(2A15.3) (2A15.4)(2A15.5)

Your call is unique. No one else in the world has one like it. You should be proud of what it represents — the license you have earned. Always use your call properly. You must identify your station with the call sign at the **end** of each transmission series and every 10 minutes in an extended conversation. In other words, you need not give your call after you say "Hi Joe, how's the weather in Moosejaw?" or when Joe says "It's a bit cold and overcast". After 10 minutes of this chit-chatting, however, you must identify. No matter when you end the conversation, you must also identify your station. It is the responsibility of the person you are talking to, to identify his or her station. (2A27.1)(2A27.2)(2A27.3)(2A27.4(2A27.5)(2A27.6)(2A27.7)

Classes Of License

There are two beginner or "entry level" points. These are the **Novice** and the **Technician Class** license. The written tests for the code-free Technician are officially designated Element 2 and Element 3(A) by the FCC. Element 2 consists of 30 questions from the Novice question pool. Element 3(A) is made up of 25 questions from the Technician question pool. Both tests consist of multiple choice questions on elementary theory, Amateur practices and basic FCC regulations.

A step up the ham radio ladder is the **Technician Plus**. To reach this level you must pass a five word-per-minute Morse code test called Element 1A. This test is conducted by three Volunteer Examiners. Once it is established that you have passed the test, you receive a *Certificate of Successful Completion of Examination (CSCE)* from the examiners. At this point you become a "Technician Plus" and you are immediately allowed to operate on certain long distance high frequency bands below 30 MHz.

Examinees who have upgraded are permitted to immediately utilize their new operating privileges. They must, however, append their call signs with an identifier to denote that they have not yet received their new license. The identifier for Technician is "temporary KT." (3AA8-1.1)

The other path for beginners is called the **Novice Class**. This license class was discussed in the Introduction Chapter. It allows Morse code operation on the high frequency (HF) bands, plus voice communications on 10 meters. (*See page 10, The Novice Class*)

Most Amateurs aspire to become **General Class** hams because it allows worldwide communications on the most popular high frequency (HF) bands. The written test for the General Class license (Element 3B) is about the same difficulty as for the Technician Element 3A test. However, the general theory questions emphasize operating on bands to which the General Class ham has access. The Morse code requirements are increased to 13 words-per-minute. This class of license gives one access to all of the Amateur bands, but not all parts of them.

The next higher class is called the **Advanced Class**, while the top of the pyramid is called the **Amateur Extra**. These licenses provide a few more privileges and total access to the Amateur bands.

Remember these five classes of license — Novice, Technician, General, Advanced and Extra. Several test questions are based on this ranking. (2A9.1)(2A9.3)

Amateur Principals

There are five principals that guide the Amateur Service. They are; (1) recognition of emergency communications; (2) advancement of the radio art; (3) improvement of communication and technical skills; (4) increase the number of trained radio operators and electronics experts; and (5) the enhancement of international goodwill. Etch these five principals into your brain. You will be asked about this in the Element 2 questions. (2A1.1)(2A1.2)(2A1.3)(2A1.4)

Emission Designators

Emission means the radio frequency signals transmitted by a radio station. Emissions can take many different forms. Until recently, the FCC liked to be much more precise than simply using the words phone or code to describe voice and Morse emissions. They used terms like A3J and F3 to describe various modulation systems and the emissions they produced. Modulation, by the way, means adding intelligence or information to a radio signal or emission. (2A17.1)

With the Part 97 rewrite, the FCC decided that such precision was not necessary. The rewrite speaks of **CW** (Morse), **phone** (voice), **image** (ham TV), **RTTY** (radio teletype), **data** (computer communications, usually packet), **test** (a blank signal with no information), **SS** (spread spectrum) and so on. There is no reference to a precise emission designator.

You've already learned about Amateur Morse and voice communication, but you might not be familiar with some of the other terms in the preceding paragraph. Did you know, for example, that Amateurs are authorized to transmit television pictures? The term RTTY may be unfamiliar these days. It stands for radio teletype which is a narrow band emission that prints directly on paper. Teletype is actually the trademark and name of the Teletype Corp. Remember those text printing machines going "chunk-chunk-chunk" in the old war movies? Those were teletype machines. (2A20.1)

Computers have virtually replaced these noisy, oily machines for the transmitting and printing of text. Computers are also used to generate the information sent on the data mode. The data mode is considered to be a wideband emission sending information in error-free packets of 128 bytes (characters) or so. Computers are also used for telemetry, that is, the control or collection of information from remote objects. (2A20.2)

Finally, spread spectrum, is a relatively new (for Amateur Radio) communication mode. Instead of an emission appearing on one frequency, it is sent on a number of frequencies. This makes the information less susceptible to interference.

Visualizing The Spectrum

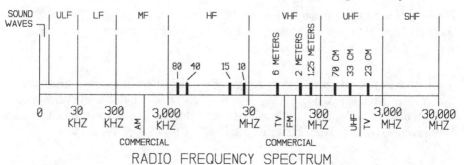

RADIO FREQUENCY SPECTRUM

In order to "understand" the Amateur bands and the frequencies we use, you have to be able to visualize the radio spectrum. You will have to learn what parts of this spectrum Amateurs are allowed to use. These are the bands that the FCC has allocated to us.

Imagine for a moment that you are standing on a high plateau of land overlooking a vast panorama in front of you. From off in the distance, to your far left, you hear the faint sounds of Motley Crue flogging their guitars to death. These are the sound frequencies with an address of 0 to .02.

Clockwise from that location, you can see numerous airplanes converging. This is the land where the navigation beacons are located at addresses between 0.2 and 0.5.

Next to this is a forest of tall steel towers supported by guy wires. These are the antenna of the AM broadcast band stations. The address of these stations is between 0.5 and 1.5.

Then arrayed in front of you are numerous towers, boats with antennas and aircraft with wires from wing tip to tail. Sprinkled among them are wires stretched between trees, and Amateur antenna systems looking like TV antennas with an overactive thyroid. This conglomeration is the high frequency band which occupies the real estate address between 3.0 and 30.

Off to your right is another forest of tall towers and buildings which represent the FM and television broadcasting stations. Again, nestled in the shadow of these monsters, are another group of antennas representing the Amateur Radio inhabitants in the land between 30 and 300. There are more huge antennas to the right owned by the UHF television stations between 500 and 800.

Off in the distance to the far right are literally millions of automobiles all with tiny tails raised in anticipation from their rear windows. A closer inspection reveals drivers in animated conversation. This is the land of the cellular telephone which has an address of approximately 800 to 900.

Next to these automobiles are almost an equal number of shiny aluminum dishes pointed skyward. These are the satellite receiving and sending terminal antenna systems. They are planted on real estate labeled 1,000 on up.

Finally, off to the extreme right is a bright illumination representing the visible light spectrum. Although you can't see the emissions, invisible tanning as well as infrared rays are being radiated from the same general area.

The panorama just described is an overview of the radio communications spectrum. The "address" referred to is the frequency. The numbers refer to millions of cycles per second. Millions of cycles is the same as megaHertz (MHz). So that you can better visualize emissions, you may want to take a "side trip" to Chapter C at this point.

With this general picture of the radio spectrum in mind, let's examine the various bands that you are allowed to utilize as a Technician Class Amateur.

The Amateur Bands

The accompanying charts show the radio spectrum and where the popular Amateur bands are located. If you would like a more elegant, full color frequency chart of the Amateur bands, write to ICOM. Ask for their high frequency (HF) and very high frequency (VHF) charts. Their address is:

ICOM America, Inc.
2380-116th Ave. N.E.
Bellevue, WA 98004

The most popular bands are located in the portion of the radio spectrum called Very High Frequencies (VHF). The VHF bands are located between 30 and 300 MHz. Between 300 and 3,000 MHz, the spectrum is considered the Ultra High Frequencies (UHF). The majority of operation on VHF and UHF is voice using the frequency modulation (FM) mode.

These are called "line-of-sight" frequencies since VHF (and higher) radio transmissions don't bend (except under unusual circumstances). Thus, these frequencies are not capable of following the curvature of the earth. As a result you can expect to talk 20 miles or so directly, or up to 100 miles via a VHF repeater. Then these "straight line" transmissions head for the cold eternity of space.

Six Meters — This is the lowest frequency VHF band on which the new "codefree" Technician is allowed to operate. The band extends from 50 to 54 MHz. All Amateur classes, except Novice, can operate on the six meter band. The band from 50.0 to 50.1 is reserved exclusively for CW. Thus, frequency modulation (FM) can only be used from 50.1 to 54.0 MHz. The only other prohibition is that stations on this band may not be used for satellite communications. (3AA2.2)(3AA4.1)(3AA17.1)

The six meter band is rather unusual from a number of standpoints. For many years six meters was shunned because of television interference. It is "located" right next to Channel 2 in the radio spectrum (Channel 2 occupies frequencies between 54 and 60 Mhz.). Because of proximity, a six meter transmitter can interfere with a nearby television set through no fault of the equipment or the Amateur. Try explaining that to an irate neighbor when "Wheel of Fortune" is getting "creamed!"

Television set designs have improved and they are now better able to reject unwanted signals. More importantly, cable television is starting to dominate the landscape. It is highly unlikely that a six meter transmitter would interfere with Channel 2 on a television connected to cable since the signal is enclosed in a shielded coaxial line.

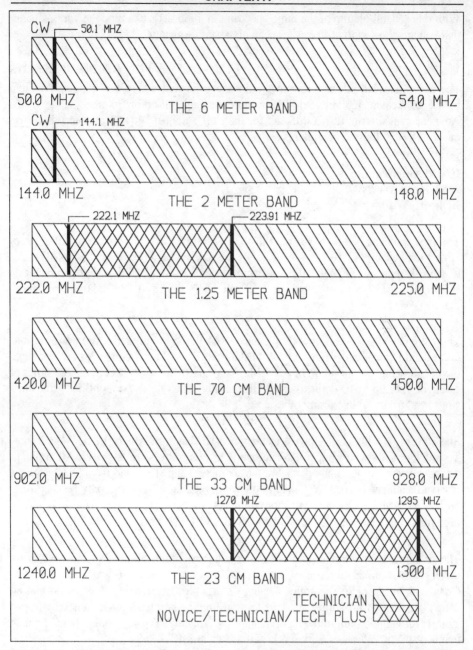

CW — 50.1 MHZ

50.0 MHZ   THE 6 METER BAND   54.0 MHZ

CW — 144.1 MHZ

144.0 MHZ   THE 2 METER BAND   148.0 MHZ

— 222.1 MHZ   — 223.91 MHZ

222.0 MHZ   THE 1.25 METER BAND   225.0 MHZ

420.0 MHZ   THE 70 CM BAND   450.0 MHZ

902.0 MHZ   THE 33 CM BAND   928.0 MHZ

1270 MHZ   1295 MHZ

1240.0 MHZ   THE 23 CM BAND   1300 MHZ

TECHNICIAN

NOVICE/TECHNICIAN/TECH PLUS

Six is an excellent band for around town communication with a simple low power transmitter. Occasionally, when the sun decides to act up (*see Chapter C*), it is possible to communicate with foreign countries. It is not unusual to tune across a "dead" band and hear a single station coming in from Buenos Aires, Argentina in South America!

Radio Control — New Technicians, interested in the radio control of models, will want to investigate this band. There is a lot of unused "space" for their control systems. The interference level should be considerably lower than the popular 72 MHz RC frequency. The band allocated to radio control of models is crowded with commercial users and subject to interference. Model hobbyists are increasingly attracted to the six meter band because of large number of clear frequencies. You can use a maximum of one watt output to control models on the Amateur bands. You need not identify your transmissions. The only requirement is that you attach a label, indicating your call letters plus name and address, to the transmitter. (3AA10.1)(3AA10.2)(3AA10.3) (3AA10.4)

Two Meters — The favorite of the new Technician Class is the two meter band which occupies 144 to 148 Mhz. The majority of people operating VHF will be found on "two." Like six meters, Novice operation is not permitted but all other Amateur classes may use the band. The maximum transmitting power permitted an Amateur station is 1,500 watts peak envelope power (PEP). Note that the band between 144.0 and 144.1 is reserved exclusively for CW. Thus, the FM emission can only be used between 144.1 and 148.0 MHz. (3AA2.3)(3AA4.2)(3AA6-3.1)

Most repeaters operate on two meters. Many of the orbital satellites carrying Amateur Radio (OSCAR) receive two meter signals. Computer communication (packet) is concentrated on two meters.

1.25 Meters — Presently Technicians are permitted to operate on the entire band between 220 and 225 MHz. But this will change when the other services occupy the 220 - 222 portion of the band. All Amateur modes and emissions are authorized for the Technician and higher license classes. Novices are only permitted operation between 222.1 and 223.91 MHz and are restricted to a transmitter power of 25 watts or less. Also, they are not allowed to establish or control a repeater. (2A10.5) (2A17.10)(2A17.13) (2A19.3)(3AA2.4)

70 Centimeters — This is an interesting band for the experimenter. The band limits are 420-450 Mhz and there are some operating restrictions near the Canadian border and adjacent to military reservations. No Novice operation is permitted, but all other classes may use the band. (3AA2.5)

Most of the present Amateur television (ATV) transmissions occur within this band. Hams in some of the larger cities have installed television repeaters. Many of the voice repeaters operating on this band belong to clubs and are closed to non-members.

33 Centimeters — There is an Amateur frequency allocation between 902 and 928 MHz. It is shared with a number of unlicensed services such as vehicle locators, video links for VCR's and wireless data links. It is likely that Amateur activity or interest in this band will further decrease as commercial use increases. There are no questions in the test pool relating to the 33 cm. band.

23 Centimeters — This band, which extends from 1240 to 1300 MHz is getting more popular as crowding increases on the lower VHF bands. New repeaters are regularly heard as more commercial equipment becomes available.

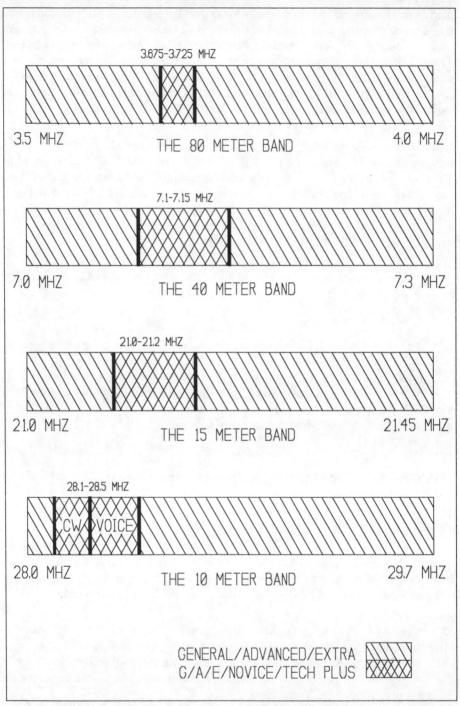

3.675-3.725 MHZ

3.5 MHZ   THE 80 METER BAND   4.0 MHZ

7.1-7.15 MHZ

7.0 MHZ   THE 40 METER BAND   7.3 MHZ

21.0-21.2 MHZ

21.0 MHZ   THE 15 METER BAND   21.45 MHZ

28.1-28.5 MHZ

CW VOICE

28.0 MHZ   THE 10 METER BAND   29.7 MHZ

GENERAL/ADVANCED/EXTRA
G/A/E/NOVICE/TECH PLUS

There is much more "real estate" for Amateur television transmissions. It is likely that most ATV operation will move up to 23 cm. Even though the wavelength is very short, the performance of equipment is excellent. Signals are more susceptible to reflection.

Thus, 23 cm. transmissions seem to bounce into areas that are not penetrated by lower band VHF signals.

Technicians are allowed to operate on any frequency within the band. Novices are restricted to the portion between **1270 and 1295 MHz**. All emissions authorized for this band may be used but transmitting output for Novices is restricted to 5 watts peak envelope power (PEP). (2A10.6)(2A17.11)(2A19.4)

There are several micro wavelength Amateur bands higher in frequency than the ones just discussed and Technician Class Amateurs can use them all. These bands will become increasingly popular as Amateur satellite activity multiplies.

The High Frequency Bands

Although the new Technician Class Amateurs are permitted all operating privileges above 30 MHz, they are not allowed to operate on the high frequency (HF) bands. The HF band is the frequency spectrum between 3.0 and 30.0 MHz. The International Telecommunications Union (ITU), requires a knowledge of Morse code for operation on the high frequency bands.

Technicians can access the high frequency bands by taking a five word-per-minute Morse test called Element 1(A). Passing this test reclassifies them as Technician Plus (plus Morse). Novice high frequency operation is permitted since this class of Amateur has already passed the Element 1(A) Morse test.

Novice and Technician Plus operators are permitted a maximum output of 200 watts peak envelope power on the high frequency bands (3-30 MHz). Even so, one should use the minimum legal power necessary to carry out the desired communications. (2A18.1) (2A18.2)(2A18.3)(2A18.4)(2A18.5)(2A19.1)(2A19.2)(2A19.5)

The following is a brief discussion of the characteristics of the high frequency Amateur bands.

80 Meters — The entire band extends from 3.5 to 4.0 MHz (3500 to 4000 kHz). Novices and "Tech-Plus" are permitted to operate between **3675 and 3725 kHz (3.675 to 3.725 MHz)** within this band. Operation is strictly by Morse code, or continuous wave (CW) as it is more correctly called. No phone operation by Novices is permitted. You can usually communicate up to 50-75 miles during the day and 400 miles or more at night. (2A10.7)(2A17.2)(2A17.5)

40 Meters — This is the favorite CW band (code emission only) of Novices and "Tech-Plus". They are permitted to operate between **7100 and 7150 kHz (7.1 to 7.15 MHz)**. During the day you can expect to "talk" with other hams around 300 miles distance. At night it's possible to work all over the United States. If the foreign shortwave broadcast interference is not too great, don't be surprised if someone from overseas answers your CQ (I'd like to communicate with someone) call. (2A10.2)(2A10.8) (2A17.3)(2A17.6)

15 Meters — This is another CW emission only band which permits worldwide communications, but mostly in the daytime. At night the band is usually dead (except during solar peaks every 11 years). Novice and "Tech-Plus" hams are permitted to thump away on their telegraph keys between 21.100 and 21.200 MHz (what is that in kiloHertz?). (2A10.3)(2A10.9)(2A17.4)(2A17.7)

10 Meters — The 10 meter band is the favorite of Novice and "Tech-Plus" operators. During periods of high solar activity one can communicate all over the world on 10 meters. It is also the only Novice and "Tech-Plus" HF band where phone communication is permitted. The full band is 28.0 to 29.7 MHz. Novice and "Tech-Plus" hams are permitted CW, RTTY and digital operation between 28.100 and 28.300 MHz. Between 28.3 and 28.5 MHz Novices and "Tech-Plus" can operate CW and phone. (2A10.4) (2A10.10)(2A17.8)(2A17.9)(2A17.12)(2A20.3)

There are several other small Amateur allocations within the HF spectrum, but a General Class or higher license is required to access them.

Beacon Stations — At various times, certain Amateur bands are capable of supporting communication over great distances (*see Chapter C-Propagation*). While there are certain patterns, it is not possible to predict with absolute certainty when a band will be "open." A popular aid to observation of propagation and reception and other related experimental activities is called a beacon station. The concept is simplicity itself. Every so often, the beacon transmits it's call letters and location. If you can hear the beacon at your location, you know the band is open and a "CQ" call is likely to result in a response.

The maximum permissible power output of a beacon station is 100 watts PEP. You must hold a Technician or higher class license to operate a beacon. Novices are not allowed to do so. (3AA6-4.1)(3AA9-1.1)(3AA9-2.1)

Who's In Charge?

The answer, in a single word, is **you**. You have (or should have) total control of your Amateur station. You, as the licensed Amateur in charge, are called the **control operator**. The **control point** is the location at which the control operator function is performed. By the way, you must always have your Amateur license (or a photocopy) in your possession whenever you are operating an Amateur Station. The license (or a photocopy) must also be retained at the station. (2A21.1)(2A23.1)(2A24.1)(2A25.1) (2A 26.1)(3AA1.1)(3AA1.2)

As the control operator, you are held responsible for the proper operation of your station whenever it is transmitting. You are always held accountable by the FCC. If someone else uses your station improperly, you are held equally responsible with the other person. You cannot permit an unlicensed person to use your station without your supervision. Any Amateur station must have a licensed control operator present whenever transmitting (unless it is remote controlled). (2A21.2)(2A21.3)(2A21.4)(2A22.1)(2A 22.2)

Miscellaneous Do's and Don't

Broadcasting — Most of the rules which regulate Amateurs are based on common sense. For example, if commercial activities were permitted, it would destroy the Amateur Service. Can you imagine some large company or distributor broadcasting advertisements on your favorite ham band? Soon everyone would do it and there would be no room left for Amateur activities.

By the same token, you cannot use your ham radio for broadcasting. Broadcasting is defined as one-way transmissions intended for reception by the general public. Broadcasting of bulletins solely of interest to radio Amateurs (such as the Newsline Report) is permitted. But there is no way you can broadcast "Hi, this is Fuzzy Fred from Farmingdale with all the latest hits and Top 40 tunes." To emphasize the point, the transmission of music on ham radio is strictly forbidden. (2A33.1)(2A35.1)(3AA12.1)

Note that beacon operation, radio control, emergency communication and information bulletins for Amateurs, and Morse code practice are **not** considered to be broadcasting. (3AA13.1)(3AA13.2)(3AA13.3)(3AA13.4)

Third Party Traffic — The same principal of common sense applies to handling messages for other people. Until the last 20 years or so, there was a paranoia on the part of governments about Amateurs. Their concern was not about spies but about revenue. They feared that their Post, Telephone and Telegraph (PTT) entities would lose business if Amateurs were allowed to handle messages into and out of their countries. As a result "third party traffic" was usually forbidden. Third party traffic is a message passed by one Amateur control operator to another Amateur control operator on behalf of an unlicensed person. The other person is called the third party. (2A34.1)(2A34.2)(2A34.3)

Over the intervening years, most governments have "mellowed". The U.S. has agreements with other governments which permit certain forms of third party traffic. If in doubt, always check with the ARRL to see if third party traffic is permitted with a specific country. The FCC also issues periodic lists of nations to which Amateurs may exchange non-commercial messages. (3AA14.3)

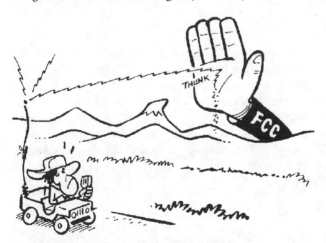

The Commission recognizes two categories of third party traffic: (1) other licensed Amateurs (who are eligible to be the control operator of the station); and (2) non-licensed people or organizations. Obviously the FCC is going to be more concerned about the later category.

If the third party is present in the Amateur "shack" (the room containing the Amateur station), they are allowed to talk on the microphone even though they may not be a licensed Amateur. The control operator must be present and continuously monitor and supervise the conversation. Normally Amateur communications need not be identified more often than every 10 minutes. However, in the case of international third party traffic, the transmissions must be identified at the end of each exchange of communications. This allows monitoring stations to quickly identify the participants in third party communications. (3AA15.1)(3AA15.2)(3AA15.3)(3AA15.4)

Business Communications — Even if your dad wants to use your radio to order a pizza, he can't. It's illegal and you have to tell him so. Business communications are never permitted unless it involves the immediate safety of life of individuals or property is threatened. (2A30.1)(2A30.2)(2A30.3)

You should exercise good judgement about the nature of the traffic, with respect to the law on business communication. "Your cousin just had a baby", or some such, is certainly permitted. "Henry, your XYL is shipping your HF rig Monday. You should have it by the end of the week" probably would not raise any eyebrows. However, "Hey Sam, the 'widgets' you ordered aren't available with .35 hole spacing. Will you accept 0.5?" is certainly "over the line". I'm sure you get the idea.

When handling messages you cannot accept any compensation for your services. If you did, it would be a business transaction, which is clearly and absolutely forbidden. By the way, compensation does not mean simply money. You cannot accept goods, services, favors or any sort of reward for handling messages. (3AA14.1)

There is one situation where you could use ham radio to aid a business. This might occur during an emergency. Let's say you are providing communications during a flood. You might say "If we don't get some sandbags down here to the Ajax building, it's going to wash away." If the sandbags were delivered and the building was saved, you certainly used Amateur Radio to aid the businesses in the building. But you also saved the building from certain destruction and maybe even saved a life (someone might try to get their belongings out of the building). While this is a hypothetical situation, I'm sure you understand the intent of the law. (3AA14.2)

Several organizations broadcast information bulletins and code practice. For example, the ARRL operates a code practice and news bulletin station for Amateurs. The call letters are W1AW, with the transmitter located in Newington, CT. W1AW is an extensive operation which requires several employees of the League to manage. Some time ago they realized that, in the strict sense, these employees were receiving compensation for sending messages on the Amateur bands. An Amateur station can never be hired to transmit messages. Thus, the rules were modified slightly to state that the control operator can be paid if they work for a station that sends code practice or news bulletins to Amateurs. (2A32.1)(2A32.2)(3AA14.1)

For various reasons, usually political, communication with Amateurs in other countries may be forbidden either by our government or theirs. Once again, the ARRL stays current on the shifting winds and can advise you on countries which should be avoided. Currently there are no countries on the banned list. (2A28.1)(2A31.1)

Emergency Communications

Amateur Radio really "shines" when there is a disaster which disrupts normal communication systems in a particular area. When this happens, the FCC may declare a **temporary state of communications emergency**. This declaration is usually initiated by the FCC Engineer-in-Charge of the affected area. This official representative of the FCC will detail any special conditions and special rules to be observed by Amateur stations during the emergency. Generally speaking, the FCC will restrict transmissions to that necessary to meet essential communication needs and to facilitate relief actions. (3A A11-2.1)(3AA11-2.2)(3AA11-2.3)(3AA11-2.4)

Normally you are not allowed to communicate with stations other than those in the Amateur Service, but this is not always the case. You can communicate with non-Amateur stations when authorized by the FCC. Exceptions are also made when safety is involved. For example in an emergency, the FCC would permit you to establish contact with the U.S. Coast Guard on frequencies outside a ham band. The FCC would also permit non-Amateur Coast Guard personnel to operate inside a band allocated to Amateur operation. This is perfectly legal. In an emergency situation, where safety of human life is involved, you would be allowed to communicate by any means or frequencies at your disposal. (2A28.2)(2A40.2)(2A40.3)

You can use you own judgement if your safety is involved. Let's say you are piloting a pleasure boat off the coast of California. In an emergency situation, where safety of life and or the craft is involved, you could use your ham rig to contact a commercial shore station. Many mariners are getting ham tickets and installing Amateur gear on their boats. Because of their wide dispersion and activity, one is far more likely to contact a ham than a specific shore station regardless of time, distance or radio conditions.

Station Location — There are no geographical limitations to the use of your ham license within the United States or on the high seas. You can operate wherever you want to without notifying the FCC. In the territorial waters of another country, you should check with the local authorities on the status of **reciprocal licensing agreements**. (2A29.1)(2A29.2)

Many years ago, the address on your license was where the FCC expected to find your station. If you operated at another location you were supposed to advise the

Courtesy SGC, Inc.

FCC Engineer-in-Charge for your radio district. This requirement was abandoned when vehicular radio operation and our mobile society flooded them with unnecessary paperwork.

Deceptive Signals — With the possible exception of "pig-Latin", you are not permitted to transmit messages in code or ciphers. The FCC must be able to monitor what you are saying. Since English is understood by all FCC monitoring stations, it must be used for station identification. The CW emission may be used anywhere in a ham band and thus it can always be used to identify an Amateur station. Abbreviations or substitutions (other than a standard phonetic alphabet) which obscure the meaning of a message are just another form of coding. They are not permitted either. (2A36.1)(2A36.2)(2A37.1) (3AA4.3)(3AA8-2.1)(3AA8.3.1)

It is inconceivable that an Amateur would send false signals or that they need to be cautioned about doing so. However, you will probably be asked a question to make sure you understand that false and deceptive signals are absolutely forbidden. For example, sending MAYDAY or SOS when there is no emergency is a "hanging offense" (not quite, but maybe it should be!). (2A37.2)

Emission Bandwidth

Not only can an Amateur transmitted signal (emission) vary up and down in amplitude, but it will also vary from side to side in width. Frequency modulation is a good example. The louder you talk (without limiting), the greater the frequency excursions of the transmitter emission. If your signal is too wide, it can also interfere with adjacent Amateurs. That's why all FM transmitters incorporate modulation deviation limiters to prevent this from happening.

The data rate of a digital transmission has a direct bearing on the bandwidth of the transmitted emission. The faster the data speed, the more "real estate" occupied by the signal. Digital modes, such as radio teletype (RTTY) and multiplexed emissions can really "spread out" as the data rate increases.

RTTY and most digital radio transmissions use two adjacent frequencies. One represents a digital zero and the other a digital one. On the HF bands (below 50 MHz), the FCC specifies the maximum spacing between the one-zero pair at 1,000 Hz or 1 kHz maximum. The maximum spacing or frequency shift is not specified above 50 MHz. (3AA7-2.1)(3AA7-2.2)

Above 50 MHz, the Commission rules specify how wide a digital signal can be. On the six and two meter band, it cannot exceed 20 kHz. On the 222 and 420 band, the width can increase to 100 kHz. (3AA7-3.1)(3AA7-3.2)(3AA7-3.3)

The FCC also specifies the maximum data rate permitted on various Amateur bands. For example, on 10 meters the maximum data rate is 1,200 baud but it increases to 19.6 kilobaud on six and two meters. On the 222 MHz band data can zip along at 56 kilobaud. (3AA7-1.1)(3AA7-1.2)(3AA7-1.3)

Power Output — The FCC is concerned that you understand the in's and out's of power (no pun intended!). Let's talk about power output. As an Amateur, you are permitted to transmit a large amount of power. For example, a Technician is permitted 1,500 watts PEP output on the two meter band (144-148 MHz). (3AA6-3.1)

Even so, there is another important rule which takes precedence over any maximum permitted power output. Part 97.313(a) states that you should *never* use more power than is necessary to carry out the desired communication. (2A19.5) (3AA6-2.1)

At what point does power become power output? So there is no confusion about power output measurement, the FCC specifies the power delivered by your transmitter or power amplifier to the terminals that connect to the antenna system. (3AA6-1.1)

In various places throughout this book you will see the term "peak envelope power" (PEP) used. This refers to the measurement of power when the information or modulation of a transmitter varies the amplitude of the power rather than the frequency. An FM transmitter doesn't have a modulation envelope and the power output is steady. But if you vary the amplitude or strength of the signal with information (data, speech, etc.), power output must be defined differently. The definition of peak envelope power is the average power supplied during one RF cycle at the crest of the modulation envelope. (3AA6-1.2)

Obscene Language — It used to be that Amateurs strictly avoided discussing sex, politics or religion. But in this liberated age, these taboos have fallen by the wayside. Sadly, too, has common decency in a few cases. There will always be those losers who hide behind the anonymity of a microphone. They use foul language and are magically transformed, for the first time in their drab lives, into someone that people notice. It is best to ignore these Neanderthals.

The rules clearly and specifically state that obscene, indecent or profane words not be transmitted by an Amateur station. (3AA16.1)(3AA16.2)(3AA16.3)

Interference

While Amateurs aren't likely to send false signals, they can interfere with other stations unintentionally. Sometimes interference cannot be avoided, like trying to move around in a crowded room. You'll always bump into people you are unaware of. This is unintentional and part of the game. However, it is clearly unlawful to **maliciously or intentionally interfere** with another station. The law states that you must always identify your transmissions with your call sign. Transmitting an unmodulated interfering signal breaks the rules twice! (2A38.1)(2A38.2)(2A38.3)(2A39.1)(2A39.2)(2A39.3)

There is concern on the part of the FCC that you understand the rules regarding interference between primary and secondary users of a frequency. For example, on the 902 MHz band, Amateurs are the secondary users. If the primary user interferes with you, you must assume that you are also interfering with them. As the secondary user, you are required to change frequency to eliminate the possibility of interference. (3AA5.1)

It's possible for an Amateur to interfere with another service in a different region of the world. For example, if you were a Technician-Plus and operated 40 CW, you might "tangle" with foreign shortwave broadcasting stations. The International Telecommunications Union allocates spectrum for different uses in different parts of the world. Thus, you have the exclusive right to be flogging away on the telegraph key between 7000 and 7100 kHz. Broadcast stations are the primary users of frequencies between 7100 and 7300 kHz and Amateurs are the secondary users. One of the advantages of CW, by the way, is the ability to copy it even in the presence of a powerful broadcasting station. Under the same conditions, you could never stand to listen to a voice transmission in the presence of such powerful interference. (3AA5.2)

Repeaters

A similar situation exists locally with radio repeaters (*see Introduction chapter*). In almost every case Amateur repeaters are coordinated by an area committee or ham group. If interference occurs between a coordinated and uncoordinated repeater, it is up to the licensee of the uncoordinated repeater to solve the problem. If two coordinated repeaters or uncoordinated repeaters interfere, the licensees of the repeaters are equally responsible for resolving the interference. (3AA11-1.1)(3AA11-1.2)(3AA11-1.3)

Auxiliary, repeater and space stations are all allowed to repeat Amateur transmissions, but beacon stations are specifically excluded from doing so. We Amateurs are also permitted to retransmit U.S. Government communications of the space shuttle with the permission of NASA. (3AA12.2)(3AA12.3)(3AA12.4)(3AA12.5)

Rule Compliance

If you break the rules (accidentally or otherwise), there is a good chance you will receive an **"Official Notice of Violation"** from the FCC. This is a serious document. You must respond to the FCC office which originated the Notice as instructed in the Notice (usually within 10 days). Your reply should describe in detail what steps you are taking to insure that the violation does not reoccur. Let's say a transistor in your radio committed "hari-kari" and put out garbage all over the band. An FCC monitoring station heard the noise and sent you a Notice. Don't wait until your radio comes back from the repair shop before writing to the FCC. As soon as you get their form, respond saying something like "A defect in my transmitter caused the problem. It has been sent in for repair and as soon as it is returned I will report the nature of the defect and verify that it has been corrected." This way the FCC knows that you have received their document and are responsive. Even if it takes several weeks to fix the radio, you have complied with the law by responding immediately. (2A40.1)

Now that you have all this information stored in the random access memory between your ears, let's take a test. The following questions are from the Novice and Technician pool section which pertains to rules and regulations. The correct answers will be found starting on page 195, near the end of the book. Don't be tempted to "sneak a peak." Also, write your answers on a separate sheet of paper, not on the pages of the book. You don't want to give your answers (right or wrong) to someone else who might like to take the test.

SUBELEMENT 2A (10 questions).

2A1.1 What are the five principles that express the fundamental purpose for which the Amateur Service rules are designed? (A) Recognition of emergency communications, advancement of the radio art, improvement of communication and technical skills, increase in the number of trained radio operators and electronics experts, and the enhancement of international goodwill; (B) Recognition of business communications, advancement of the radio art, improvement of communication and business skills, increase in the number of trained radio operators and electronics experts, and the enhancement of international goodwill; (C) Recognition of emergency communications, preservation of the earliest radio techniques, improvement of communication and technical skills, maintain a pool of people familiar with early tube-type equipment, and the enhancement of international goodwill; (D) Recognition of emergency communications, advancement of the radio art, improvement of communication and technical skills, increase in the number of trained radio operators and electronics experts, and the enhancement of a sense of patriotism.

2A1.2 Which of the following is not one of the basic principles for which the Amateur Service rules are designed? (A) Providing emergency communications; (B) Improvement of communication and technical skills; (C) Advancement of the radio art; (D) Enhancement of a sense of patriotism and nationalism.

2A1.3 The Amateur Service rules were designed to provide a radio communications service that meets five fundamental purposes. Which of the following is not one of those principles? (A) Improvement of communication and technical skills; (B) Enhancement of international goodwill; (C) Increase the number of trained radio operators and electronics experts; (D) Preserving the history of radio communications.

2A1.4 The Amateur Service rules were designed to provide a radio communications service that meets five fundamental purposes. What are those principles? (A) Recognition of business communications, advancement of the radio art, improvement of communication and business skills, increase in the number of trained radio operators and electronics experts, and the enhancement of international goodwill; (B) Recognition of emergency communications, advancement of the radio art, improvement of communication and technical skills, increase in the number of trained radio operators and electronics experts, and the enhancement of international goodwill; (C) Recognition of emergency communications, preservation of the earliest radio techniques, improvement of communication and technical skills, maintain a pool of people familiar with early tube-type equipment, and the enhancement of international goodwill; (D) Recognition of emergency communications, advancement of the radio art, improvement of communication and technical skills, increase in the number of trained radio operators and electronics experts, and the enhancement of a sense of patriotism.

2A2.1 What is the definition of the Amateur Service? (A) A private radio service used for personal gain and public benefit; (B) A public radio service used for public service communications; (C) A radio communication service for the purpose of self-training, intercommunication and technical investigations; (D) A private radio service intended for the furtherance of commercial radio interests.

2A2.2 What name is given to the radio communication service that is designed for self-training, intercommunication, and technical investigation? (A) The Amateur Service; (B) The Citizen's Radio Service; (C) The Experimenter's Radio Service; (D) The Maritime Radio Service.

2A3.1 What document contains the specific rules and regulations governing the Amateur Service in the United States? (A) Part 97 of title 47 CFR (Code of Federal Regulations); (B) The Communications Act of 1934 (as amended); (C) The Radio Amateur's Handbook; (D) The minutes of the International Telecommunication Union meetings.

2A3.2 Which one of the following topics is not addressed in the rules and regulations of the Amateur Service? (A) Station operation standards; (B) Technical standards; (C) Providing emergency communications; (D) Station construction standards.

2A4.1 What is the definition of an Amateur operator? (A) A person who has not received any training in radio operations; (B) A person holding a written authorization to be the control operator of an Amateur station; (C) A person who performs private radio communications for hire; (D) A trainee in a commercial radio station.

2A4.2 What term describes a person holding a written authorization to be the control operator of an Amateur station? (A) A Citizen Radio operator; (B) A Personal Radio operator; (C) A Radio Service operator; (D) An Amateur operator.

2A5.1 What is the portion of an Amateur operator/primary station license that conveys operator privileges? (A) The verification section; (B) Form 610; (C) The operator license; (D) The station license.

2A5.2 What authority is derived from an operator/primary station license? (A) The authority to operate any shortwave radio station; (B) The authority to be the control operator of an Amateur station; (C) The authority to have an Amateur station at a particular location; (D) The authority to transmit on either Amateur or Class D citizen's band frequencies.

2A6.1 What authority is derived from a written authorization for an Amateur station? (A) The authority to use specified operating frequencies; (B) The authority to operate an Amateur station; (C) The authority to enforce FCC Rules when violations are noted on the part of other operators; (D) The authority to transmit on either Amateur or Class D citizen's band frequencies.

2A6.2 What part of your Amateur license gives you authority to operate an Amateur station? (A) The operator license; (B) The FCC Form 610; (C) The station license; (D) An Amateur operator/primary station license does not specify a station location.

2A7.1 What is an Amateur station? (A) A licensed radio station engaged in broadcasting to the public in a limited and well-defined area; (B) A radio station used to further commercial radio interests; (C) A private radio service used for personal gain and public service; (D) A station in an Amateur Service consisting of the apparatus necessary for carrying on radio communications.

2A8.1 Who is a control operator? (A) An Amateur operator designated by the licensee of a station to be responsible for the transmissions from that station to assure compliance with the FCC rules; (B) A person, either licensed or not, who controls the emissions of an Amateur station; (C) An unlicensed person who is speaking over an Amateur station's microphone while a licensed person is present; (D) A government official who comes to an Amateur station to take control for test purposes.

2A8.2 If you designate another Amateur operator to be responsible for the transmissions from your station, what is the other operator called? (A) Auxiliary operator; (B) Operations coordinator; (C) Third party; (D) Control operator.

2A9.1 List the five United States Amateur operator/primary station license Classes in order of increasing privileges. (A) Novice, General, Technician, Advanced, Amateur Extra; (B) Novice, Technician, General, Advanced, Digital; (C) Novice, Technician, General, Amateur, Extra; (D) Novice, Technician, General, Advanced, Amateur Extra.

2A9.3 What is the license Class immediately above Novice Class? (A) The Digital Class license; (B) The Technician Class license; (C) The General Class license; (D) The Experimenter's Class license.

2A10.2 What frequencies are available in the Amateur 40-meter wavelength band for a control operator holding a Novice Class operator license in ITU Region 2? (A) 3500 to 4000 kHz; (B) 3700 to 3750 kHz; (C) 7100 to 7150 kHz; (D) 7000 to 7300 kHz.

2A10.3 What frequencies are available in the Amateur 15-meter wavelength band for a control operator holding a Novice Class operator license? (A) 21.100 to 21.200 MHz; (B) 21.000 to 21.450 MHz; (C) 28.000 to 29.700 MHz; (D) 28.100 to 28.200 MHz.

2A10.4 What frequencies are available in the Amateur 10-meter wavelength band for a control operator holding a Novice Class operator license? (A) 28.000 to 29.700 MHz; (B) 28.100 to 28.300 MHz; (C) 28.100 to 28.500 MHz; (D) 28.300 to 28.500 MHz.

2A10.5 What frequencies are available in the Amateur 220-MHz band for a control operator holding a Novice Class operator license in ITU Region 2? (A) 225.0 to 230.5 MHz; (B) 222.1 to 223.91 MHz; (C) 224.1 to 225.1 MHz; (D) 222.2 to 224.0 MHz.

2A10.6 What frequencies are available in the Amateur 1270-MHz band for a control operator holding a Novice Class operator license? (A) 1260 to 1270 MHz; (B) 1240 to 1300 MHz; (C) 1270 to 1295 MHz; (D) 1240 to 1246 MHz.

2A10.7 If you are operating your Amateur station on 3725 kHz, in what meter band are you operating? (A) 80 meters; (B) 40 meters; (C) 15 meters; (D) 10 meters.

2A10.8 If you are operating your Amateur station on 7125 kHz, in what meter band are you operating? (A) 80 meters; (B) 40 meters; (C) 15 meters; (D) 10 meters.

2A10.9 If you are operating your Amateur station on 21150 kHz, in what meter band are you operating? (A) 80 meters; (B) 40 meters; (C) 15 meters; (D) 10 meters.

2A10.10 If you are operating your Amateur station on 28150 kHz, in what meter band are you operating? (A) 80 meters; (B) 40 meters; (C) 15 meters; (D) 10 meters.

2A11.1 Who is eligible to obtain a U.S. Amateur operator/primary station license? (A) Anyone except a representative of a foreign government; (B) Only a citizen of the United States; (C) Anyone; (D) Anyone except an employee of the United States Government.

2A11.2 Who is not eligible to obtain a U.S. Amateur operator/primary station license? (A) Any citizen of a country other than the United States; (B) A representative of a foreign government; (C) No one; (D) An employee of the United States Government.

2A12.1 What FCC examination elements are required for a Novice Class license? (*See page 10*) (A) Elements 1(A) and 2(A); (B) Elements 1(A) and 3(A); (C) Elements 1(A) and 2; (D) Elements 2 and 4.

2A12.2 What is an FCC Element 1(A) examination intended to prove? (*See page 10*) (A) The applicant's ability to send and receive texts in the international Morse code at not less than 5 words per minute; (B) The applicant's ability to send and receive texts in the international Morse code at not less than 13 words per minute; (C) The applicant's knowledge of Novice Class theory and regulations; (D) The applicant's ability to recognize Novice frequency assignments and operating modes.

2A12.3 What is an FCC Element 2 examination? (*See page 10*) (A) A test of the applicant's ability to send and receive Morse code at 5 words per minute; (B) The written examination concerning the privileges of a Technician Class operator license; (C) A test of the applicant's ability to recognize Novice frequency assignments; (D) The written examination concerning the privileges of a Novice Class operator license.

2A13.1 Who is eligible to obtain an FCC-issued written authorization for an Amateur station? (A) A licensed Amateur operator; (B) Any unlicensed person, except an agent of a foreign government; (C) Any unlicensed person, except an employee of the United States Government; (D) Any unlicensed United States Citizen.

2A14.1 Why is an Amateur operator required to furnish the FCC with a current mailing address served by the U.S. Postal service? (A) So the FCC has a record of the location of each Amateur station; (B) In order to comply with the Commission's rules and so the FCC can correspond with the licensee; (C) So the FCC can send license-renewal notices; (D) So the FCC can compile a list for use in a call sign directory.

2A15.1 Which one of the following call signs is a valid U.S. Amateur call? (A) UA4HAK; (B) KBL7766; (C) KA9OLS; (D) BY7HY.

2A15.2 Which one of the following call signs is a valid U.S. Amateur call? (A) CE2FTF; (B) G3GVA; (C) UA1ZAM; (D) AA2Z.

2A15.3 Which one of the following call signs is not a valid U.S. Amateur call? (A) KDV5653; (B) WA1DVU; (C) KA5BUG; (D) NT0Z.

2A15.4 What letters may be used for the first letter in a valid U.S. Amateur call sign? (A) K, N, U and W; (B) A, K, N and W; (C) A, B, C and D; (D) A, N, V and W.

2A15.5 Excluding special-event call signs that may be issued by the FCC, what numbers may be used in a valid U.S. call sign? (A) Any double-digit number, 10 through 99; (B) Any double-digit number, 22 through 45; (C) Any single digit, 1 through 9; (D) A single digit, 0 through 9.

2A16.1 Your Novice license was issued on November 1, 1988. When will it expire? (A) On the date specified on the license; (B) November 30, 1998; (C) November 1, 1993; (D) November 1, 1990.

2A17.1 What does the term emission mean? (A) RF signals transmitted from a radio station; (B) Signals refracted by the E layer; (C) Filter out the carrier of a received signal; (D) Baud rate.

2A17.2 What emission types are Novice control operators permitted to use on the 80-meter wavelength band? (A) CW only; (B) Data only; (C) RTTY only; (D) Phone only.

2A17.3 What emission types are Novice control operators permitted to use in the 40-meter wavelength band? (A) CW only; (B) Data only; (C) RTTY only; (D) Phone only.

2A17.4 What emission types are Novice control operators permitted to use in the 15-meter wavelength band? (A) CW only; (B) Data only; (C) RTTY only; (D) Phone only.

2A17.5 What emission types are Novice control operators permitted to use from 3675 to 3725 kHz? (A) Phone only; (B) CW and phone; (C) All Amateur emission privileges authorized for use on those frequencies; (D) CW only.

2A17.6 What emission types are Novice control operators permitted to use from 7100 to 7150 kHz in ITU Region 2? (A) CW and data; (B) Phone; (C) All Amateur emission privileges authorized for use on those frequencies; (D) CW only.

2A17.7 What emission types are Novice control operators permitted to use on frequencies from 21.1 to 21.2 MHz? (A) CW and data only; (B) CW and phone only; (C) All Amateur emission privileges authorized for use on those frequencies; (D) CW only.

2A17.8 What emission types are Novice control operators permitted to use on frequencies from 28.1 to 28.3 MHz? (A) All authorized Amateur emission privileges; (B) Data or phone only; (C) CW, RTTY and data; (D) CW and phone only.

2A17.9 What emission types are Novice control operators permitted to use on frequencies from 28.3 to 28.5 MHz? (A) All authorized Amateur emission privileges; (B) CW and data only; (C) CW and single-sideband phone only; (D) Data and phone only.

2A17.10 What emission types are Novice control operators permitted to use on the Amateur 220-MHz band in ITU Region 2? (A) CW and phone only; (B) CW and data only; (C) Data and phone only; (D) All Amateur emission privileges authorized for use on 220 MHz.

2A17.11 What emission types are Novice control operators permitted to use on the Amateur 1270-MHz band? (A) Data and phone only; (B) CW and data only; (C) CW and phone only; (D) All Amateur emission privileges authorized for use on 1270 MHz.

2A17.12 On what frequencies in the 10-meter wavelength band may a Novice control operator use single-sideband phone? (A) 3700 to 3750 kHz; (B) 7100 to 7150 kHz; (C) 21100 to 21200 kHz; (D) 28300 to 28500 kHz.

2A17.13 On what frequencies in the 1.25-meter wavelength band in ITU Region 2 may a Novice control operator use FM phone emission? (A) 28.3 to 28.5 MHz; (B) 144.0 to 148.0 MHz; (C) 222.1 to 223.91 MHz; (D) 1240 to 1270 MHz.

2A18.1 What amount of output transmitting power may a Novice Class control operator use when operating below 30 MHz? (A) 200 watts input; (B) 250 watts output; (C) 1500 watts PEP output; (D) The minimum legal power necessary to carry out the desired communications.

2A18.2 What is the maximum transmitting power ever permitted to be used by an Amateur station transmitting in the 80, 40 and 15-meter Novice bands? (A) 75 watts PEP output; (B) 100 watts PEP output; (C) 200 watts PEP output; (D) 1500 watts PEP output.

2A18.3 What is the maximum transmitting power permitted an Amateur station transmitting on 3725 kHz? (A) 75 watts PEP output; (B) 100 watts PEP output; (C) 200 watts PEP output; (D) 1500 watts PEP output.

2A18.4 What is the maximum transmitting power permitted an Amateur station transmitting on 7125 kHz? (A) 75 watts PEP output; (B) 100 watts PEP output; (C) 200 watts PEP output; (D) 1500 watts PEP output.

2A18.5 What is the maximum transmitting power permitted an Amateur station transmitting on 21.125 MHz? (A) 75 watts PEP output; (B) 100 watts PEP output; (C) 200 watts PEP output; (D) 1500 watts PEP output.

2A19.1 What is the maximum transmitting power permitted an Amateur station with a Novice control operator transmitting on 28.125 MHz? (A) 75 watts PEP output; (B) 100 watts PEP output; (C) 200 watts PEP output; (D) 1500 watts PEP output.

2A19.2 What is the maximum transmitting power permitted an Amateur station with a Novice control operator transmitting in the Amateur 10-meter wavelength band? (A) 25 watts PEP output; (B) 200 watts PEP output; (C) 1000 watts PEP output; (D) 1500 watts PEP output.

2A19.3 What is the maximum transmitting power permitted an Amateur station with a Novice control operator transmitting in the Amateur 220-MHz band? (A) 5 watts PEP output; (B) 10 watts PEP output; (C) 25 watts PEP output; (D) 200 watts PEP output.

2A19.4 What is the maximum transmitting power permitted an Amateur station with a Novice control operator transmitting in the Amateur 1270-MHz band? (A) 5 milliwatts PEP output; (B) 500 milliwatts PEP output; (C) 1 watt PEP output; (D) 5 watts PEP output.

2A19.5 What amount of transmitting power may an Amateur station with a Novice control operator use in the Amateur 220-MHz band? (A) Not less than 5 watts PEP output; (B) The minimum legal power necessary to maintain reliable communications; (C) Not more than 50 watts PEP output; (D) Not more than 200 watts PEP output.

2A20.1 What term is used to describe narrow-band direct-printing telegraphy emissions? (A) Teleport communications; (B) Direct communications; (C) RTTY communications; (D) Third-party communications.

2A20.2 What term is used to describe telemetry, telecommand and computer communications emissions? (A) Teleport communications; (B) Direct communications; (C) Data communications; (D) Third-party communications.

2A20.3 On what frequencies in the 10-meter wavelength band are Novice control operators permitted to transmit RTTY? (A) 28.1 to 28.5 MHz; (B) 28.0 to 29.7 MHz; (C) 28.1 to 28.2 MHz; (D) 28.1 to 28.3 MHz.

2A21.1 Who is held responsible for the proper operation of an Amateur station? (A) Only the control operator; (B) Only the station licensee; (C) Both the control operator and the station licensee; (D) The person who owns the property where the station is located.

2A21.2 You allow another Amateur operator to use your Amateur station. What are your responsibilities, as the station licensee? (A) You and the other Amateur operator are equally responsible for the proper operation of your station; (B) Only the control operator is responsible for the proper operation of the station; (C) As the station licensee, you must be at the control point of your station whenever it is operated; (D) You must notify the FCC when another Amateur will be the control operator of your station.

2A21.3 What is your primary responsibility as the station licensee? (A) You must permit any licensed Amateur operator to operate your station at any time upon request; (B) You must be present whenever the station is operated; (C) You must notify the FCC in writing whenever another Amateur operator will act as the control operator; (D) You are responsible for the proper operation of the station for which you are licensed.

2A21.4 If you are the licensee of an Amateur station when are you not responsible for its proper operation? (A) Only when another licensed Amateur is the control operator; (B) The licensee is always responsible for the proper operation of the station for which he or she is licensed; (C) Only after notifying the FCC in writing that another licensed Amateur will assume responsibility for the proper operation of your station; (D) Only when your station is in repeater operation.

2A22.1 When must an Amateur station have a control operator? (A) A control operator is only required for training purposes; (B) Whenever the station receiver is operated; (C) Whenever the station is transmitting; (D) A control operator is not required.

2A22.2 Another Amateur gives you permission to use her Amateur station. What are your responsibilities, as the control operator? (A) Both you and she are equally responsible for the proper operation of her station; (B) Only the station licensee is responsible for the proper operation of the station, not you the control operator; (C) You must be certain the station licensee has given proper FCC notice that you will be the control operator; (D) You must inspect all antennas and related equipment to ensure they are working properly.

2A23.1 Who may be the control operator of an Amateur station? (A) Any person over 21 years of age; (B) Any properly licensed Amateur operator that is designated by the station licensee; (C) Any licensed Amateur operator with an Advanced Class license or higher; (D) Any person over 21 years of age with a General Class license or higher.

2A24.1 Where must an Amateur operator be when he or she is performing the duties of control operator? (A) Anywhere in the same building as the transmitter; (B) At the control point of the Amateur station; (C) At the station entrance, to control entry to the room; (D) Within sight of the station monitor, to view the output spectrum of the transmitter.

2A25.1 Where must you keep your Amateur operator license when you are operating a station? (A) Your original operator license must always be posted in plain view; (B) Your original operator license must always be taped to the inside front cover of your station log; (C) You must have the original or a photocopy of your operator license in your possession; (D) You must have the original or a photocopy of your operator license posted at your primary station location. You need not have the original license nor a copy in your possession to operate another station.

2A26.1 Where must you keep your written authorization for an Amateur station? (A) Your original station license must always be taped to the inside front cover of your station log; (B) Your original station license must always be posted in plain view; (C) You must post the original or a photocopy of your station license at the main entrance to the transmitter building; (D) The original or a photocopy of the written authorization for an Amateur station must be retained at the station.

2A27.1 How often must an Amateur station be identified? (A) At the beginning of the contact and at least every ten minutes during a contact; (B) At least once during each transmission; (C) At least every ten minutes during a contact and at the end of the contact; (D) Every 15 minutes during a contact and at the end of the contact.

2A27.2 As an Amateur operator, how should you correctly identify your station? (A) With the name and location of the control operator; (B) With the station call sign; (C) With the call of the control operator, even when he or she is visiting another radio Amateur's station; (D) With the name and location of the station licensee, followed by the two-letter designation of the nearest FCC field office.

2A27.3 What station identification, if any, is required at the beginning of communication? (A) The operator originating the contact must transmit both call signs; (B) No identification is required at the beginning of the contact; (C) Both operators must transmit their own call signs; (D) Both operators must transmit both call signs.

2A27.4 What station identification, if any, is required at the end of a communication? (A) Both stations must transmit their own call sign, assuming they are FCC-licensed; (B) No identification is required at the end of the contact; (C) The station originating the contact must always transmit both call signs; (D) Both stations must transmit their own call sign followed by a two-letter designator for the nearest FCC field office.

2A27.5 What do the FCC rules for Amateur station identification generally require? (A) Each Amateur station shall give its call sign at the beginning of each communication, and every ten minutes or less during a communication; (B) Each Amateur station shall give its call sign at the end of each communication, and every ten minutes or less during a communication; (C) Each Amateur station shall give its call sign at the beginning of each communication, and every five minutes or less during a communication; (D) Each Amateur station shall give its call sign at the end of each communication, and every five minutes or less during a communication.

2A27.6 What is the fewest number of times you must transmit your Amateur station identification during a 25 minute QSO? (A) 1; (B) 2; (C) 3; (D) 4.

2A27.7 What is the longest period of time during a QSO that an Amateur station does not need to transmit its station identification? (A) 5 minutes; (B) 10 minutes; (C) 15 minutes; (D) 20 minutes.

2A28.1 With which Amateur stations may an FCC-licensed Amateur station communicate? (A) All Amateur stations; (B) All public noncommercial radio stations unless prohibited by the station's government; (C) Only with U.S. Amateur stations; (D) All Amateur stations, unless prohibited by the Amateur's government.

2A28.2 With which non-Amateur stations may an FCC-licensed Amateur station communicate? (A) No non-Amateur stations; (B) All such stations; (C) Only those authorized by the FCC; (D) Only those who use the International Morse code.

2A29.1 When must the licensee of an Amateur station in portable or mobile operation notify the FCC? (A) One week in advance if the operation will last for more than 24 hours; (B) FCC notification is not required for portable or mobile operation; (C) One week in advance if the operation will last for more than a week; (D) One month in advance of any portable or mobile operation.

2A29.2 When may you operate your Amateur station at a location within the United States, its territories or possessions other than the one listed on your station license? (A) Only during times of emergency; (B) Only after giving proper notice to the FCC; (C) During an emergency or an FCC-approved emergency preparedness drill; (D) Whenever you want to.

2A30.1 When are communications pertaining to the business or commercial affairs of any party permitted in the Amateur Service? (A) Only when the immediate safety of human life or immediate protection of property is threatened; (B) There are no rules against conducting business communications in the Amateur Service; (C) No business communications of any kind are ever permitted in the Amateur service; (D) Business communications are permitted between the hours of 9 AM to 5 PM, only on weekdays.

2A30.2 You wish to obtain an application for membership in the American Radio Relay League. When would you be permitted to send an Amateur Radio message requesting the application? (A) At any time, since the ARRL is a not-for-profit organization; (B) Never. This would facilitate the commercial affairs of the ARRL; (C) Only during normal business hours, between 9 AM and 5 PM; (D) At any time, since there are no rules against conducting business communications in the Amateur Service.

2A30.3 On your way home from work you decide to order pizza for dinner. When would you be permitted to use the autopatch on your radio club repeater to order the pizza? (A) At any time, since you will not profit from the communications; (B) Only during normal business hours, between 9 AM and 5 PM; (C) At any time, since there are no rules against conducting business communications in the Amateur Service; (D) Never. This would facilitate the commercial affairs of a business.

2A31.1 When may an FCC-licensed Amateur operator communicate with an Amateur operator in a foreign country? (A) Only when the foreign operator uses English as his primary language; (B) All the time, except on 28.600 to 29.700 MHz; (C) Only when a third party agreement exists between the U.S. and the foreign country; (D) At any time unless prohibited by either the U.S. or the foreign government.

2A32.1 When may an Amateur station be used to transmit messages for hire? (A) Under no circumstances may an Amateur station be hired to transmit messages; (B) Modest payment from a non-profit charitable organization is permissible; (C) No money may change hands, but a radio Amateur may be compensated for services rendered with gifts of equipment or services rendered as a returned favor; (D) All payments received in return for transmitting messages by Amateur radio must be reported to the IRS.

2A32.2 When may the control operator be paid to transmit messages from an Amateur station? (A) The control operator may be paid if he or she works for a public service agency such as the Red Cross; (B) The control operator may not be paid under any circumstances; (C) The control operator may be paid if he or she reports all income earned from operating an Amateur station to the IRS as receipt of tax-deductible contributions; (D) The control operator may accept compensation if he or she works for a club station during the period in which the station is transmitting telegraphy practice or information bulletins if certain exacting conditions are met.

2A33.1 When is an Amateur operator permitted to broadcast information intended for the general public? (A) Amateur operators are not permitted to broadcast information intended for the general public; (B) Only when the operator is being paid to transmit the information; (C) Only when such transmissions last less than 1 hour in any 24-hour period; (D) Only when such transmissions last longer than 15 minutes.

2A34.1 What is third-party communications? (A) A message passed from the control operator of an Amateur station to another control operator on behalf of another person; (B) Public service communications handled on behalf of a minor political party; (C) Only messages that are formally handled through Amateur radio channels; (D) A report of highway conditions transmitted over a local repeater.

2A34.2 Who is a third party in Amateur communications? (A) The Amateur station that breaks into a two-way contact between two other Amateur stations; (B) Any person for whom a message is passed through Amateur communication channels other than the control operators of the two stations handling the message; (C) A shortwave listener monitoring a two-way Amateur communication; (D) The control operator present when an unlicensed person communicates over an Amateur station.

2A34.3 When is an Amateur operator permitted to transmit a message to a foreign country for a third party? (A) Anytime; (B) Never; (C) Anytime, unless there is a third-party communications agreement between the U.S. and the foreign government; (D) When there is a third-party communications agreement between the U.S. and the foreign government, or when the third party is eligible to be the control operator of the station.

2A35.1 Is an Amateur station permitted to transmit music? (A) The transmission of music is not permitted in the Amateur Service; (B) When the music played produces no dissonances or spurious emissions; (C) When it is used to jam an illegal transmission; (D) Only above 1280 MHz.

2A36.1 Is the use of codes or ciphers where the intent is to obscure the meaning permitted during a two-way communication in the Amateur Service? (A) Codes and ciphers are permitted during ARRL-sponsored contests; (B) Codes and ciphers are permitted during nationally declared emergencies; (C) The transmission of codes and ciphers where the intent is to obscure the meaning is not permitted in the Amateur Service; (D) Codes and ciphers are permitted above 1280 MHz.

2A36.2 When is an operator in the Amateur Service permitted to use abbreviations that are intended to obscure the meaning of the message? (A) Only during ARRL-sponsored contests; (B) Only on frequencies above 222.5 MHz; (C) Only during a declared communications emergency; (D) Abbreviations that are intended to obscure the meaning of the message may never be used in the Amateur Service.

2A37.1 Under what circumstances, if any, may the control operator cause false or deceptive signals or communications to be transmitted? (A) Under no circumstances; (B) When operating a beacon transmitter in a "fox hunt" exercise; (C) When playing a harmless "practical joke" without causing interference to other stations that are not involved; (D) When you need to obscure the meaning of transmitted information to ensure secrecy.

2A37.2 If an Amateur operator transmits the word "MAYDAY" when no actual emergency has occurred, what is this called? (A) A traditional greeting in May; (B) An Emergency Action System test transmission; (C) False or deceptive signals; (D) "MAYDAY" has no significance in an emergency situation.

2A38.1 When may an Amateur station transmit unidentified communications? (A) A transmission need not be identified if it is restricted to brief tests not intended for reception by other parties; (B) A transmission need not be identified when conducted on a clear frequency or "dead band" where interference will not occur; (C) An Amateur operator may never transmit unidentified communications; (D) A transmission need not be identified unless two-way communications or third-party communications handling are involved.

2A38.2 What is the meaning of the term unidentified radio communications or signals? (A) Radio communications in which the transmitting station's call sign is transmitted in modes other than CW and voice; (B) Radio communications approaching a receiving station from an unknown direction; (C) Radio communications in which the operator fails to transmit his or her name and QTH; (D) Radio communications in which the station identification is not transmitted.

2A38.3 What is the term used to describe a transmission from an Amateur station that does not transmit the required station identification? (A) Unidentified communications or signals; (B) Reluctance modulation; (C) N0N emission; (D) Tactical communication.

2A39.1 When may an Amateur operator willfully or maliciously interfere with a radio communication or signal? (A) You may jam another person's transmissions if that person is not operating in a legal manner; (B) You may interfere with another station's signals if that station begins transmitting on a frequency already occupied by your station; (C) You may never willfully or maliciously interfere with another station's transmissions; (D) You may expect, and cause, deliberate interference because it is unavoidable during crowded band conditions.

2A39.2 What is the meaning of the term malicious interference? (A) Accidental interference; (B) Intentional interference; (C) Mild interference; (D) Occasional interference.

2A39.3 What is the term used to describe an Amateur radio transmission that is intended to disrupt other communications in progress? (A) Interrupted CW; (B) Malicious interference; (C) Transponded signals; (D) Unidentified transmissions.

2A40.1 As an Amateur operator, you receive an Official Notice of Violation from the FCC. How promptly must you respond? (A) Within 90 days; (B) Within 30 days; (C) As specified in the Notice; (D) The next day.

2A40.2 If you were to receive a voice distress signal from a station on a frequency outside your operator privileges, what restrictions would apply to assisting the station in distress? (A) You would not be allowed to assist the station because the frequency of its signals were outside your operator privileges; (B) You would be allowed to assist the station only if your signals were restricted to the nearest frequency band of your privileges; (C) You would be allowed to assist the station on a frequency outside of your operator privileges only if you used international Morse code; (D) You would be allowed to assist the station on a frequency outside of your operator privileges using any means of radio communications at your disposal.

2A40.3 If you were in a situation where normal communication systems were disrupted due to a disaster, what restrictions would apply to essential communications you might provide in connection with the immediate safety of human life? (A) You would not be allowed to communicate at all except to the FCC Engineer in Charge of the area concerned; (B) You would be restricted to communications using only the emissions and frequencies authorized to your operator privileges; (C) You would be allowed to communicate on frequencies outside your operator privileges only if you used international Morse code; (D) You would be allowed to use any means of radio communication at your disposal.

SUBELEMENT 3AA (5 questions).

3AA1.1 What is the control point of an Amateur station? (A) The location at which the control operator function is performed; (B) The operating position of any Amateur Radio station operating as a repeater user station; (C) The physical location of any Amateur Radio transmitter, even if it is operated by radio link from some other location; (D) The variable frequency oscillator (VFO) of the transmitter.

3AA1.2 What is the term for the location at which the control operator function is performed? (A) The operating desk; (B) The control point; (C) The station location; (D) The manual control location.

3AA2.2 Which operator licenses authorize privileges on 52.525 MHz? (A) Extra, Advanced only; (B) Extra, Advanced, General only; (C) Extra, Advanced, General, Technician only; (D) Extra, Advanced, General, Technician, Novice.

3AA2.3 Which operator licenses authorize privileges on 146.52 MHz? (A) Extra, Advanced, General, Technician, Novice; (B) Extra, Advanced, General, Technician only; (C) Extra, Advanced, General only; (D) Extra, Advanced only.

3AA2.4 Which operator licenses authorize privileges on 223.50 MHz? (A) Extra, Advanced, General, Technician, Novice; (B) Extra, Advanced, General, Technician only; (C) Extra, Advanced, General only; (D) Extra, Advanced only.

3AA2.5 Which operator licenses authorize privileges on 446.0 MHz? (A) Extra, Advanced, General, Technician, Novice; (B) Extra, Advanced, General, Technician only; (C) Extra, Advanced, General only; (D) Extra, Advanced only.

3AA3.1 How often do Amateur service licenses generally need to be renewed? (A) Every 10 years; (B) Every 5 years; (C) Every 2 years; (D) They are lifetime licenses.

3AA3.2 The FCC currently issues Amateur licenses carrying 10-year terms. What is the "grace period" during which the FCC will renew an expired 10-year license? (A) 2 years; (B) 5 years; (C) 10 years; (D) There is no grace period.

3AA3.3 What action would you take to modify your operator/primary station license? (A) Properly fill out FCC Form 610 and send it to the FCC in Gettysburg, PA; (B) Properly fill out FCC Form 610 and send it to the nearest FCC field office; (C) Write the FCC at their nearest field office; (D) There is no need to modify an Amateur license between renewals.

3AA4.1 On what frequencies within the 6-meter wavelength band may FM phone emissions be transmitted? (A) 50.0-54.0 MHz only; (B) 50.1-54.0 MHz only; (C) 51.0-54.0 MHz only; (D) 52.0-54.0 MHz only.

3AA4.2 On what frequencies within the 2-meter wavelength band may FM image emissions be transmitted? (A) 144.1-148.0 MHz only; (B) 146.0-148.0 MHz only; (C) 144.0-148.0 MHz only; (D) 146.0-147.0 MHz only.

3AA4.3 What emission type may always be used for station identification, regardless of the transmitting frequency? (A) CW; (B) RTTY; (C) MCW; (D) Phone.

3AA5.1 If you are using a frequency within a band designated to the Amateur service on a secondary basis and another station assigned to a primary service on that band causes interference, what action should you take? (A) Notify the FCC's regional Engineer in Charge of the interference; (B) Increase your transmitter's power to overcome the interference; (C) Attempt to contact the station and request that it stop the interference; (D) Change frequencies; you may also be causing interference to the other station and that would be a violation of FCC rules.

3AA5.2 What is the basic principle of frequency sharing between two stations allocated to a primary service within a frequency band, but each in a different ITU Region or Subregion? (A) The station with a control operator holding a lesser Class of license must yield the frequency to the station with a control operator holding a higher Class license; (B) The station with a lower power output must yield the frequency to the station with a higher power output; (C) Both stations have an equal right to operate on the frequency; (D) Stations in ITU Regions 1 and 3 must yield the frequency to stations in ITU Region 2.

3AA6-1.1 FCC Rules specify the maximum transmitter power that you may use with your Amateur Radio station. At what point in your station is the transmitter power measured? (A) By measuring the final amplifier supply voltage inside the transmitter or amplifier; (B) By measuring the final amplifier supply current inside the transmitter or amplifier; (C) At the antenna terminals of the transmitter or amplifier; (D) On the antenna itself, after the feed line.

3AA6-1.2 What is the term used to define the average power supplied to the antenna transmission line during one RF cycle at the crest of the modulation envelope? (A) Peak transmitter power; (B) Peak output power; (C) Average radio-frequency power; (D) Peak envelope power.

3AA6-2.1 Notwithstanding the numerical limitations in the FCC Rules, how much transmitting power shall be used by an Amateur station? (A) There is no regulation other than the numerical limits; (B) The minimum power level required to achieve S9 signal reports; (C) The minimum power necessary to carry out the desired communication; (D) The maximum power available, as long as it is under the allowable limit.

3AA6-3.1 What is the maximum transmitting power permitted an Amateur station on 146.52 MHz? (A) 200 watts PEP output; (B) 500 watts ERP; (C) 1000 watts DC input; (D) 1500 watts PEP output.

3AA6-4.1 What is the maximum transmitting power permitted an Amateur station in beacon operation? (A) 10 watts PEP output; (B) 100 watts PEP output; (C) 500 watts PEP output; (D) 1500 watts PEP output.

3AA7-1.1 What is the maximum sending speed permitted for a RTTY transmission between 28 and 50 MHz? (A) 56 kilobauds; (B) 19.6 kilobauds; (C) 1200 bauds; (D) 300 bauds.

3AA7-1.2 What is the maximum sending speed permitted for a RTTY transmission between 50 and 220 MHz? (A) 56 kilobauds; (B) 19.6 kilobauds; (C) 1200 bauds; (D) 300 bauds.

3AA7-1.3 What is the maximum sending speed permitted for a RTTY transmission above 220 MHz? (A) 300 bauds; (B) 1200 bauds; (C) 19.6 kilobauds; (D) 56 kilobauds.

3AA7-2.1 What is the maximum frequency shift permitted for RTTY when transmitted below 50 MHz? (A) 100 Hz; (B) 500 Hz; (C) 1000 Hz; (D) 5000 Hz.

3AA7-2.2 What is the maximum frequency shift permitted for RTTY when transmitted above 50 MHz? (A) 100 Hz or the sending speed, in bauds, whichever is greater; (B) 500 Hz or the sending speed, in bauds, whichever is greater; (C) The FCC rules do not specify a maximum frequency shift above 50 MHz; (D) 5000 Hz or the sending speed, in bauds, whichever is greater.

3AA7-3.1 What is the maximum authorized bandwidth of an RTTY, data or multiplexed emission using a specified digital code within the frequency range of 50 to 225 MHz? (A) 20 kHz; (B) 50 kHz; (C) The total bandwidth shall not exceed that of a single-sideband emission; (D) The total bandwidth shall not exceed 10 times that of a CW emission.

3AA7-3.2 What is the maximum authorized bandwidth of a RTTY, data or multiplexed emission using an unspecified digital code within the frequency range of 220 to 450 MHz? (A) 50 kHz; (B) 150 kHz; (C) 200 kHz; (D) 100 kHz.

3AA7-3.3 What is the maximum authorized bandwidth of an RTTY, data or multiplexed emission using an unspecified digital code within the 420 to 450 MHz Amateur band? (A) 50 kHz; (B) 200 kHz; (C) 300 kHz; (D) 100 kHz.

3AA8-1.1 How must a control operator who has a Novice license and a Certificate of Successful Completion of Examination for Technician privileges identify the station when transmitting on 146.34 MHz? (A) The new Technician may not operate on 146.34 until his or her new license arrives; (B) The licensee gives his or her call sign, followed by any suitable word that denotes the slant mark and the identifier "KT"; (C) No special form of identification is needed; (D) The licensee gives his or her call sign and states the location of the VE examination where he or she obtained the certificate of successful completion.

3AA8-2.1 Which language(s) must be used when making the station identification by telephony? (A) The language being used for the contact may be used if it is not English, providing the U.S. has a third-party traffic agreement with that country; (B) English must be used for identification; (C) Any language may be used, if the country which uses that language is a member of the International Telecommunication Union; (D) The language being used for the contact must be used for identification purposes.

3AA8-3.1 What does the FCC recommend to aid correct station identification when using phone? (A) A speech compressor; (B) Q signals; (C) A recognized phonetic alphabet; (D) Unique words of the operator's choice.

3AA9-1.1 What is the term used to describe an Amateur station transmitting communications for the purpose of observation of propagation and reception or other related experimental activities? (A) Beacon operation; (B) Repeater operation; (C) Auxiliary operation; (D) Radio control operation.

3AA9-2.1 What Class of Amateur operator license must you hold to operate a beacon station? (A) Technician, General, Advanced or Amateur Extra Class; (B) General, Advanced or Amateur Extra Class; (C) Amateur Extra Class only; (D) Any license Class.

3AA10.1 What is the maximum transmitter power an Amateur station is permitted when transmitting signals to control a model craft? (A) One watt; (B) One milliwatt; (C) Two watts; (D) Three watts.

3AA10.2 What minimum information must be indicated on the label affixed to a transmitter transmitting signals to control a model craft? (A) Station call sign; (B) Station call sign and operating times; (C) Station call sign and the station licensee's name and address; (D) Station call sign, Class of license, and operating times.

3AA10.3 What are the station identification requirements for an Amateur station transmitting signals to control a model craft? (A) Once every ten minutes, and at the beginning and end of each transmission; (B) Once every ten minutes; (C) At the beginning and end of each transmission; (D) Station identification is not required provided that a label indicating the station call sign and the station licensee's name and address is affixed to the station transmitter.

3AA10.4 Where must the writing indicating the station call sign and the licensee's name and address be affixed in order to operate under the special rules for radio control of remote model craft and vehicles? (A) It must be in the operator's possession; (B) It must be affixed to the transmitter; (C) It must be affixed to the craft or vehicle; (D) It must be filed with the nearest FCC field office.

3AA11-1.1 If an Amateur repeater is causing harmful interference to another Amateur repeater and a frequency coordinator has coordinated (recommends) the operation of one station and not the other, who is primarily responsible for resolving the interference? (A) The licensee of the non-coordinated (unrecommended) repeater; (B) Both repeater licensees; (C) The licensee of the coordinated (recommended) repeater; (D) The frequency coordinator.

3AA11-1.2 If an Amateur repeater is causing harmful interference to another Amateur repeater and a frequency coordinator has coordinated (recommends) the operation of both stations, who is primarily responsible for resolving the interference? (A) The licensee of the repeater which has been coordinated for the longest period of time; (B) Both repeater licensees; (C) The licensee of the repeater which has been coordinated the most recently; (D) The frequency coordinator.

3AA11-1.3 If an Amateur repeater is causing harmful interference to another Amateur repeater and a frequency coordinator has not coordinated the operation of either station, who is primarily responsible for resolving the interference? (A) Both repeater licensees; (B) The licensee of the repeater which has been in operation for the longest period of time; (C) The licensee of the repeater which has been in operation for the shortest period of time; (D) The frequency .

3AA11-2.1 Under what circumstances does the FCC declare a temporary state of communication emergency? (A) When a declaration of war is received from Congress; (B) When the maximum usable frequency goes above 28 MHz; (C) When communications facilities in Washington, DC, are disrupted; (D) When a disaster disrupts normal communications systems in a particular area.

3AA11-2.2 By what means should a request for a declaration of a temporary state of communication emergency be initiated? (A) Communication with the FCC Engineer-In-Charge of the affected area; (B) Communication with the U.S. senator or congressman for the area affected; (C) Communication with the local Emergency Coordinator; (D) Communication with the Chief of the FCC Private Radio Bureau.

3AA11-2.3 What information is included in an FCC declaration of a temporary state of communication emergency? (A) Designation of the areas affected and of organizations authorized to use radio communications in the affected area; (B) Designation of Amateur frequency bands for use only by Amateurs participating in emergency communications in the affected area, and complete suspension of Novice operating privileges for the duration of the emergency; (C) Any special conditions and special rules to be observed during the communication emergency; (D) Suspension of Amateur rules regarding station identification and business communication.

3AA11-2.4 If a disaster disrupts normal communication systems in an area where the Amateur service is regulated by the FCC, what kinds of transmissions are authorized to Amateur stations in such an area? (A) Communications which are necessary to meet essential communication needs and facilitate relief actions; (B) Communications which allow a commercial business to continue to operate in the affected area; (C) Communications for which material compensation has been paid to the Amateur operator for delivery into the affected area; (D) Communications which are to be used for program production or newsgathering for broadcasting purposes.

3AA12.1 What is meant by the term broadcasting? (A) Transmissions intended for reception by the general public, either direct or relayed; (B) Retransmission by automatic means of programs or signals emanating from any Class of station other than Amateur; (C) The transmission of any one-way radio communication, regardless of purpose or content; (D) Any one-way or two-way radio communication involving more than two stations.

3AA12.2 Which of the following is an Amateur station that cannot automatically retransmit signals of other Amateur stations? (A) Auxiliary station; (B) Repeater station; (C) Beacon station; (D) Space station.

3AA12.3 Which of the following is an Amateur station that is permitted to automatically retransmit signals of other Amateur stations? (A) Beacon station; (B) Space station; (C) Official bulletin station; (D) RACES station.

3AA12.4 Signals from what type of radio station may be directly retransmitted by an Amateur station? (A) AM radio station; (B) Police or fire department radio station; (C) NOAA weather station; (D) U.S. Government communications between the space shuttle and associated Earth stations with prior approval from the National Aeronautics and Space Administration (NASA).

3AA12.5 When may U.S. Government communications between the space shuttle and associated Earth stations be directly retransmitted by an Amateur station? (A) After prior approval has been obtained from the FCC in Washington, DC; (B) No radio stations other than Amateur may be retransmitted in the Amateur service; (C) After prior approval has been obtained from the National Aeronautics and Space Administration (NASA); (D) After prior approval has been obtained from the nearest FCC Engineer-In-Charge.

3AA13.1 What kinds of one-way communications by Amateur stations are not considered broadcasting? (A) All types of one-way communications by Amateurs are considered by the FCC as broadcasting; (B) Beacon operation, remote control of a device, emergency communications, information bulletins consisting solely of subject matter of direct interest to the Amateur service, and telegraphy practice; (C) Only code-practice transmissions conducted simultaneously on all available Amateur bands below 30 MHz and conducted for more than 40 hours per week are not considered broadcasting; (D) Only actual emergency communications during a declared communications emergency are exempt.

3AA13.2 Which of the following one-way communications may not be transmitted in the Amateur service? (A) Transmissions to remotely control a device at a distant location; (B) Transmissions to assist persons learning or improving their proficiency in Morse code; (C) Brief transmissions to make adjustments to the station; (D) Transmission of music.

3AA13.3 What kinds of one-way information bulletins may be transmitted by Amateur stations? (A) NOAA weather bulletins; (B) Commuter traffic reports from local radio stations; (C) Regularly scheduled announcements concerning Amateur Radio equipment for sale or trade; (D) Messages directed only to Amateur operators consisting solely of subject matter of direct interest to the Amateur service.

3AA13.4 What types of one-way Amateur communications may be transmitted by an Amateur station? (A) Beacon operation, radio control, code practice, retransmission of other services; (B) Beacon operation, radio control, transmitting an unmodulated carrier, NOAA weather bulletins; (C) Beacon operation, remote control of a device, information bulletins consisting solely of subject matter of direct interest to the Amateur service, telegraphy practice and emergency communications; (D) Beacon operation, emergency-drill-practice transmissions, automatic retransmission of NOAA weather transmissions, code practice.

3AA14.1 What types of material compensation, if any, may be involved in third-party traffic transmitted by an Amateur station? (A) Payment of an amount agreed upon by the Amateur operator and the parties involved; (B) Assistance in maintenance of auxiliary station equipment; (C) Donation of Amateur equipment to the control operator; (D) No compensation may be accepted.

3AA14.2 What types of business communications, if any, may be transmitted by an Amateur station on behalf of a third party? (A) The FCC rules specifically prohibit communications with a business for any reason; (B) Business communications involving the sale of Amateur Radio equipment; (C) Communications to a business may be provided during an emergency as provided by the FCC rules; (D) Business communications aiding a broadcast station.

3AA14.3 Does the FCC allow third-party messages when communicating with Amateur Radio operators in a foreign country? (A) Third-party messages with a foreign country are only allowed on behalf of other Amateurs.; (B) Yes, provided the third-party message involves the immediate family of one of the communicating Amateurs; (C) Under no circumstances may U.S. Amateurs exchange third-party messages with an Amateur in a foreign country; (D) Yes, when communicating with a person in a country with which the U.S. shares a third-party agreement.

3AA15.1 Under what circumstances, if any, may a third party participate in radio communications from an Amateur station if the third party is ineligible to be a control operator of one of the stations? (A) A control operator must be present at the control point and continuously monitor and supervise the third party participation. Also, contacts may only be made with Amateurs in the U.S. and countries with which the U.S. has a third-party communications agreement; (B) A control operator must be present and continuously monitor and supervise the radio communication to ensure compliance with the rules only if contacts are made with Amateurs in countries with which the U.S. has no third-party traffic agreement; (C) A control operator must be present and continuously monitor and supervise the radio communication to ensure compliance with the rules. In addition, the control operator must key the transmitter and make the station identification.; (D) A control operator must be present and continuously monitor and supervise the radio communication to ensure compliance with the rules. In addition, if contacts are made on frequencies below 30 MHz, the control operator must transmit the call signs of both stations involved in the contact at 10-minute intervals.

3AA15.2 Where must the control operator be situated when a third party is participating in radio communications from an Amateur station? (A) If a radio remote control is used, the control operator may be physically separated from the control point, when provisions are incorporated to shut off the transmitter by remote control; (B) If the control operator supervises the third party until he or she is satisfied of the competence of the third party, the control operator may leave the control point; (C) The control operator must be present at the control point; (D) If the third party holds a valid radiotelegraph license issued by the FCC, no supervision is necessary.

3AA15.3 What must the control operator do while a third party is participating in radio communications? (A) If the third party holds a valid commercial radiotelegraph license, no supervision is necessary; (B) The control operator must tune up and down 5 kHz from the transmitting frequency on another receiver, to ensure that no interference is taking place; (C) If a radio control link is available, the control operator may leave the room; (D) The control operator must continuously monitor and supervise the third party's participation.

3AA15.4 In an exchange of international third-party communications, when is the station identification procedure required? (A) Only at the beginning of the communications; (B) At the end of each exchange of communications; (C) The station identification procedure is not required during international third-party communications; (D) Only at the end of multiple exchanges of communications.

3AA16.1 Under what circumstances, if any, may an Amateur station transmit radio communications containing obscene words? (A) Obscene words are permitted when they do not cause interference to any other radio communication or signal; (B) Obscene words are prohibited in Amateur Radio transmissions; (C) Obscene words are permitted when they are not retransmitted through repeater or auxiliary stations; (D) Obscene words are permitted, but there is an unwritten rule among Amateurs that they should not be used on the air.

3AA16.2 Under what circumstances, if any, may an Amateur station transmit radio communications containing indecent words? (A) Indecent words are permitted when they do not cause interference to any other radio communication or signal; (B) Indecent words are permitted when they are not retransmitted through repeater or auxiliary stations; (C) Indecent words are permitted, but there is an unwritten rule among Amateurs that they should not be used on the air; (D) Indecent words are prohibited in Amateur Radio transmissions.

3AA16.3 Under what circumstances, if any, may an Amateur station transmit radio communications containing profane words? (A) Profane words are permitted when they are not retransmitted through repeater or auxiliary stations; (B) Profane words are permitted, but there is an unwritten rule among Amateurs that they should not be used on the air; (C) Profane words are prohibited in Amateur Radio transmissions; (D) Profane words are permitted when they do not cause interference to any other radio communication or signal.

3AA17.1 Which of the following VHF/UHF bands may not be used by Earth stations for satellite communications? (A) 6 meters; (B) 2 meters; (C) 1.25 meters; (D) 70 centimeters.

Chapter

B

Operating Procedures

When you are issued an Amateur license, it is done on the assumption you know how to properly control your station. A number of test questions are written to insure this assumption is correct. Two questions of the 30 you will be asked from Subelement 2B and three questions from Subelement 3AB are taken from the section called Operating Procedures.

Interference

As an Amateur, you are permitted to operate a high power radio transmitter. In the last chapter, we discussed the rules regarding intentional interference with another station. Unless you observe good operating practice, your transmitter can also cause unintentional interference.

Just think what would happen if anyone could transmit anywhere they wanted to at any time. The feuding would make the Hatfield and McCoy battles seem like a sewing circle competition. The FCC would probably assign the frequencies to the public and give it a name like "The Citizens Band".

When selecting a frequency for your transmitter, the most important consideration is to insure that you minimize the interference with other Amateurs. It is common courtesy to say "Is this frequency in use?", before calling another specific Amateur or calling CQ. By the way, CQ is a general call meaning "I want to make a contact." (2B1-1.1)(2B2 4.1)

There's nothing subtle about having someone start transmitting on top of you. There are other forms of interference which are subtle, however. For example, droning "CQ" on-and-on without signing your call is a form of on-the-air pollution. Rather than making filibuster CQ's, you should make crisp, short transmissions. When trying to contact another station using CW, the correct format is to send CQ three times followed by the letters DE (from, or this is) and your call letters three times. At this point you can let up on the key long enough to see if anyone returns your call. If the band is dead or conditions are poor, you may wish to repeat the sequence a few times before listening. (2B2-1.1)(2B2-4.2)

If you answer someone else's CQ, you should send their call twice followed by the characters DE followed by your call sign twice. Then standby to see if you were heard. Incidentally, your CW sending speed should be paced to the speed of the Amateur you heard sending CQ. You should never call a station at a speed faster than you can reliably copy. Otherwise it is necessary to take time to tell the sender to QRS (slow down). This transmission would not have been necessary if you had responded at the speed at which you wished to receive. (2B2-1.2)(2B2-2.1)

If there is a lot of QRM (interference) you may need to repeat the send/listen sequence a couple of times before giving up. Obviously, if the station you are calling goes back to someone else, you should stop calling.

On 10 meters, you might want to listen for beacon stations (*see Chapter A*) below 28.3 MHz. before transmitting. Amateur beacons are low power automatic CW stations that transmit the call letters and location of the station. It is not unusual to hear an Australian beacon when the Novice/Technician phone portion of the band (28.3-28.5 MHz) seems totally dead.

On phone, the standard format is similar to a CW call except that you do not use the term DE. Normally, you would say CQ three times, then "this is" and your call letters three times. If you respond to someone else's CQ, you should give their call once followed by "this is" and your call letters spelled out phonetically. (2B3-1.1)(2B3-1.2)

As a practical matter, calls are often paced according to band conditions. If the band is very active, it means that many people will be tuning around looking for a CQ. A short "CQ, CQ, CQ 10 meters, this is K6HX located in Del Mar, California calling CQ 10 meters" will often suffice. If the band seems dead, you may wish to repeat the sequence several times.

Band propagation, as well as band conditions should be considered when trying to contact a specific station. For example, if you live in Seattle and wish to contact a friend in San Diego, you wouldn't try to do it on the two meter band. Why not? Two meters, for the most part, is a VHF **line-of-sight** band (an exception, of course, is the use of an OSCAR satellite). Calling a station which is out of range for the band propagation and characteristic is a subtle form of interference for other users of the band.

To work the Seattle/San Diego path (about 1,500 miles) a "Tech-Plus" or Novice would use the 10 or 15 meter band. Before calling your friend, you should tune around to see if there are other stations coming from that area. If not, it is likely that the call to your friend will be unsuccessful. (2B1-1.2)

One of the most annoying forms of interference is not confined to newcomers. Some Amateurs persist in tuning up their transmitters into an antenna. Occasionally they do not listen (or ask) to see if the frequency is clear. Their unmodulated signal can cause annoying interfering whistles or entirely "blot out" weak signals. Transmitter tune up should always be done using a device called a **dummy load**. This device is sometimes called a dummy antenna. (*See Chapter D - Test Equipment*). The dummy load appears just like an antenna as far as the transmitter is concerned except that it does not radiate a signal. Thus there is no radio frequency energy to interfere with other operators. (2B1-1.3)(3AB3.2)

Procedural Signals

Amateurs use a form of shorthand to speed up their CW transmissions. These are called **procedural signals** which are one or two letters sent together as one code character. An example, mentioned earlier, was the substitution of "DE" for the word "from" or "this is." The most common procedural signal is "CQ". Another is "AR" which means "over" or signifies the end of a transmission. This is different from "SK" which signifies the end of the contact or good-bye. Some of the less common procedural signals are "BT" (a double dash or equal sign), "DN" (the fraction bar, often used in call letter strings to indicate portable operation in another call area — i.e. W6TNS/7, Seattle). One that confuses everyone is "KN", which means that only the called station should transmit. A similar pool question asks the meaning of "K" at the end of a transmission. The "K" (not "KN") means that any station can transmit. Commit these abbreviations to the frontal lobe of your brain, as you will probably be asked about them during your test. (2B2-3.1)(2B2-3.2)(2B2-3.3)(2B2-3.4)(2B2-3.5)(2B2-4.3)

How Do You Copy Me?

Amateurs have also devised a standardized shorthand method of indicating how a station sounds. This is called the **R-S-T** reporting system. The "R" part means the readability on a scale of one to five (barely to perfect copy). The "S" designator tells the other ham, on a scale of one to nine, their signal strength.

The Microcraft "Code-Star" makes it easy to copy Morse code.

A one would be extremely weak and unreadable, while nine would be a "rock crushing" strong signal. The ending "T" is used to indicate the tone of the CW note, again on a scale of one to nine (badly distorted to a pure musical note). A good signal from a nearby station would probably get an RST report of 599.

Most modern communication products include a signal strength meter. These indicators used to be calibrated with a 0-9 relative reading which used to correspond to the "S" in the RST. In the 1950's, a famous ham radio manufacturing company decided to calibrate their meters in decibels (a relative strength measurement). The upper limit of the scale was 60 db (decibels). This made their products seem better than the competition so everyone starting printing a decibel scale on the meter (few, if any, calibrated their receiver to the meter scale!). Most modern Amateur radios have a signal strength indicator calibrated zero to nine (which appears about mid-scale) and further graduations up to 60 on the right half of the meter. Thus, the typical signal report today might be "You are 20 db over 9 at this QTH". CW operators stick to tradition and anything over nine on the meter gets a nine in the RST report. (3AB1.3)

The "T" (tone) designator is dropped for phone and there is no correlation with the old RST system. One often hears the "Q" designator substituted for the "R". The "Q" stands for a general, overall indication of quality. It is correct etiquette to say "I hear you Q5-S9, OM" or simply "you are 5-9." (2B2-5.1)(2B2-5.2)(2B2-5.3)(3AB1.1)(3AB1.2)

By the way, the term "OM" deserves explanation. It stands for "old man" and is ham radio generic-talk for a male ham of **any age**. If your dad is a ham, he is also an "old man" but you may wish to exhibit a bit of discretion with the use of the term! Female hams don't seem to have an equivalent term, probably for very good reasons.

What's A Que-Tee-Ach?

Amateurs use another form of shorthand, called **Q-signals**. They were developed many years ago by hams to save time sending telegraphic messages. Here are a few of the more common Q-signals (some of which you may be asked on the Novice test).

QRL- Used to ask if the frequency is in use.
QRS- This Q-signal means "Send more slowly".
QRT- Means to stop sending as in "I have to QRT now for dinner".
QRZ- "Who is the station calling me?"
QSL- Acknowledgement of transmission copy such as "QSL your message number five". A QSL card is a document which confirms a two-way transmission.
QTH- A location of the ham radio station such as "QTH- Mercer Island".

These Q-signals are in the question pool and you may be asked to identify one of them. (2B2-6.1)(2B2-6.2)(2B2-6.3)(2B2-6.4)(2B2-6-5)(3AB3.3)

Here are some of the other commonly used Q-signals for your information.

QRK- "What is my signal like?" You would probably respond with a Q-signal. Consider the elegant simplicity of three CW letters (QRK) and the response, "479". It may not seem important with an occasional ham contact but what if you were a telegrapher handling hundreds of messages each day?

QRM- Man-made interference such as other nearby signals, motors, ignition noise, etc.

QRN- Natural static such as lightning bursts and static crashes.

QRX- "Please stand by" or "I am standing by", depending on how it is used. For example, "Please QRX while I answer the phone".

QSB- Fading of signals due to atmospheric conditions.

QSM- "Can you repeat the last message?"

QSO- A conversation on the ham radio.

QSY- To change frequency such as "QSY down 15" (kHz).

The Phonetic Alphabet

In the presence of fading, static or other forms of QRM, it is easy to mistake A6HX for K6HX. To avoid this, the International Telecommunication Union, in Geneva, Switzerland, has developed a standard **phonetic alphabet**. The words they have picked to represent the 26 letters of the alphabet are those which are least likely to be confused with other words on a world-wide basis.

The phonetic representations are shown in the accompanying chart. It is unlikely that Kilo Six Hotel X-Ray would be mistaken for A6HX. Kilo and Alpha do not sound alike but "K" and "A" sound almost the same, particularly at the other end of a noisy or weak communications circuit.

A- Alpha	J- Juliette	S- Sierra	You must memorize the correspondence
B- Bravo	K- Kilo	T- Tango	between letters and the standard pho-
C- Charlie	L- Lima	U- Uniform	netic words. You will be using these
D- Delta	M- Mike	V- Victor	forever (at least until the ITU changes
E- Echo	N- November	W- Whiskey	them) so long as you are an Amateur. In
F- Foxtrot	O- Oscar	X- X-Ray	addition you will probably be asked for
G- Golf	P- Papa	Y- Yankee	the phonetic representation of various
H- Hotel	Q- Quebec	Z- Zulu	call letters in your Technician test.
I- India	R- Romeo		There are 11 questions on phonetics and

The International Telecommunication Union Phonetic Alphabet you will almost certainly get one of them. The best way to commit these to memory is to spell out words phonetically on the signs you see along the highway as you are traveling. After a while they will become second nature to you. Have you got that Oscar-Kilo?(2B3-2.1)(2B3-2.2)(2B3-2.3)(2B3-2.4)(2B3-2.5)(2B3-2.6)(2B3-2.7)(2B3-2.8)(2B-3-2.9)(2B3-2.10)(2B3-2.11)

Digital Procedures

Long before the computer era, Amateurs were engaging in an early form of digital communications called radio teletype (RTTY). A teletype machine is a mechanical device designed to reproduce alphanumeric characters sent from one place to another. The transport medium can be wire or by radio.

The teletype machine has a selector mechanism which determines what character is printed on a paper roll or strip fed through the RTTY machine. A train of ones and zeros determines what character is selected and printed each time the motorized distributor revolves. The speed of the motor rotation determines the data or "baud" rate. Most Amateurs used 45 baud for sending and receiving communication. This amounts to about five printed characters per second. (2B4-2.1)

In actual practice, few Amateurs followed a "standard RTTY CQ format" such as alluded to in the question pool. Rather, they used paper punch tapes (holes represented ones, no holes represented a zero) to call CQ. They would make the tape (called "brag tapes") into a loop by glueing the ends together. As the tape rotated in a distributor/reader, the transmitter would be activated to call CQ in a unique, customized style.

This is not the correct answer for the VEC Question pool, however. If you are asked for the proper format for a standard RTTY CQ call, the correct answer is "CQ three to six times, followed by DE with your call sign sent three times." (2B4-1.1)

In addition to the machines being slow, noisy and cantankerous, RTTY is prone to errors. The error correction and message addressing and routing is very rudimentary. RTTY was revolutionized (as was most everything else) with the introduction of computers. Amateurs carried the revolution one step further with the introduction of packet radio. This scheme splits any message into packets of information by a device called a **Terminal Node Controller (TNC)**. Each packet has the sender and recipients address or identification. In addition, packet communication includes a fool-proof method of telling if the message has been corrupted by one or more errors. If so, the sending station receives a retransmission request. Thus, the data you receive is error-free.

The TNC has the capability of storing an incoming message (to any addressee) and then repeating it error-free to the recipient. When used in this mode, the TNC is called a digital repeater or "**digipeater**". Because of this capability, an unlimited number of TNC's can be interconnected into a packet radio network for passing messages. The network can move information anywhere a TNC is located. (2B5-2.1)(2B5-2.2)

By using an addressing scheme, many messages for different Amateurs can fly back and forth on the same frequency. You normally do not see any messages except those addressed to you. Your equipment simply monitors the traffic flow on a channel. You can display messages meant for others by entering the monitoring mode of your TNC. The message content will appear on your CRT screen even though the message is not addressed to you. Your TNC will not correct errors since this is done by the TNC of the addressee. (2B5-1.2)

If a transmitting station sends data specifically addressed to your receiving site, you will see the words **CONNECTED** on your screen. The term is so universal that Jim Grubs, K9EI, used it in the title of his book *"Getting ***CONNECTED***"*. If you are interested in computer communications, be certain to pick up a copy of Jim's book at a store selling Amateur products. (2B5-1.1)

Repeater Communication

Once again, in this chapter, the subject of repeaters comes up. The Commission wants to be sure that you have a complete understanding of repeater operation.

As mentioned in the first chapter, repeaters are used to extend the operating range of portable and mobile stations. You will recall that the repeater receives on frequency "A" and retransmits whatever it picks up on frequency "B." The receiving frequency is called the input and the transmitting frequency is called the output. (2B6-2.1)(2B6-3.1)(3AB2-1.5)

You should use proper etiquette on a repeater just as you would on any other Amateur frequency. Since the reception is so crystal clear, there is no need to repeat calls several times. If you do, it brands you as a "lid" (a poor operator). When using the repeater, simply call the station you want to talk to and identify your own station. (2B6-1.1)(3AB2-1.1)

Most repeaters use a "courtesy tone" or "beep" to indicate a station has stopped transmitting. You should wait a few seconds after the "beep" before transmitting. This allows a station to break in, if they need access to the repeater. (3AB2-1.2)(3AB2-1.4)

If you are physically near the station you wish to contact, there is no need to use the wide area capability of a repeater. Usually you establish contact on the repeater, then switch over to a mutually agreed simplex frequency or channel. Simplex means that you transmit and listen on the same frequency. Always use a simplex channel whenever a contact is possible without using the repeater. This leaves the repeater channel clear for someone else. (2B6-4.1)(3AB2-2.1)

Common sense dictates that you would not use a high frequency (HF) band to chat with someone across town. Your local transmissions would also traverse great distances by skywave and might interfere with communications in another state or country. (3AB3.1)

There are other good manners which should be observed if the repeater has an autopatch function. An autopatch is a device that allows repeater users to make telephone calls from their portable handheld or mobile station. Make your calls short and to the point so that you do not tie up the repeater excessively. (2B6-5.1)

I cannot overstress the importance of not "hogging" the repeater. If you are talking to someone else, try to keep your transmissions short so that someone could call in an emergency. Repeaters are required by the FCC to have a time-out device (appropriately called a timer). It is set to switch off after three minutes of continuous transmission so that the repeater cannot be accidentally stuck in the transmitting mode. (2B6-5.2)(3AB2-1.3)(3AB2-1.6)

Repeater Interference

Let's say you are visiting a friend in a nearby state. You both operate two meters. By telephone, you tell the friend to listen for you on 147.60 MHz simplex. As you approach your friends city, you hear him calling you and he "talks you in", right to his driveway. Everything worked out great. Or did it?

The frequency of 147.60 happens to be the input for the local repeater. While you and your friend are chatting away, the repeater is picking you up and retransmitting your conversations on 147.00 MHz. This, of course, totally locks up the repeater for anyone else to use. It's unintentional, of course, and you are unaware of it, but it still drives the repeater users "up the wall."

For this reason, the FCC wants you to understand about repeater input-output spacing. On the six meter band, the I/O spacing is one megaHertz (MHz). On two meters it is 600 kiloHertz (kHz). The output frequency that you hear may be 600 kHz higher or lower than the input or receive frequency. A repeater directory will indicate which it is with a plus or minus sign specifying your transmit frequency. The I/O spacing increases to 1.6 MHz (1600 kHz) on the 1.25 meter band and 5 MHz on the 70 cm. band. If you know these spacings and have a repeater directory, you can avoid operating on one of the repeater input frequencies. (3AB2-3.1)(3AB2-3.2)(3AB2-3.3)(3AB2-3.4)

If you operate simplex and interfere with a repeater, good Amateur practice dictates that you change frequency for several reasons. The repeater is probably frequency coordinated and has a right to be on the assigned frequency. Further, a repeater is usually crystal controlled which makes it very difficult to change frequency. (3AB2-2.2)

What is frequency coordination? To minimize interference between repeaters in each area, a person or group studies the situation and recommends frequency input-output pairs for repeater usage. (3AB2-4.1)

During periods when usage is low, repeaters often handle nets (shorthand for "networks"). Nets are groups of people who have a common interest. The activity may involve personally owned equipment trading, YL (young lady) meetings and third party message handling. Naturally these nets should avoid tying up the repeater during traffic rush hours. (3AB2-1.7)

Emergency Communications

One never knows when an emergency is going to occur. You could be chatting away with a friend on the local repeater or talking with a ham across the country on 10 meters. Suddenly, you hear someone say "break-break with emergency traffic." What should you do? The law requires that you immediately standby to copy the emergency communications. (2B1-2.1)

You might use the above procedure to report an accident where injuries appear to be involved. In more serious situations (there's more water inside the boat than outside!), you would simply say the word "MAYDAY" several times along with your call. On CW, the equivalent of "MAYDAY" is the famous three letters "SOS." (3AB4.1)(3AB4.2)

You will recall from Chapter A, the first Amateur Principle is the "recognition of emergency communications." Amateurs have banded into an important group called The Radio Amateur Civil Emergency Service (RACES). If you are interested in using your Amateur station to serve the public, you should contact your local civil defense agency for information and enrollment forms.

To participate in RACES drills and exercises, you must be registered with your local civil defense organization. To avoid excessive use of Amateur frequencies, RACES drills are limited to one hour per week. Messages sent during a drill must be identified as simply tests so as not to unduly alarm the casual listener. (3AB5-1.1)(3AB5-1.2)(3A B5-2.1)

During the first stages of an emergency situation, the traffic is called **tactical communications**. In such cases, some of the more structured Amateur formats described in this book are modified. For example, one might use tactical call signs such as "command post," "hospital" or "weather center." (3AB6-1.1)(3AB6-1.2)

Most of the traffic (messages) in and out of a disaster area will relate to the status of people living in the area and affected by the situation. This is called **health and welfare** traffic. (3AB6-2.1)

Would you like to configure your station to be ready in the case of a disaster? It can be easily accomplished. Let's say you have a two meter base station in your bedroom. It probably operates from a 12 volt power supply connected to the commercial power lines. Of course, if the power fails, you rig is useless. However, you can continue to operate by connecting a 12 volt sealed (gel-cell) motorcycle battery across the power leads of your AC supply. If the commercial AC power fails, your two meter rig will then draw power from the battery. (3AB6-3.1)

You will be able to maintain communications for many hours, with this setup, depending on how long you transmit. The exact time can be calculated by dividing 3 (a typical two meter base station draws 3 amperes on transmit) into the ampere rating of the battery. For example, you could transmit continuously for four hours with a 12 ampere-hour sealed motorcycle battery.

There is one other situation that can put you "out of business" in an emergency. Let's say you are caught in a hurricane. The chances are that your antenna will be blown down. You may be able to transmit with emergency power but the signal will not go anywhere without an antenna. It is an excellent idea to have a dipole antenna rolled up and stashed in the closet "just in case." Once the wind dies down, you can easily erect the antenna. A dipole will even work with a volunteer holding each insulated end in the air over their head! (3AB6-3.2)

SUBELEMENT 2B (2 questions)

2B1-1.1 What is the most important factor to consider when selecting a transmitting frequency within your authorized sub-band? (A) The frequency should not be in use by other Amateurs; (B) You should be able to hear other stations on the frequency to ensure that someone will be able to hear you; (C) Your antenna should be resonant at the selected frequency; (D) You should ensure that the SWR on the antenna feed line is high enough at the selected frequency.

2B1-1.2 You wish to contact an Amateur station more than 1,500 miles away on a summer afternoon. Which band is most likely to provide a successful contact? (A) The 80-or 40-meter wavelength bands; (B) The 40-or 15-meter wavelength bands; (C) The 15-or 10-meter wavelength bands; (D) The 1-1/4 meter or 23-centimeter wavelength bands.

2B1-1.3 How can on-the-air transmitter tune-up be kept as short as possible? (A) By using a random wire antenna; (B) By tuning up on 40 meters first, then switching to the desired band; (C) By tuning the transmitter into a dummy load; (D) By using twin lead instead of coaxial-cable feed lines.

2B1-2.1 You are having a QSO with your uncle in Pittsburgh when you hear an emergency call for help on the frequency you are using. What should you do? (A) Inform the station that the frequency is in use; (B) Direct the station to the nearest emergency net frequency; (C) Call your local Civil Preparedness Office and inform them of the emergency; (D) Immediately stand by to copy the emergency communication.

2B2-1.1 What is the format of a standard Morse code CQ call? (A) Transmit the procedural signal "CQ" three times, followed by the procedural signal "DE", followed by your call three times; (B) Transmit the procedural signal "CQ" three times, followed by the procedural signal "DE", followed by your call one time; (C) Transmit the procedural signal "CQ" ten times, followed by the procedural signal "DE", followed by your call one time; (D) Transmit the procedural signal "CQ" continuously until someone answers your call.

2B2-1.2 How should you answer a Morse code CQ call? (A) Send your call sign four times; (B) Send the other station's call sign twice, followed by the procedural signal "DE", followed by your call sign twice; (C) Send the other station's call sign once, followed by the procedural signal "DE", followed by your call sign four times; (D) Send your call sign followed by your name, station location and a signal report.

2B2-2.1 At what telegraphy speed should a "CQ" message be transmitted? (A) Only speeds below five WPM; (B) The highest speed your keyer will operate; (C) Any speed at which you can reliably receive; (D) The highest speed at which you can control the keyer.

2B2-3.1 What is the meaning of the Morse code character AR? (A) Only the called station transmit; (B) All received correctly; (C) End of transmission; (D) Best regards.

2B2-3.2 What is the meaning of the Morse code character SK? (A) Received some correctly; (B) Best regards; (C) Wait; (D) End of contact.

2B2-3.3 What is the meaning of the Morse code character BT? (A) Double dash "="; (B) Fraction bar "/"; (C) End of contact; (D) Back to you.

2B2-3.4 What is the meaning of the Morse code character DN? (A) Double dash "="; (B) Fraction bar "/"; (C) Done now (end of contact)(D) Called station only transmit.

2B2-3.5 What is the meaning of the Morse code character KN? (A) Fraction bar "/"; (B) End of contact; (C) Called station only transmit; (D) Key now (go ahead to transmit).

2B2-4.1 What is the procedural signal "CQ" used for? (A) To notify another station that you will call on the quarter hour; (B) To indicate that you are testing a new antenna and are not listening for another station to answer; (C) To indicate that only the called station should transmit; (D) A general call when you are trying to make a contact.

2B2-4.2 What is the procedural signal "DE" used for? (A) To mean "from" or "this is," as in "W9NGT DE N9BTT"; (B) To indicate directional emissions from your antenna; (C) To indicate "received all correctly"; (D) To mean "calling any station".

2B2-4.3 What is the procedural signal "K" used for? (A) To mean "any station transmit"; (B) To mean "all received correctly"; (C) To mean "end of message"; (D) To mean "called station only transmit".

2B2-5.1 What does the R in the RST signal report mean? (A) The recovery of the signal; (B) The resonance of the CW tone; (C) The rate of signal flutter; (D) The readability of the signal.

2B2-5.2 What does the S in the RST signal report mean? (A) The scintillation of a signal; (B) The strength of the signal; (C) The signal quality; (D) The speed of the CW transmission.

2B2-5.3 What does the T in the RST signal report mean? (A) The tone of the signal; (B) The closeness of the signal to "telephone" quality; (C) The timing of the signal dot to dash ratio; (D) The tempo of the signal.

2B2-6.1 What is one meaning of the Q signal "QRS"? (A) Interference from static; (B) Send more slowly; (C) Send RST report; (D) Radio station location is...

2B2-6.2 What is one meaning of the Q signal "QRT"? (A) The correct time is; (B) Send RST report; (C) Stop sending; (D) Send more slowly.

2B2-6.3 What is one meaning of the Q signal "QTH"? (A) Time here is; (B) My name is; (C) Stop sending; (D) My location is...

2B2-6.4 What is one meaning of the Q signal "QRZ," when it is followed with a question mark? (A) Who is calling me?; (B) What is your radio zone?; (C) What time zone are you in?; (D) Is this frequency in use?

2B2-6.5 What is one meaning of the Q signal "QSL," when it is followed with a question mark? (A) Shall I send you my log?; (B) Can you acknowledge receipt (of my message)?; (C) Shall I send more slowly?; (D) Who is calling me?

2B3-1.1 What is the format of a standard radiotelephone CQ call? (A) Transmit the phrase "CQ" at least ten times, followed by "this is," followed by your call sign at least two times; (B) Transmit the phrase "CQ" at least five times, followed by "this is," followed by your call sign once; (C) Transmit the phrase "CQ" three times, followed by "this is," followed by your call sign three times; (D) Transmit the phrase "CQ" at least ten times, followed by "this is," followed by your call sign once.

2B3-1.2 How should you answer a radiotelephone CQ call? (A) Transmit the other station's call sign at least ten times, followed by "this is," followed by your call sign at least twice; (B) Transmit the other station's call sign at least five times phonetically, followed by "this is," followed by your call sign at least once; (C) Transmit the other station's call sign at least three times, followed by "this is," followed by your call sign at least five times phonetically; (D) Transmit the other station's call sign once, followed by "this is," followed by your call sign given phonetically.

2B3-2.1 How is the call sign "KA3BGQ" stated in Standard International Phonetics? (A) Kilo Alfa Three Bravo Golf Quebec; (B) King America Three Bravo Golf Quebec; (C) Kilowatt Alfa Three Bravo George Queen; (D) Kilo America Three Baker Golf Quebec.

2B3-2.2 How is the call sign "WE5TZD" stated phonetically? (A) Whiskey Echo Foxtrot Tango Zulu Delta; (B) Washington England Five Tokyo Zanzibar Denmark; (C) Whiskey Echo Five Tango Zulu Delta; (D) Whiskey Easy Five Tear Zebra Dog.

2B3-2.3 How is the call sign "KC4HRM" stated phonetically? (A) Kilo Charlie Four Hotel Romeo Mike; (B) Kilowatt Charlie Four Hotel Roger Mexico; (C) Kentucky Canada Four Honolulu Radio Mexico; (D) King Charlie Foxtrot Hotel Roger Mary.

2B3-2.4 How is the call sign "AF6PSQ" stated phonetically? (A) America Florida Six Portugal Spain Quebec; (B) Adam Frank Six Peter Sugar Queen; (C) Alfa Fox Sierra Papa Santiago Queen; (D) Alfa Foxtrot Six Papa Sierra Quebec.

2B3-2.5 How is the call sign "NB8LXG" stated phonetically? (A) November Bravo Eight Lima Xray Golf; (B) Nancy Baker Eight Love Xray George; (C) Norway Boston Eight London Xray Germany; (D) November Bravo Eight London Xray Germany.

2B3-2.6 How is the call sign "KJ1UOI" stated phonetically? (A) King John One Uncle Oboe Ida; (B) Kilowatt George India Uncle Oscar India; (C) Kilo Juliette One Uniform Oscar India; (D) Kentucky Juliette One United Ontario Indiana.

2B3-2.7 How is the call sign "WV2BPZ" stated phonetically? (A) Whiskey Victor Two Bravo Papa Zulu; (B) Willie Victor Two Baker Papa Zebra; (C) Whiskey Victor Tango Bravo Papa Zulu; (D) Willie Virginia Two Boston Peter Zanzibar.

2B3-2.8 How is the call sign "NY3CTJ" stated phonetically? (A) Norway Yokohama Three California Tokyo Japan; (B) Nancy Yankee Three Cat Texas Jackrabbit; (C) Norway Yesterday Three Charlie Texas Juliette; (D) November Yankee Three Charlie Tango Juliette.

2B3-2.9 How is the call sign "KG7DRV" stated phonetically? (A) Kilo Golf Seven Denver Radio Venezuela; (B) Kilo Golf Seven Delta Romeo Victor; (C) King John Seven Dog Radio Victor; (D) Kilowatt George Seven Delta Romeo Video.

2B3-2.10 How is the call sign "WX9HKS" stated phonetically? (A) Whiskey Xray Nine Hotel Kilo Sierra; (B) Willie Xray November Hotel King Sierra; (C) Washington Xray Nine Honolulu Kentucky Santiago; (D) Whiskey Xray Nine Henry King Sugar.

2B3-2.11 How is the call sign "AE0LQY" stated phonetically? (A) Able Easy Zero Lima Quebec Yankee; (B) Arizona Equador Zero London Queen Yesterday; (C) Alfa Echo Zero Lima Quebec Yankee; (D) Able Easy Zero Love Queen Yoke.

2B4-1.1 What is the format of a standard RTTY CQ call? (A) Transmit the phrase "CQ" three times, followed by "DE", followed by your call sign two times; (B) Transmit the phrase "CQ" three to six times, followed by "DE", followed by your call sign three times; (C) Transmit the phrase "CQ" ten times, followed by the procedural signal

"DE", followed by your call one time; (D) Transmit the phrase "CQ" continuously until someone answers your call.

2B4-2.1 You receive an RTTY CQ call at 45 bauds. At what speed should you respond? (A) 22-1/2 bauds; (B) 45 bauds; (C) 90 bauds; (D) Any speed, since radioteletype systems adjust to any signal rate.

2B5-1.1 What does the term "connected" mean in a packet-radio link? (A) A telephone link has been established between two Amateurs; (B) An Amateur Radio message has reached the station for local delivery; (C) The transmitting station is sending data specifically addressed to the receiving station, and the receiving station is acknowledging that the data has been received correctly; (D) The transmitting station and a receiving station are using a certain digipeater, so no other contacts can take place until they are finished.

2B5-1.2 What does the term monitoring mean on a frequency used for packet radio? (A) The FCC is copying all messages to determine their content; (B) A member of the Amateur Auxiliary to the FCC's Field Operations Bureau is copying all messages to determine their content; (C) The receiving station's video monitor is displaying all messages intended for that station, and is acknowledging correct receipt of the data; (D) The receiving station is displaying information that may not be addressed to that station, and is not acknowledging correct receipt of the data.

2B5-2.1 What is a digipeater? (A) A packet-radio station used to retransmit data that is specifically addressed to be retransmitted by that station; (B) An Amateur Radio repeater designed to retransmit all audio signals in a digital form; (C) An Amateur Radio repeater designed using only digital electronics components; (D) A packet-radio station that retransmits any signals it receives.

2B5-2.2 What is the meaning of the term network in packet radio? (A) A system of telephone lines interconnecting packet-radio stations to transfer data; (B) A method of interconnecting packet-radio stations so that data can be transferred over long distances; (C) The interlaced wiring on a terminal- node-controller board; (D) The terminal-node-controller function that automatically rejects another caller when the station is connected.

2B6-1.1 What is a good way to establish contact on a repeater? (A) Give the call sign of the station you want to contact three times; (B) Call the other operator by name and then give your call sign three times; (C) Call the desired station and then identify your own station; (D) Say, "Breaker, breaker," and then give your call sign.

2B6-2.1 What is the main purpose of a repeater? (A) To provide a station that makes local information available 24 hours a day; (B) To provide a means of linking Amateur stations with the telephone system; (C) To retransmit NOAA weather information during severe storm warnings; (D) Repeaters extend the operating range of portable and mobile stations.

2B6-3.1 What does it mean to say that a repeater has an input and an output frequency? (A) The repeater receives on one frequency and transmits on another; (B) All repeaters offer a choice of operating frequency, in case one is busy; (C) One frequency is used to control repeater functions and the other frequency is the one used to retransmit received signals; (D) Repeaters require an access code to be transmitted on one frequency while your voice is transmitted on the other.

2B6-4.1 When should simplex operation be used instead of using a repeater? (A) Whenever greater communications reliability is needed; (B) Whenever a contact is possible without using a repeater; (C) Whenever you need someone to make an emergency telephone call; (D) Whenever you are traveling and need some local information.

2B6-5.1 What is an autopatch? (A) A repeater feature that automatically selects the strongest signal to be repeated; (B) An automatic system of connecting a mobile station to the next repeater as it moves out of range of the first; (C) A device that allows repeater users to make telephone calls from their portable or mobile stations; (D) A system that automatically locks other stations out of the repeater when there is a QSO in progress.

2B6-5.2 What is the purpose of a repeater time-out timer? (A) It allows the repeater to have a rest period after heavy use; (B) It logs repeater transmit time to determine when the repeater mean time between failure rating is exceeded; (C) It limits repeater transmission time to no more than ten minutes; (D) It limits repeater transmission time to no more than three minutes.

SUBELEMENT 3AB (3 questions).

3AB1.1 What is the meaning of: "Your report is five seven..."? (A) Your signal is perfectly readable and moderately strong; (B) Your signal is perfectly readable, but weak; (C) Your signal is readable with considerable difficulty; (D) Your signal is perfectly readable with near pure tone.

3AB1.2 What is the meaning of: "Your report is three three..."? (A) The contact is serial number thirty-three; (B) The station is located at latitude 33 degrees; (C) Your signal is readable with considerable difficulty and weak in strength; (D) Your signal is unreadable, very weak in strength.

3AB1.3 What is the meaning of: "Your report is five nine plus 20 dB..."? (A) Your signal strength has increased by a factor of 100; (B) Repeat your transmission on a frequency 20 kHz higher; (C) The bandwidth of your signal is 20 decibels above linearity; (D) A relative signal-strength meter reading is 20 decibels greater than strength 9.

3AB2-1.1 How should a QSO be initiated through a station in repeater operation? (A) Say "breaker, breaker 79"; (B) Call the desired station and then identify your own station; (C) Call "CQ" three times and identify three times; (D) Wait for a "CQ" to be called and then answer it.

3AB2-1.2 Why should users of a station in repeater operation pause briefly between transmissions? (A) To check the SWR of the repeater; (B) To reach for pencil and paper for third party traffic; (C) To listen for any hams wanting to break in; (D) To dial up the repeater's autopatch.

3AB2-1.3 Why should users of a station in repeater operation keep their transmissions short and thoughtful? (A) A long transmission may prevent someone with an emergency from using the repeater; (B) To see if the receiving station operator is still awake; (C) To give any non-hams that are listening a chance to respond; (D) To keep long-distance charges down.

3AB2-1.4 What is the proper procedure to break into an on-going QSO through a station in repeater operation? (A) Wait for the end of a transmission and start calling; (B) Shout, "break, break!" to show that you're eager to join the conversation; (C) Turn on your 100-watt amplifier and override whoever is talking; (D) Send your call sign during a break between transmissions.

3AB2-1.5 What is the purpose of repeater operation? (A) To cut your power bill by using someone's higher power system; (B) To enable mobile and low-power stations to extend their usable range; (C) To reduce your telephone bill; (D) To call the ham radio distributor 50 miles away.

3AB2-1.6 What is meant by "making the repeater time out"? (A) The repeater's battery supply has run out; (B) The repeater's transmission time limit has expired during a single transmission; (C) The warranty on the repeater duplexer has expired; (D) The repeater is in need of repairs.

3AB2-1.7 During commuting rush hours, which types of operation should relinquish the use of the repeater? (A) Mobile operators; (B) Low-power stations; (C) Highway traffic information nets; (D) Third-party communications nets.

3AB2-2.1 Why should simplex be used where possible instead of using a station in repeater operation? (A) Farther distances can be reached; (B) To avoid long distance toll charges; (C) To avoid tying up the repeater unnecessarily; (D) To permit the testing of the effectiveness of your antenna.

3AB2-2.2 When a frequency conflict arises between a simplex operation and a repeater operation, why does good Amateur practice call for the simplex operation to move to another frequency? (A) The repeater's output power can be turned up to ruin the front end of the station in simplex operation; (B) There are more repeaters than simplex operators; (C) Changing the repeater's frequency is not practical; (D) Changing a repeater frequency requires the authorization of the Federal Communications Commission.

3AB2-3.1 What is the usual input/output frequency separation for stations in repeater operation in the 2-meter wavelength band? (A) 1 MHz; (B) 1.6 MHz; (C) 170 Hz; (D) 0.6 MHz.

3AB2-3.2 What is the usual input/output frequency separation for stations in repeater operation in the 70-centimeter band? (A) 1.6 MHz; (B) 5 MHz; (C) 600 kHz; (D) 5 kHz.

3AB2-3.3 What is the usual input/output frequency separation for a 6-meter station in repeater operation? (A) 1 MHz; (B) 600 kHz; (C) 1.6 MHz; (D) 20 kHz.

3AB2-3.4 What is the usual input/output frequency separation for a 1.25-meter station in repeater operation? (A) 1000 kHz; (B) 600 kHz; (C) 1600 kHz; (D) 1.6 GHz.

3AB2-4.1 What is a repeater frequency coordinator? (A) Someone who coordinates the assembly of a repeater station; (B) Someone who provides advice on what kind of system to buy; (C) The club's repeater trustee; (D) A person or group that recommends frequency pairs for repeater usage.

3AB3.1 Why should local Amateur communications be conducted on VHF and UHF frequencies? (A) To minimize interference on HF bands capable of long-distance sky-wave communication; (B) Because greater output power is permitted on VHF and UHF; (C) Because HF transmissions are not propagated locally; (D) Because absorption is greater at VHF and UHF frequencies.

3AB3.2 How can on-the-air transmissions be minimized during a lengthy transmitter testing or loading up procedure? (A) Choose an unoccupied frequency; (B) Use a dummy antenna; (C) Use a non-resonant antenna; (D) Use a resonant antenna that requires no loading up procedure.

3AB3.3 What is the proper Q signal to use to determine whether a frequency is in use before making a transmission? (A) QRV?; (B) QRU?; (C) QRL?; (D) QRZ?

3AB4.1 What is the proper distress calling procedure when using telephony? (A) Transmit MAYDAY; (B) Transmit QRRR; (C) Transmit QRZ; (D) Transmit SOS.

3AB4.2 What is the proper distress calling procedure when using telegraphy? (A) Transmit MAYDAY; (B) Transmit QRRR; (C) Transmit QRZ; (D) Transmit SOS.

3AB5-1.1 What is one requirement you must meet before you can participate in RACES drills? (A) You must be registered with ARRL; (B) You must be registered with a local racing organization; (C) You must be registered with the responsible civil defense organization; (D) You need not register with anyone to operate RACES.

3AB5-1.2 What is the maximum amount of time allowed per week for RACES drills? (A) Eight hours; (B) One hour; (C) As many hours as you want; (D) Six hours, but not more than one hour per day.

3AB5-2.1 How must you identify messages sent during a RACES drill? (A) As emergency messages; (B) As Amateur traffic; (C) As official government messages; (D) As drill or test messages.

3AB6-1.1 What is the term used to describe first-response communications in an emergency situation? (A) Tactical communications; (B) Emergency communications; (C) Formal message traffic; (D) National Traffic System messages.

3AB6-1.2 What is one reason for using tactical call signs such as "command post" or "weather center" during an emergency? (A) They keep the general public informed about what is going on; (B) They promote efficiency and coordination in public-service communications activities; (C) They are required by the FCC; (D) They promote goodwill among Amateurs.

3AB6-2.1 What is the term used to describe messages sent into or out of a disaster area that pertain to a person's well being? (A) Emergency traffic; (B) Tactical traffic; (C) Formal message traffic; (D) Health and welfare traffic.

3AB6-3.1 Why is it important to provide a means of operating your Amateur station separate from the commercial AC power lines? (A) So that you can take your station mobile; (B) So that you can provide communications in an emergency; (C) So that you can operate field day; (D) So that you will comply with Subpart 97.169 of the FCC Rules.

3AB6-3.2 Which type of antenna would be a good choice as part of a portable HF Amateur station that could be set up in case of a communications emergency? (A) A three-element quad; (B) A three-element Yagi; (C) A dipole; (D) A parabolic dish.

Chapter

C

Radio Propagation

This is a "fun" chapter. It discusses a number of interesting aspects of how radio signals get from one place to another. The questions are easy too. You will be asked only one question from the Novice pool and three from the Technician pool (2A and 3AA respectively).

The "Exciting" Word of Ham Radio

How does one Amateur communicate with another? By means of invisible waves which are radiated from an antenna connected to a transmitter. The radio frequency (RF) energy produced by the transmitter travels up to the antenna via one or more wires called a **transmission line**. The antenna accepts this energy and uses it to excite the environment surrounding the antenna.

True enough, but why can't one talk a thousand miles on a handheld transceiver? How is it possible to hear stations from thousands of miles away on a portable shortwave receiver? Clearly, there's a lot more going on here than the first paragraph would seem to indicate.

Exciting the environment is a confusing concept and it doesn't mean shaking your "booty" at the disco! We cannot see, feel or hear this "excitation". Even so, we know there is a coupling between the antenna and the space surrounding it.

Ham Radio Billiards

You can think of the radio frequency excitation as an almost endless series of invisible billiard balls. They stretch out from the antenna in all directions and pass the excitation along by clicking ball-to-ball. No single ball moves very far but the energy is imparted ball-to-ball. This continues until they either run out of energy or bang into another antenna.

When our imaginary billiard balls reach another antenna, they induce a weak voltage in it. The receiver connected to the antenna converts the tiny signal back into the original information.

Several volts of energy will be delivered to and radiated by a transmitting antenna. Only a few millionths of a volt will be induced in the receiving antenna. Obviously banging all those billiard balls around dissipates a lot of energy!

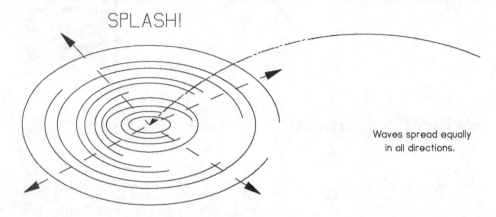

SPLASH!

Waves spread equally in all directions.

Figure C.1 - There are analogies between water action and radio signals

The billiard balls are actually electrons that vibrate and pass along their energy (*see Chapter E*). The electrical signal that radiates from the antenna does so in undulations similar to waves traveling across water. If you could, by magic, make the waves visible, you would see ripples spreading out from the antenna very much as if you had thrown a pebble into a still pond. The waves would radiate out in concentric circles consisting of a series of crests and valleys. Near the impact point of the pebble (the antenna), the waves would be strongest. They would diminish in strength as they traveled across the water.

If the pond was not too wide and the force of the thrown pebble was sufficient, the waves might make an impact on the shore. The size of the pebble and the force accompanying it, represent the transmitter **power**. The water surface, and the loss of strength resulting from trying to move the water, represents **resistance**.

VHF and UHF Characteristics

The last chapter presented a simple chart of the various radio frequencies. The section also described the characteristics of Amateur bands on which the Novice and Technician licensee are permitted operate. You will recall there was a remarkable difference in the communication range between say 10 meters (HF) and the 3/4 meter (UHF) band.

With a couple of exceptions, VHF and UHF signals are relatively undisturbed by external forces. They are radiated by the antenna, travel by direct waves in a straight line and are intercepted by a distant antenna. Contrary to what the "Flat Earth Society" believes,

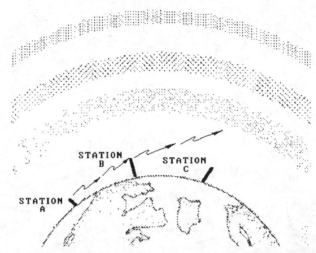

Figure C.1- VHF signals travel in a straight line. They can be intercepted by an antenna which is close but will pass above (and not be heard by) a distant reception point.

the earth is round. Since the signals do not bend around the earth, they will pass high over your head (and your antenna) if you are distant from the transmitting point. This is called **line-of-sight** communication. In other words, if the antennas can "see" each other, the radio stations connected to the antennas can communicate. (2C1.1)(2C1.2) (3AC6.1)(3AC6.2)

What are the exceptions mentioned above? Well for one, VHF signals are easily re-flected. It is not at all unusual for two distant VHF stations to communicate with each other with the help of a mountain. If the Amateurs were to point their directional anten-nas at each other, most of the signal strength might pass overhead and be lost in space. However, by pointing their antennas at a mutually visible mountain, enough signal is re-flected between stations to permit communications. (2C6.1)(2C6.2)

High Frequency Signal Characteristics

The transmission or propagation of signals on the HF bands (3-30 MHz) is fascinating. Unlike VHF, high frequency (HF) signals are almost completely influenced by external factors.

The energy which departs the HF antenna actually has two components, the **sky wave** and the **ground wave**. The ground wave "slithers" electronically along the surface of the earth. It is dissipated within a few miles of the transmitter due to the resistance it en-counters from the dry earth. Because of this, working distant stations solely by means of the ground wave is actually quite difficult. The sky wave travels many times further and can even reach foreign countries. (2C2.1)(2C2.2)(2C2.3)(2C2.4)

Ultraviolet rays from the sun beam down on the earth each day. The excitation causes an effect called **ionization**. The sun's rays excite the electrons in the ionosphere, caus-ing them to behave in a strange way. When the excitation is high enough, radio signals

which strike the ionosphere can be repelled or reflected back to earth at a point far distant from their origin. This signal bending is called **ionospheric refraction.** (3AC1-1.2)(3AC1-1.3)

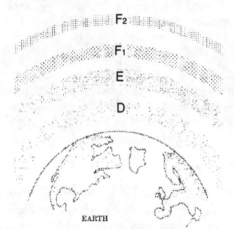

Figure C.2 - The ionosphere layers actually merge and are not distinct.

During the night the free electrons dissipate. Thus the minimum ionization level occurs just before dawn. The ionosphere absorbs radiation very quickly. By noon the ionization reaches a maximum. This does not mean that this is the best time to communicate over long distances. Remember that the ionosphere has to be percolating along at both ends of the circuit. Thus the best time for DX'ing is right after dawn and just before sunset. (3AC3.1)(3AC3.2)(3AC3.3)(3AC3.4)

This is what causes the difference in characteristics between HF and VHF. The ionosphere, well above the atmosphere, contains enough ions and free electrons that it is capable of reflecting high frequency signals. Signals transmitted via this medium are called **skywave communications.** (2C3.1)(2C3.2)(2C3.6)(3AC1-1.1)

For the most part, VHF signals are not affected by the ionosphere and pass straight through. If this were not the case, we would be unable to communicate with our satellites which orbit above the ionosphere and travel to other planetary systems.

While we cannot see the ionosphere, we think it looks something like the drawing in Figure C.2. The sketch is a little misleading. Actually there are no distinct layers like a

Jello desert. Rather, one layer blends into the next. The regions are labeled **D, E, F1** and **F2** because certain layers of the ionosphere have different characteristics. Some layers influence the lower frequencies. For example, the ionized D layer (the lowest) limits daytime 80-meter communications to short distances due to radio waves entering at a low angle. This causes absorption of the energy. (3AC1-2.1)(3AC1-2.2)(3AC2.1)(3AC 2.2)(3AC2.3)(3AC2.4)

The E layer is the lowest region that is useful for long distance propagation. It also creates erratic propagation conditions at the upper end of the high frequency spectrum. When this occurs, it is called **sporadic-E.** (3AC1-3.1)

The F layers (F1 and F2) are capable of supporting worldwide communications on a consistent basis. The F2 layer is mainly responsible for long distance skywave communications. At night the F1 and F2 layers combine as shown in Figure C4. (3AC1-4.1)(3AC1-4.2)(3AC1-4.3)

Although we cannot see the ionosphere, we can certainly observe and describe its effects. The ionosphere acts very much like an **electronic mirror** which reflects radio signals back to earth at some distant point. Unfortunately the "mirror" is not as consistent as the one you stare at each morning. The ionosphere is constantly in motion and in a state of turmoil. The "reflectability" varies from transparent to nearly perfect. It can also move up and down, thereby increasing or decreasing the angle of the signals bounced back to earth (and therefore the impact point). We refer to those signals which are reflected by the ionosphere as **skip transmissions**. The signals actually leave the surface of the earth and are bent (or reflected) by the ionosphere. They arrive back at the earth's surface at some distance from the point of origin. (2C3.3)

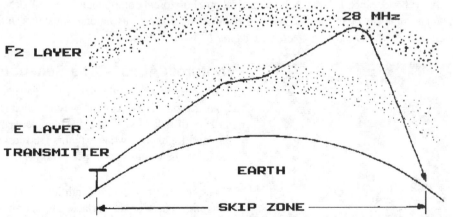

Figure C.3 - The distance between the transmitter and the point of closest reception is called the skip zone.

Note that between the transmission and reception point, the signal cannot be received. The ground wave has long since dissipated. This area of no reception is called the **skip zone**. Typically, the 10 meter skip zone is 500-1,000 miles but can be considerably shorter or longer under unusual conditions. (2C3.4)(2C3.5)

Antenna Polarization

The pebble explanation mentioned earlier denotes radiation solely in a horizontal plane. However, the transmitting antenna could just as well be rotated 90 degrees. Now our imaginary pond would have to be turned on its side to simulate vertical polarization.

There can be a significant amount of signal loss between cross polarized antennas. The reason is quite simple to understand. If our imaginary billiard balls were traveling in a horizontal plane, not as many of them would strike a vertical antenna element.

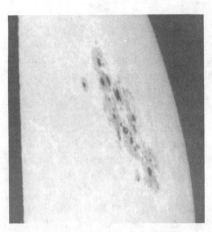

Virtually all mobile antennas are vertically polarized. Fixed stations, communicating with these mobiles, must also have vertically polarized antennas or a significant loss of signal strength would result. Since there are so many mobile stations, most VHF base station antennas are vertically polarized.

Playing tricks with the antenna polarity can sometimes reduce interference from other stations. One can use the polarization effect to advantage by receiving with the antenna polarity opposite that of an interfering station.

For working long distances on the lower frequencies, horizontal polarization of the antenna seems to be more effective. Some Amateurs will argue that a vertical antenna is better for working the really distant stations. Others contend that the cubical quad antenna is better since it radiates both vertical and horizontal components. The subject of antennas can result in long heated and opinionated discussions among Amateurs. *For more information on this subject, see Chapter I - Polarization.*

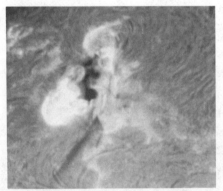

Two views of sunspots taken by high altitude rockets.

Nature's Acne — The Sunspots

The ionosphere is highly charged by particles from the sun. This explains why the characteristics of radio signals are different between day and night. But what explains the reason the ionosphere sometimes "goes crazy"?

The sun exhibits a cyclic condition in which **sunspots** appear on the surface. The action of the sun over this period is called the **sunspot cycle**. Approximately every 11 years, these solar "pimples" reach a peak as shown in Figure C.6. For two or three years on either side of the peak, all heck breaks loose in the HF portion of the radio spectrum. The effect is particularly noticeable on the 10 meter band. (2C4.1)(2C4.2)

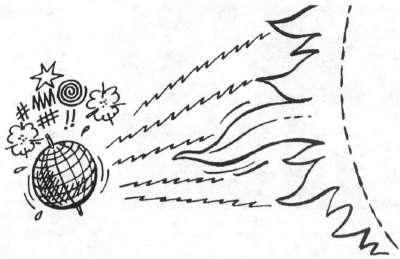

Occasionally one of the sunspots erupts into a solar flare. Electrons shower the earth like an oil leak from an old Volkswagen. When this occurs, the ionosphere blows its chromosomes and becomes paralyzed at all frequencies. This can completely disrupt radio communications circuits and cause radio "blackouts". The intensity of the solar radiation can even disrupt telephone cables lying on the ocean floor! The blackout can last for hours or days, depending on the intensity and duration of the flare. During the Spring of 1990, Amateurs experienced a total blackout of the 10 meter band, even though we are at a peak in the sunspot cycle. The ionization level was so high that 10 meter signals were absorbed, rather than being passed or reflected, by the ionosphere.

Sunspots are magnetic field blemishes on the surface of the sun which can be observed and photographed. The spots seem to be directly related with how much radiation strikes the ionosphere and its level of ionization. The fact that the sun plays such an important part in the functioning of the ionosphere also causes a number of associated phenomena. The seasons will affect propagation differently. Usually distant signals are much stronger in the Winter than in the Summer. Just the opposite is true for sporadic-E, which accounts for the reception of distant television stations in the summer.

The ionosphere of the northern hemisphere reacts differently from that of the southern hemisphere, since their seasons are opposite. Some radio conditions will improve at night, as shown in Figure C.4, while on other bands the signals will disappear altogether. No doubt you've heard broadcast stations coming in from great distances on your car radio. This usually happens at night during the Winter. In the southern hemisphere, the effect is most noticeable in the Summer.

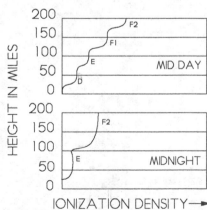

Figure C.4 - At night the F-layers, as well as the D and E-layers, merge together

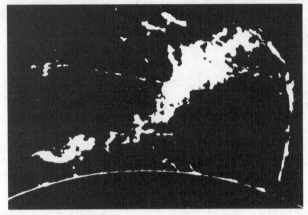

A looping flare from the surface of the sun. The arrow points to a dot of burning gas about the size of the earth!

The Maximum Usable Frequency

The ionosphere has some of the properties of a photographic filter. Some of the "colors" (frequencies) will pass through, while others will be absorbed or reflected.

The ionization level determines how high a frequency will be reflected by the ionosphere. The more sunspots there are, the greater the ionization. By observing the onset of the spots near the sun's rim, we can predict what radio conditions will be like in the following weeks. (2C5.2)

If we were to beam signals of an increasingly higher frequency at the ionosphere, they would be reflected farther and farther from their origin. Finally, a point where reflection no longer occurs would be reached. At this point, the angle would be so sharp and the ionization level sufficiently low that reflection can no longer occur. Above this critical point, signals will pass through the ionosphere and be lost forever in space as illustrated in Figure C.5.

The highest or **critical frequency** which can be reflected by the ionosphere is called the **maximum usable frequency** or **MUF**. This is defined as the highest frequency that will reach its destination in a single hop. As the sunspot number and activity increases, so does the radiation reaching the earth and the MUF increases. (2C5.1)(3AC-4.1) (3AC 4.2)(3AC4.3)

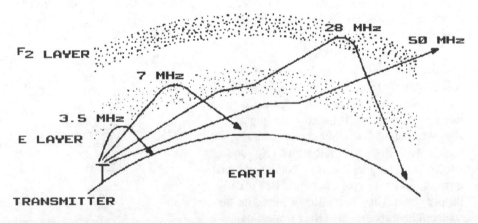

Figure C.5 - The Maximum Usable Frequency (MUF) is somewhere between 28 and 50 MHz in this drawing.

During periods of peak solar activity, MUF can reach 50 MHz or higher. When the MUF gets this high, the ol' ionosphere really gets swinging like a Jai alai champion. World wide communication becomes commonplace on the 10 meter band and even occurs on the 6 meters (50 MHz). It is not at all unusual to work European or Asian stations from your car on 10 meters during these peaks. The current peak in sunspot activity occurred in Winter of 1990 or early in 1991.

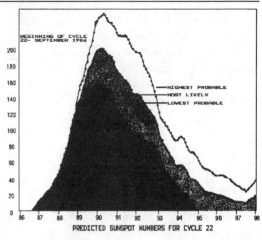

Figure C.6 - The most recent sun-spot cycle peak occurred in early 1991.

One might think that the MUF would drop to a very low value at night when the sun is illuminating the other side of the earth. This is not the case fortunately. Usually at night the F layers merge together, as do the D and E layers. Dr. Van Allen's satellite experiments discovered a radiation doughnut around the earth (the Van Allen belt). The belt follows the earth's magnetic lines of force and serves to trap solar radiation in its electronic spider web. As a result, ionization can continue long after the sun has set. Because of the Van Allen belt, ionization will be minimal at the earth's poles and maximum near the equator. This accounts for the fact that we hear a preponderance of Central and South American stations when the skip really starts coming in. (3AC1-4.3)

Selective Fading

The ionosphere has another phenomenon which you might find interesting. The ionosphere is not smooth, like the mirror we talked about earlier. Rather, it is highly irregular and has areas of ion concentration. As a result, signals transmitted from point A can arrive at point B simultaneously over a number of different paths. Often the paths shift around, some getting longer and others getting shorter, and signal cancellation, or fading (*remember QSB from Chapter B?*), can occur. When this happens, it is actually possible to have carrier cancellation of an AM station while the modulation sidebands are left intact. This selective fading causes horrible distortion of an AM signal (such as a shortwave broadcast station) which makes it totally unreadable. The same effect can destroy data transmissions. The effect does not arise on SSB because there is no carrier to selectively fade. Fading simply causes the volume of the SSB station to rise and fall with the gyrations of the ionosphere. The automatic volume control (AVC) circuit in most SSB receivers can easily cope with this fading and level out large signal variations. Thus, the effects of selective fading are hardly noticeable on SSB while they make AM reception intolerable.

The ionosphere can tell you when it's about to "close shop" for the day, if you know what signs to look for. At times (not just in the evening) you may hear tremendous signal strengths from distant stations. The signal strength meter may read as high as for a station a few miles away. This effect is often noted just as the band "shuts down", usually in the evening, but not always. Just before everything gets quiet, there is a peaking of signals which will last for several minutes. The observance of abnormally strong transmissions usually signifies the party is over. When it happens, it is just as if someone flipped a switch and turned off the ionosphere. Signals can go from S9 plus 20 db to inaudible within 30-40 seconds.

Other Propagation Modes

Sporadic-E — Occasionally "hot spots" develop in the ionosphere around the E layer. This effect is stronger in the summer months, while longer distance (because it is higher) F layer propagation is stronger in the Winter. These hot patches of ionosphere are called sporadic-E and may be only a few hundred miles across. Between any two points that are able to bounce a signal off the hotspot, extremely strong signal strengths can occur. The MUF can actually double due to this invisible ionized cloud. When sporadic-E hits, it is not at all unusual to have contacts with South America on the 6 meter (50 MHz) Amateur band. On 10 meters you may hear the band open up suddenly to a specific area and then, sometime later, shut down just as quickly as it started. This is the effect of sporadic-E.

Scatter — It is possible for two stations within each others skip zone to communicate. As we've seen, the ionosphere is not a smooth continuous surface. Some radiation will scatter at angles that reach stations within a skip zone. The signals will be weak and hollow sounding but if the stations have enough power and interference is low, they can hear each other. This mode is called "**scatter communications**." (3AC5.1)

Backscatter — When calling DX, several Amateurs may have their directional antenna's pointed toward the DX station. Since the antennas are pointed in the same general direction, it is possible for stations within a skip zone to hear each other. Like the scatter mode mentioned previously, the ionosphere can reflect signals toward the source. This mode is called **backscatter propagation**. Backscatter reception sounds much the same as scatter communications. (3AC5.2)

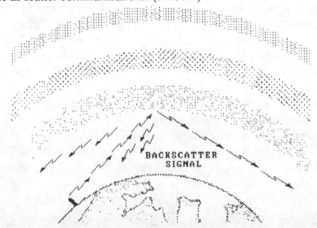

Figure C.7 - Signals striking the ionosphere will be "scattered" weakly back toward the source , in addition to being reflected toward distant locations.

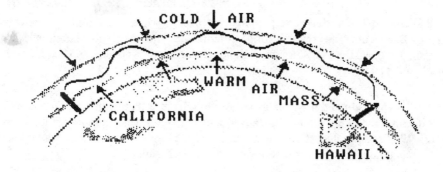

Figure C.8 - Large warm air masses can actually function like a "waveguide" to bend VHF signals around the curvature of the earth.

Tropospheric Propagation — DX communication is actually possible on VHF which is normally line-of-sight. The effect is called atmospheric ducting or **tropospheric propagation**. How does DX on VHF happen? Occasionally, when a layer of cool air stalls over an area of warm air, the temperature inversion acts as a "pipe" for VHF radio signals. Many Southern California Amateurs have communicated with Hawaii via widespread temperature inversions over the ocean. (3AC7.1)(3AC7.2)(3AC7.3) (3AC7.4) (3AC7.5)(3AC7.6)

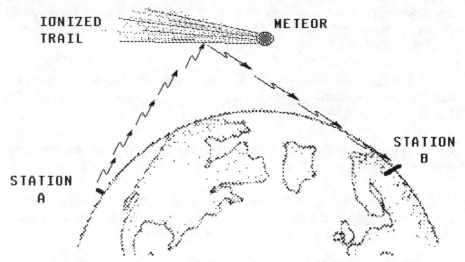

Figure C.9 - Meteors hurtling through the upper atmosphere leave an ionized trail that is capable of reflecting radio signals over great distances.

Much of the information in this chapter is not required knowledge to pass the Technician test. Hopefully you found the subject interesting and informative. On the following pages, you will find the questions relating to propagation and what happens to emissions when they travel from one place to another. (Subelement 2C and 3AC from the Novice and Technician question pool).

SUBELEMENT 2C (1 question).

2C1.1 What type of radio-wave propagation occurs when the signal travels in a straight line from the transmitting antenna to the receiving antenna? (A) Lineofsight propagation; (B) Straight-line propagation; (C) Knifeedge diffraction; (D) Tunnel propagation.

2C1.2 What path do radio waves usually follow from a transmitting antenna to a receiving antenna at VHF and higher frequencies? (A) A bent path through the ionosphere; (B) A straight line; (C) A great circle path over either the North or South pole; (D) A circular path going either east or west from the transmitter.

2C2.1 What type of propagation involves radio signals that travel along the surface of the Earth? (A) Sky-wave propagation; (B) Knifeedge diffraction; (C) E layer propagation; (D) Groundwave propagation.

2C2.2 What is the meaning of the term groundwave propagation? (A) Signals that travel along seismic fault lines; (B) Signals that travel along the surface of the earth; (C) Signals that are radiated from a groundplane antenna; (D) Signals that are radiated from a ground station to a satellite.

2C2.3 Two Amateur stations a few miles apart and separated by a low hill blocking their lineofsight path are communicating on 3.725 MHz. What type of propagation is probably being used? (A) Tropospheric ducting; (B) Ground wave; (C) Meteor scatter; (D) Sporadic-E.

2C2.4 When compared to sky-wave propagation, what is the usual effective range of groundwave propagation? (A) Much smaller; (B) Much greater; (C) The same; (D) Dependent on the weather.

2C3.1 What type of propagation uses radio signals refracted back to earth by the ionosphere? (A) Sky wave; (B) Earth-moon-earth; (C) Ground wave; (D) Tropospheric.

2C3.2 What is the meaning of the term sky-wave propagation? (A) Signals reflected from the moon; (B) Signals refracted by the ionosphere; (C) Signals refracted by water-dense cloud formations; (D) Signals retransmitted by a repeater.

2C3.3 What does the term skip mean? (A) Signals are reflected from the moon; (B) Signals are refracted by water-dense cloud formations; (C) Signals are retransmitted by repeaters; (D) Signals are refracted by the ionosphere.

2C3.4 What is the area of weak signals between the ranges of ground waves and the first hop called? (A) The skip zone; (B) The hysteresis zone; (C) The monitor zone; (D) The transequatorial zone.

2C3.5 What is the meaning of the term skip zone? (A) An area covered by skip propagation; (B) The area where a satellite comes close to the earth, and skips off the ionosphere; (C) An area that is too far for groundwave propagation, but too close for skip propagation; (D) The area in the atmosphere that causes skip propagation.

2C3.6 What type of radio wave propagation makes it possible for Amateur stations to communicate long distances? (A) Direct-inductive propagation; (B) Knifeedge diffraction; (C) Groundwave propagation; (D) Sky-wave propagation.

2C4.1 How long is an average sunspot cycle? (A) 2 years; (B) 5 years; (C) 11 years; (D) 17 years.

2C4.2 What is the term used to describe the long-term variation in the number of visible sunspots? (A) The 11-year cycle; (B) The solar magnetic flux cycle; (C) The hysteresis count; (D) The sunspot cycle.

2C5.1 What effect does the number of sunspots have on the maximum usable frequency (MUF)? (A) The more sunspots there are, the higher the MUF will be; (B) The more sunspots there are, the lower the MUF will be; (C) The MUF is equal to the square of the number of sunspots; (D) The number of sunspots effects the lowest usable frequency (LUF) but not the MUF.

2C5.2 What effect does the number of sunspots have on the ionization level in the atmosphere? (A) The more sunspots there are, the lower the ionization level will be; (B) The more sunspots there are, the higher the ionization level will be; (C) The ionization level of the ionosphere is equal to the square root of the number of sunspots; (D) The ionization level of the ionosphere is equal to the square of the number of sunspots.

2C6.1 Why can a VHF or UHF radio signal that is transmitted toward a mountain often be received at some distant point in a different direction? (A) You can never tell what direction a radio wave is traveling in; (B) These radio signals are easily bent by the ionosphere; (C) These radio signals are easily reflected by objects in their path; (D) These radio signals are sometimes scattered in the ectosphere.

2C6.2 Why can the direction that a VHF or UHF radio signal is traveling be changed if there is a tall building in the way? (A) You can never tell what direction a radio wave is traveling in; (B) These radio signals are easily bent by the ionosphere; (C) These radio signals are easily reflected by objects in their path; (D) These radio signals are sometimes scattered in the ectosphere.

SUBELEMENT 3AC (3 questions).

3AC1-1.1 What is the ionosphere? (A) That part of the upper atmosphere where enough ions and free electrons exist to affect radio-wave propagation; (B) The boundary between two air masses of different temperature and humidity, along which radio waves can travel; (C) The ball that goes on the top of a mobile whip antenna; (D) That part of the atmosphere where weather takes place.

3AC1-1.2 What is the region of the outer atmosphere that makes long-distance radio communications possible as a result of bending of radio waves? (A) Troposphere; (B) Stratosphere; (C) Magnetosphere; (D) Ionosphere.

3AC1-1.3 What type of solar radiation is most responsible for ionization in the outer atmosphere? (A) Thermal; (B) Ionized particle; (C) Ultraviolet; (D) Microwave.

3AC1-2.1 Which ionospheric layer limits daytime radio communications in the 80-meter wavelength band to short distances? (A) D layer; (B) F1 layer; (C) E layer; (D) F2 layer.

3AC1-2.2 What is the lowest ionospheric layer? (A) The A layer; (B) The D layer; (C) The E layer; (D) The F layer.

3AC1-3.1 What is the lowest region of the ionosphere that is useful for long- distance radio-wave propagation? (A) The D layer; (B) The E layer; (C) The F1 layer; (D) The F2 layer.

3AC1-4.1 Which layer of the ionosphere is mainly responsible for long- distance sky-wave radio communications? (A) D layer; (B) E layer; (C) F1 layer; (D) F2 layer.

3AC1-4.2 What are the two distinct sub-layers of the F layer of the ionosphere during the daytime? (A) Troposphere and stratosphere; (B) F1 and F2; (C) Electrostatic and electromagnetic; (D) D and E.

3AC1-4.3 Which two daytime ionospheric layers combine into one layer at night? (A) E and F1; (B) D and E; (C) F1 and F2; (D) E1 and E2.

3AC2.1 Which layer of the ionosphere is most responsible for absorption of radio signals during daylight hours? (A) The E layer; (B) The F1 layer; (C) The F2 layer; (D) The D layer.

3AC2.2 When is ionospheric absorption most pronounced? (A) When tropospheric ducting occurs; (B) When radio waves enter the D layer at low angles; (C) When radio waves travel to the F layer; (D) When a temperature inversion occurs.

3AC2.3 During daylight hours, what effect does the D layer of the ionosphere have on 80-meter radio waves? (A) The D layer absorbs the signals; (B) The D layer bends the radio-waves out into space; (C) The D layer refracts the radio-waves back to earth; (D) The D layer has little or no effect on 80-meter radio-wave propagation.

3AC2.4 What causes ionospheric absorption of radio waves? (A) A lack of D layer ionization; (B) D layer ionization; (C) The presence of ionized clouds in the E layer; (D) Splitting of the F layer.

3AC3.1 What is usually the condition of the ionosphere just before sunrise? (A) Atmospheric attenuation is at a maximum; (B) Ionization is at a maximum; (C) The E layer is above the F layer; (D) Ionization is at a minimum.

3AC3.2 At what time of day does maximum ionization of the ionosphere occur? (A) Dusk; (B) Midnight; (C) Midday; (D) Dawn.

3AC3.3 Minimum ionization of the ionosphere occurs daily at what time? (A) Shortly before dawn; (B) Just after noon; (C) Just after dusk; (D) Shortly before midnight.

3AC3.4 When is E layer ionization at a maximum? (A) Dawn; (B) Midday; (C) Dusk; (D) Midnight.

3AC4.1 What is the name for the highest radio frequency that will be refracted back to earth? (A) Lowest usable frequency; (B) Optimum working frequency; (C) Ultra high frequency; (D) Critical frequency.

3AC4.2 What causes the maximum usable frequency to vary? (A) Variations in the temperature of the air at ionospheric levels; (B) Upper-atmospheric wind patterns; (C) The amount of ultraviolet and other types of radiation received from the sun; (D) Presence of ducting.

3AC4.3 What does the term maximum usable frequency refer to? (A) The maximum frequency that allows a radio signal to reach its destination in a single hop; (B) The minimum frequency that allows a radio signal to reach its destination in a single hop; (C) The maximum frequency that allows a radio signal to be absorbed in the lowest ionospheric layer; (D) The minimum frequency that allows a radio signal to be absorbed in the lowest ionospheric layer.

3AC5.1 When two stations are within each other's skip zone on the frequency being used, what mode of propagation would it be desirable to use? (A) Groundwave propagation; (B) Sky-wave propagation; (C) Scatter-mode propagation; (D) Ionospheric ducting propagation.

3AC5.2 You are in contact with a distant station and are operating at a frequency close to the maximum usable frequency. If the received signals are weak and somewhat distorted, what type of propagation are you probably experiencing? (A) Tropospheric ducting; (B) Line-of-sight propagation; (C) Backscatter propagation; (D) Waveguide propagation.

3AC6.1 What is the transmission path of a wave that travels directly from the transmitting antenna to the receiving antenna called? (A) Line of sight; (B) The sky wave; (C) The linear wave; (D) The plane-wave.

3AC6.2 How are VHF signals within the range of the visible horizon propagated? (A) By sky wave; (B) By direct wave; (C) By plane wave; (D) By geometric-wave.

3AC7.1 Ducting occurs in which region of the atmosphere? (A) F2; (B) Ionosphere; (C) Troposphere; (D) Stratosphere.

3AC7.2 What effect does tropospheric bending have on 2-meter radio waves? (A) It increases the distance over which they can be transmitted; (B) It decreases the distance over which they can be transmitted; (C) It tends to garble 2-meter phone transmissions; (D) It reverses the sideband of 2-meter phone transmissions.

3AC7.3 What atmospheric phenomenon causes tropospheric ducting of radio waves? (A) A very low pressure area; (B) An aurora to the north; (C) Lightning between the transmitting and receiving station; (D) A temperature inversion.

3AC7.4 Tropospheric ducting occurs as a result of what phenomenon? (A) A temperature inversion; (B) Sunspots; (C) An aurora to the north; (D) Lightning between the transmitting and receiving station.

3AC7.5 What atmospheric phenomenon causes VHF radio waves to be propagated several hundred miles through stable air masses over oceans? (A) Presence of a maritime polar air mass; (B) A widespread temperature inversion; (C) An overcast of cirriform clouds; (D) Atmospheric pressure of roughly 29 inches of mercury or higher.

3AC7.6 In what frequency range does tropospheric ducting occur most often? (A) LF; (B) MF; (C) HF; (D) VHF.

Chapter

D

Amateur Radio Practice

> To see if you understand safety and good practice, you will be asked four questions from Subelement 2D and four questions from the Subelement 3AD question pool.

Safety Practices

Hobbies are generally rather benign. One might cut a lip while licking a stamp hinge or get a bruised ankle from a runaway RC model car. Unless you collect dangerous snakes or navigate hot air balloons, your hobby probably does not involve personal safety.

Amateur Radio is not a benign hobby. But don't get the impression that it is a dangerous hobby, either. However, there are a number of areas where care must be exercised to avoid harmful situations.

Antennas and Towers

All too often we hear of an unfortunate Amateur who, in erecting an antenna, comes in contact with power lines and is electrocuted. Everything seems to be under control, then someone loses their grip or stumbles, the tower falls and poof!

Some thoughtless Amateurs do not wear a **safety belt** (in good condition!) when climbing an antenna tower. Seldom a year goes by without a ham falling and breaking bones, or worse. It seems so simple, but up about the 40-foot level of the tower, Harry Ham's high blood pressure kicks in, he gets a little dizzy and loses his grip. Presto — he is transported to the emergency entrance of the local hospital for treatment of multiple broken bones. (2D-6.1)(2D-6.2)

You would be surprised at the number of hams, working under a friend's antenna, who get "beaned" by wrenches and screwdrivers. Hams are pretty "thick-skulled" but a Philips screwdriver traveling at 40 miles an hour makes a very effective arrow. One should always wear a **hard-hat** in any area where there is any possibility of falling objects. It has nothing to do with macho — it has to do with "smarts". (2D-6.4)(2D-6.5)

Electrical Shock

Most Amateur equipment today is all solid state and operates from a 12 volt DC power supply. A ham rig seldom presents a serious safety hazard except for the occasional RF burn from an antenna. Since this can happen, an antenna should be mounted high enough that a person cannot touch it. (2D-6.3)

RF burns are painful but seldom lethal since radio frequency energy travels on the surface of objects (including the human body). Thus the RF is not able to reach the heart and paralyze the muscles which keep it pumping. Even so, radio frequency energy can be very dangerous. Not only can it burn and cook you, but evidence indicates there may be harmful long-term effects of exposure to radio frequency energy. We'll look at some of the dangers of RF shortly.

The ETO "Alpha 87" linear power amplifier can continuously deliver 1500 watts output.

Amateur high power radio frequency amplifiers can legally deliver 1500 watts of power. Most of these amplifiers still use vacuum tubes and employ a thousand or more volts in the power supply circuit. The result of contacting this voltage is often fatal. Always make certain the power cannot be energized when you are exposed to lethal voltages. In case you forget this precaution, any equipment employing voltages greater than 50 volts should employ an **interlock**. This device, usually a power switch attached to the removable covers, automatically disables the power supply whenever entry is made into the cabinet. The covers also prevent radiation of RF energy. Sometimes it is necessary to troubleshoot a "hot box". If you **absolutely must** work on equipment which uses lethal voltages, always keep one hand in your pocket when the safety covers are off. (2D-4.3)(2D-5.1)(2D-5.2)(2D8-2.4)(3AD11-3.1)

Fire!

The voltages used in most modern solid state transmitter/receivers will not cause electrical shock. The current available, however, can easily start a fire. As an example, if a paper clip should happen to short an unfused 12 volt, 40 ampere power supply, the metal clip would glow red-hot just like an automobile cigarette lighter. This can easily ignite combustible materials.

An Ounce of Prevention

Obviously you should not leave metal objects near your high amperage power supplies. Even with precautions, however, accidents can and do happen in the ham shack.

For a number of reasons, it is an excellent idea to install a key operated power switch in your Amateur station. This will prevent your pesky kid brother or sister from tampering with your gear or creating an unsafe condition. (2D-1.1)(2D-1.2)

Electrical Storms

Lightening can cause havoc in your ham shack. It is not necessary for a "bolt" to strike your antenna in order to cause damage. Electrically charged clouds, passing overhead, can cause a buildup of electricity on antennas. The buildup, or charge, will eventually jump or discharge to ground. With proper grounding the charge will not accumulate on the antenna.

Even when lightning strikes hundreds of yards away, an enormous electromagnetic field is generated. This field will induce voltage in any metal objects within the field. Remember Hertz's spark experiments mentioned in Chapter One? Exactly the same thing can happen with your antenna. Very little voltage is required to damage the transistors in your radio equipment. In fact, it takes far less than the voltage required to create a spark.

If the lightning stroke is sufficiently strong, and your station is not adequately grounded, it can cause sparks to jump between your radio equipment. Even if the level is not lethal, it might be sufficient to start a fire. A key operated power switch won't solve this problem.

Grounding Protection

It is not possible to stop the phenomena of lightning induced voltage and static electricity. We can, however, take steps to minimize the damage or harm caused by it. The first step is to properly ground all your radio equipment. The metal chassis of each piece of equipment should be connected together with a heavy copper wire. The gauge used for house wiring, #10 or #12 (available at most hardware stores), is quite adequate. This wire should run to ground by a short direct route. (2D-2.4)(2D-3.2)

In addition, you must ground the antenna and (if used) rotor or control wires with a switch (such as a knife switch) whenever there is a storm in the vicinity. Several companies sell grounding devices which can be left connected at all times. These are usually mounted outside the house. (2D-2.1)(2D-2.2)

This covers the situation when a storm comes up while you are away from home. If you don't install static discharge devices, it is a good idea to always ground the wires entering your station whenever you are not using your station. It's also a good idea to unplug your valuable equipment when it is not in use. (2D-2.3)

Where do you find a good ground connection? The preferred method is to install a ground rod in the earth just outside the window nearest the radio equipment. The ground rod should be at least 8 foot long and plated with copper, to be effective. These can be purchased at most Amateur Radio stores. They are driven into the ground with a sledge hammer. (2D-3.3)(2D-3.4)

Sometimes it is just not practical to install a ground rod. You may be on the upper story of an apartment building or your folks may object to your drilling holes in the wall of their tidy mortgaged bungalow. A "second best" ground is to connect all your equipment to a cold water pipe. Why second best? Usually the plumber puts compound on the pipe joints. This may prevent a good electrical connection between pipes. (2D-3.1)

Why a cold water pipe? The hot water pipes go to the water heater which is probably not grounded. In this case, static discharges are more likely to head for the electrical circuits or natural gas pipes instead of going directly to an earth ground. Even so, the static electricity will ultimately reach ground.

There is another way that your radio equipment is grounded which should always be respected. Virtually all electronic equipment found in the hamshack uses a three wire plug. Two lugs carry the power, while a round center pin is used for ground. This is where the green ground wire is connected. At the other end, the green wire is connected to the metal frame of a drill, electric saw or the metal chassis of an electronic product. Never cut off this safety pin or use an adapter that has no provision for grounding the green wire to the wall outlet. (3AD-1-1.1)

The MFJ AC voltmeter has an expanded scale for accurate measurement of AC line voltage

While speaking of electrical wiring, we should mention the correct connection of the current carrying wires. Anything that breaks the electrical circuit (a fuse or switch) should be connected in series with the black (or red) wire of the power cord or house wiring. By the same token, the unswitched side of the wiring should use the white wire. (3AD-1-1.2)(3AD-1-1.3)

Maintaining these relationships is very important to minimize shock hazard in electronic equipment. Look at the two lugs that carry the current in the power cord. Did you ever notice they are a different size. This insures that you insert the plug correctly when there is no ground pin. This respect for polarity explains why the screws that secure the wiring on each side of a switch or light socket are different color. (3AD-1-1.4)

This single-sideband linear power amplifier (the Ten-Tec "Titan") is rated at 1500 watts output.

Electric Shock — Why all this concern about proper wiring? The answer is simple. An electric current flowing through your body can kill you. Even voltages as low as 30 volts can be dangerous under certain conditions. However, it is not the voltage, but rather the current level that matters. Ever work on an automobile engine and get shocked by the ignition circuit? If so, it's likely that something in the order of 20,000 volts was conducted through your ole "bod." Fortunately, there is not enough conducted current to hurt you. (3AD1-2.2)

How does current affect you? Anything below five milliamperes (mA) is probably harmless. If the current increases to 50 mA, you will experience pain and muscular contractions that may prevent you from "letting go." Over 100 mA, the heart will be affected and may cause death in people with heart problems or if the current is sustained. (3AD-1-2.1)(3AD-1-2.3)

For safety sake, always place the power switch (either the master switch or transmitter high voltage power switch) where it is obvious to anyone and can be easily reached. Someone else may have to throw the switch if you can't let go! (3AD-1-3.1)

RF Exposure

If you doubt that RF has the ability to cook things, ask for a demonstration of a microwave oven at the local discount store. Any concentration of radio frequency energy will raise the temperature of material in its' field. Dish shaped antennas, designed to work at microwave frequencies (above 1,000 MHz or 1 GigaHertz) concentrate RF energy so that it may be directed like a flashlight beam. If you happen to be standing at the focus point, you will quickly realize how that meatloaf feels in the microwave oven. You should never stand near any kind of antenna which concentrates RF energy (or open waveguide transmission line, for that matter) when the transmitter power is on. Always use a good quality of coaxial cable transmission line to minimize RF leakage. (2D-4.1)(2D4.4)

Insofar as possible, your antenna (regardless of frequency) must be mounted high enough so that people cannot touch it. Even if the antenna is out of reach, you should never transmit if someone is standing near it. The strong field around an antenna can be very intense. There is growing concern that the radiation from hand-held transceivers may be harmful if used constantly over long periods of time. There is no direct evidence to support this, but it is an excellent idea to keep the whip or "rubber duck" antenna on your hand-held away from your head. (2D-4.2)

Scientists at the American National Standards Institute (ANSI) have established maximum level standards for exposure to RF energy. These standards state the maximum RF exposure limits. (3AD-11-2.1)(3AD-11-2.2)

ANSI is concerned about the heating caused by RF energy. The eyes are particularly sensitive to heating caused by this form of radiation. The standards in 300 to 3,000 MHz range are the most stringent since RF energy can be concentrated into powerful beams in this region. (3AD-11-1.1)(3AD-11-1.2)(3AD-11-2.3)(3AD-11-2.4)

Hand-held units, which are operated near the head and eyes, should not have a power rating in excess of 7 watts according to ANSI. (3AD-11-2.5)

Antenna Tuning and SWR — The last chapter mentioned that energy from the transmitter is fed through the transmission line to the antenna, where it is coupled to the environment. For this to occur, the antenna must be the **correct length** for the frequency in question. If it is too long or too short, it will lose efficiency as a coupling device. This can also happen if the electrical resistance (the impedance) of the antenna is incorrect.

In this case, what happens to the energy sent up to the antenna? Most of it will be radiated into space, but some will not. A portion of the energy will be reflected back down the transmission line to the transmitter. The antenna "says" "Hey, I can't handle this" and sends some of the energy back to the transmitter. The transmitter doesn't want it either. It just got rid of it, and back up the transmission line it goes.

The reflected energy back and forth, is called **standing waves**. The intensity of these waves is measured with a device called an **SWR meter**. An SWR meter can also be used to indicate the **impedance matching** condition between the transmitter and the antenna. A reading of 1:1 indicates a perfect condition, while anything above 2:1 is an unacceptable match which can damage your transmitter. The SWR meter can also indicate an open or shorted transmission line with an exceptionally high SWR reading. A poor or intermittent connection might be indicated by an erratic meter reading. (2D-7-1.1)(2D-7-1.2)(2D-7-2.1)(2d-7-2.2)(2D-7-2.3)(2D-7-2.4)(2D-7-3.1)(2D-7-3.2)

As mentioned, the antenna must be the correct length to be most efficient at a specific frequency. If the antenna is too long it will tune lower than the desired frequency. If the antenna is too short, it will tune above the desired frequency. The SWR meter can be used to indicate the frequency to which the antenna is tuned. Let's say, for example, you measure an SWR of 2.5:1 at the low end of the Amateur band and 5:1 at the high end. Both numbers are excessively high but improving at the low end. Just like a golf score, 2.5 is better than 5 so the SWR is improving at the low frequency. This means that the antenna is probably tuned below the low end of the band. Remember that "long is low" so the antenna is probably too long for the band in question. (2D-7-3.3)(2D-7-3.4)

If you are adjusting an antenna for lowest SWR, the meter should be connected right **at the antenna terminals** for best accuracy. This is because a long transmission line can mask poor SWR readings. (3AD-8-2.1) (3AD-8-2.2)

One occasionally hears the standing wave radio meter called an SWR bridge or **reflectometer**. The reflectometer or SWR meter is connected between the 50 ohm impedance transmitter output and the transmission line to the antenna. If the antenna system (including transmission line) also measures 50 ohms impedance there will be no reflected power. The SWR meter will indicate a perfect 1:1 impedance match. It the reading is higher than 1:1,

The MFJ SWR meter has a dual meter scale which shows the forward and reverse energy at the same time.

it indicates an impedance mismatch. (3AD-5-1.1)(3AD-5-1.3) (3AD-8-1.1)(3AD-8-1.2)

The transmitter antenna jack is also where a power output measuring device should be connected for best accuracy. (3AD-5-1.2)

A simple SWR meter measures the **relative** power delivered to, and reflected by, the antenna system. More elegant versions are called directional watt-meters and are calibrated in watts forward and watts reflected. (3AD-5-1.4)

The only time the forward power reading will be accurate is when there is no reflected power. The reflected power will artificially add to the forward power reading and the forward reading will by higher than the actual level. For example, let's say a transmitter that produces 80 watts is connected to an antenna that shows 10 watts reflected power on the directional watt-meter. In this circumstance, the forward power will actually read 90 watts, 10 watts more than the transmitter is capable of producing. If a transmitter shows 96 watts forward and 4 watts reflected, the transmitter is actually producing 92 watts. (3AD-5-2.1)(3AD-5-2.2)

The previous explanation is the correct answer for the Technician test, but may not always be true in practice. Most modern (meaning all solid-state) transmitters and transceivers (a combination transmitter-receiver) employ a circuit to protect the power amplifier transistors against excessive SWR. When the SWR value rises above a certain point, the transmitter may shut down and provide little or no power output. This can be somewhat inconvenient when you are trying to tune an antenna system. But it is even more annoying to take your rig to the repair shop to have the power amplifier transistors replaced!

Television Interference

As more and more people become radio Amateurs, interference due to close proximity of an Amateur station becomes more common. The energy from a nearby Amateur can be so strong where you live, that it might completely paralyze your ham radio receiver. Technically this is called receiver overload. A typical Amateur receiver is designed to "hear" signals in the order of a millionth of a volt (a microvolt). The signal from another ham down the street could induce several volts at your receiver antenna terminal. This would certainly overload your receiver, no matter how much you paid for it. An indication of **receiver overload** is reception of the local Amateur all over the dial, independent of frequency, no matter where you tune. (2D-8-1.1)(2D-8-1.2)

Another manifestation of receiver overload is interference by your transmitter with nearby television receivers. The signal radiated by your antenna can also induce several volts of energy in a nearby TV antenna. If the TV set connected to this antenna is not designed to reject the interference, your signal can "chop up" the picture on all channels. If this occurs no matter where you are transmitting, it is almost certainly due to overload of the television receiver. (2D-8-1.3)

W3EFG transmits Amateur television on 70 cm from New Smyrna Beach, Florida

How do you design a TV set to reject this sort of interference? By incorporating a simple device which passes the high frequency television signals but rejects your low frequency transmitter signals. The device is called a **high pass filter** and is discussed in Chapter G (Filters). (2D-8-1.4)

Some TV manufacturers do not include high pass filters in order to reduce costs. A high pass filter can be added to eliminate this sort of interference. This is done right at the antenna terminals of the television set.

If your transmitter bothers TV reception only on specific channels (usually the lower two or three), it indicates that your rig is emitting spurious signals. The most common spurious is called a **harmonic**. Harmonics can cause interference to other services and can result in out-of-band transmissions. (2D-8-2.2)

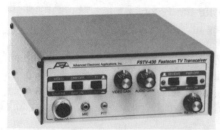

The FSTY-430 Fastscan TV transmitter from AEA duplicates most of the functions of a commercial TV station.

A harmonic is a **mathematical multiple** of the transmitting frequency. For example, if you operate on the 28 MHz band, your second harmonic at 56 MHz is very close to Channel 2 (56-60 MHz). Other harmonics might interfere with commercial frequencies rather than a television channel. (2D-8-2.1)(2D-8-2.5)

A high pass filter on the TV set will not solve this problem. The spurious signal from your transmitter is near the desired television channel or station so there is no way to filter it out at the receiver. In this instance you must add a filter between your transmitter and the transmission line. This harmonic filter is called **a low pass filter**. It lets the low frequencies you are transmitting pass through, but suppresses the high frequency harmonics that interfere with other services. (2D-8-2.6)

An improperly tuned transmitter or poorly matched antenna (or a multi-band antenna) can agitate the problem of harmonic radiation. Because of this, it is a good idea to incorporate a low pass filter in your transmission line, even if you do not hear reports of television interference by your station. (2D-8-2.3)

If you are notified that your station is interfering with someones' TV reception, what should you do? First, be responsive and friendly. Check your own television set to see if you also have interference. If your set is bothered also, it probably means that your transmitter is putting out some "garbage" and you should add a low pass filter.

If your set is "clean", it means that your neighbor's television is not well equipped to reject Amateur Radio interference. In almost every case a simple high pass filter (available from an Amateur Radio store) will solve the problem. (2D-8-3.1)(2D-8-3.2)

Test Equipment

The most important devices an Amateur can own are used to make measurements. The SWR meter mentioned earlier is probably the most useful. Let's discuss some of the other types of Amateur test equipment.

Marker Generators — Equipment that produce test signals are quite useful in the ham radio "shack." For example a **marker generator** places an accurate, stable, crystal controlled marker (a tone or whistle) at various intervals on the receiver dial. In the last chapter, we learned that the frequencies between 50.0 and 50.1 MHz are reserved for CW operation. A 100 kHz (0.1 MHz) marker generator would cause a tone to be heard as you tuned to these frequencies. This can be used to warn you of the band edges. Naturally, you can switch off the marker generator once you have noted where the limits are. A marker generator is sometimes called a **crystal calibrator** since it can be used to accurately calibrate the receiver dial. (3AD-6.1)(3-6.2)(3AD-6.3)

Signal Generators — A similar device, but variable in frequency, is called an **RF signal generator**. This device produces a stable, low level variable signal that can be used for receiver testing and checking alignment. (3AD-7.1)(3AD-7.2)

The Multimeter — One of the most useful pieces of test equipment found in the ham shack is called a **multimeter** or V-O-M (volt-ohm-milliampere) meter. As the name implies, it will measure electromotive force (voltage), resistance (ohms) and current (amperes).(3AD-4.1)

The multimeter has a switch on the front panel to select the function and range. To measure voltage, the test leads are placed across or in parallel with the source. To measure current, the meter leads are connected in series with the source of current. (3AD-2-1.1)(3AD-3-1.1)

The switch changes the range of the multimeter by connecting resistors to the meter. To decrease the reading of a voltmeter, resistors would be connected in series with the meter movement. Thus it would be possible to read 0-1, 0-10 and 0-100 volts with the same zero to ten meter scale. (3AD-2-2.1)

To decrease the reading of an ammeter, resistors would be connected in parallel with the meter movement. Again, the same zero to ten meter scale calibration could be used to read 0-100 mA, 0-1 ampere and 0-10 amperes. (3AD-3-2.1)

Dummy Antenna — This piece of test equipment, also called a **dummy load**, should be found in every hamshack. It is used for off-the-air transmitter testing and tuning. (3AD-9.1)(3AD-9.5)

The dummy antenna is connected in place of the antenna transmission line. It tricks the transmitter into thinking it is connected to a perfect antenna. The dummy load is far from perfect, however. It does not radiate any signal. (3AD-9.2)(3AD-9.4)

The main component of the device is a large carbon composition resistor (*see Chapter F*). Resistors made with resistance wire (such as sometimes seen on old fashioned electric stoves) are never used. The wire will have inductance which can confuse the SWR meter. Sometimes the resistor is immersed in a container of mineral oil to keep it cool and increase its power rating. (3AD-9.3)

The power rating should be observed to avoid damaging the resistive element. Always use a dummy antenna load which matches the power rating of the transmitter to which it is connected. (3AD-9.6)

S-Meter — While this is not a separate instrument, it is a useful meter. The **S-meter** is included in most Amateur receivers to indicate relative signal strength (*see Chapter B- "How Do You Copy Me?"*). (3AD-10.1)(3AD-10.2)

Now it's time to see if you absorbed all this knowledge. Here are the questions from the Novice and Technician pools.

SUBELEMENT 2D (4 questions).

2D1.1 How can you prevent the use of your Amateur station by unauthorized persons? (A) Install a carrier-operated relay in the main power line; (B) Install a key-operated "ON/OFF" switch in the main power line; (C) Post a "Danger - High Voltage" sign in the station; (D) Install AC line fuses in the main power line.

2D1.2 What is the purpose of a key-operated "ON/OFF" switch in the main power line? (A) To prevent the use of your station by unauthorized persons; (B) To provide an easy method for the FCC to put your station off the air; (C) To prevent the power company from inadvertently turning off your electricity during an emergency; (D) As a safety feature, to kill all power to the station in the event of an emergency.

2D2.1 Why should all antenna and rotator cables be grounded when an Amateur station is not in use? (A) To lock the antenna system in one position; (B) To avoid radio frequency interference; (C) To save electricity; (D) To protect the station and building from damage due to a nearby lightning strike.

2D2.2 How can an antenna system be protected from damage caused by a nearby lightning strike? (A) Install a balun at the antenna feed point; (B) Install an RF choke in the feed line; (C) Ground all antennas when they are not in use; (D) Install a line fuse in the antenna wire.

2D2.3 How can Amateur station equipment be protected from damage caused by voltage induced in the power lines by a nearby lightning strike? (A) Use heavy insulation on the wiring; (B) Keep the equipment on constantly; (C) Disconnect the ground system; (D) Disconnect all equipment after use, either by unplugging or by using a main disconnect switch.

2D2.4 For proper protection from lightning strikes, what equipment should be grounded in an Amateur station? (A) The power supply primary; (B) All station equipment; (C) The feed line center conductors; (D) The AC power mains.

2D3.1 What is a convenient indoor grounding point for an Amateur station? (A) A metallic cold water pipe; (B) PVC plumbing; (C) A window screen; (D) A natural gas pipe.

2D3.2 To protect against electrical shock hazards, what should you connect the chassis of each piece of your equipment to? (A) Insulated shock mounts; (B) The antenna; (C) A good ground connection; (D) A circuit breaker.

2D3.3 What type of material should a driven ground rod be made of? (A) Ceramic or other good insulator; (B) Copper or copper-clad steel; (C) Iron or steel; (D) Fiberglass.

2D3.4 What is the shortest ground rod you should consider installing for your Amateur station RF ground? (A) 4 foot; (B) 6 foot; (C) 8 foot; (D) 10 foot.

2D4.1 What precautions should you take when working with 1270-MHz waveguide? (A) Make sure that the RF leakage filters are installed at both ends of the waveguide; (B) Never look into the open end of a waveguide when RF is applied; (C) Minimize the standing wave ratio before you test the waveguide; (D) Never have both ends of the waveguide open at the same time when RF is applied.

2D4.2 What precautions should you take when you mount a UHF antenna in a permanent location? (A) Make sure that no one can be near the antenna when you are transmitting; (B) Make sure that the RF field screens are in place; (C) Make sure that the antenna is near the ground to maximize directional effect; (D) Make sure you connect a RF leakage filter at the antenna feed point.

2D4.3 What precautions should you take before removing the shielding on a UHF power amplifier? (A) Make sure all RF screens are in place at the antenna; (B) Make sure the feed line is properly grounded; (C) Make sure the amplifier cannot be accidentally energized; (D) Make sure that the RF leakage filters are connected.

2D4.4 Why should you use only good-quality, well-constructed coaxial cable and connectors for a UHF antenna system? (A) To minimize RF leakage; (B) To reduce parasitic oscillations; (C) To maximize the directional characteristics of your antenna; (D) To maximize the standing wave ratio of the antenna system.

2D4.5 Why should you be careful to position the antenna of your 220-MHz hand-held transceiver away from your head when you are transmitting? (A) To take advantage of the directional effect; (B) To minimize RF exposure; (C) To use your body to reflect the signal, improving the directional characteristics of the antenna; (D) To minimize static discharges.

2D4.6 Which of the following types of radiation produce health risks most like the risks produced by radio frequency radiation? (A) Microwave oven radiation and ultraviolet radiation; (B) Microwave oven radiation and radiation from an electric space heater; (C) Radiation from Uranium or Radium and ultraviolet radiation; (D) Sunlight and radiation from an electric space heater.

2D5.1 Why is there a switch that turns off the power to a high-voltage power supply if the cabinet is opened? (A) To prevent RF from escaping from the supply; (B) To prevent RF from entering the supply through the open cabinet; (C) To provide a way to turn the power supply on and off; (D) To reduce the danger of electrical shock.

2D5.2 What purpose does a safety interlock on an Amateur transmitter serve? (A) It reduces the danger that the operator will come in contact with dangerous high voltages when the cabinet is opened while the power is on; (B) It prevents the transmitter from being turned on accidentally; (C) It prevents RF energy from leaking out of the transmitter cabinet; (D) It provides a way for the station licensee to ensure that only authorized operators can turn the transmitter on.

2D6.1 What type of safety equipment should you wear when you are working at the top of an antenna tower? (A) A grounding chain; (B) A reflective vest; (C) Loose clothing; (D) A carefully inspected safety belt.

2D6.2 Why should you wear a safety belt when you are working at the top of an antenna tower? (A) To provide a way to safely hold your tools so they don't fall and injure someone on the ground; (B) To maintain a balanced load on the tower while you are working; (C) To provide a way to safely bring tools up and down the tower; (D) To prevent an accidental fall.

2D6.3 For safety purposes, how high should you locate all portions of your horizontal wire antenna? (A) High enough so that a person cannot touch them from the ground; (B) Higher than chest level; (C) Above knee level; (D) Above electrical lines.

2D6.4 What type of safety equipment should you wear when you are on the ground assisting someone who is working on an antenna tower? (A) A reflective vest; (B) A safety belt; (C) A grounding chain; (D) A hard hat.

2D6.5 Why should you wear a hard hat when you are on the ground assisting someone who is working on an antenna tower? (A) To avoid injury from tools dropped from the tower; (B) To provide an RF shield during antenna testing; (C) To avoid injury if the tower should accidentally collapse; (D) To avoid injury from walking into tower guy wires.

2D7-1.1 What accessory is used to measure standing wave ratio? (A) An ohm meter; (B) An ammeter; (C) A SWR meter; (D) A current bridge.

2D7-1.2 What instrument is used to indicate the relative impedance match between a transmitter and antenna? (A) An ammeter; (B) An ohmmeter; (C) A voltmeter; (D) A SWR meter.

2D7-2.1 What does a SWR-meter reading of 1:1 indicate? (A) An antenna designed for use on another frequency band is probably connected; (B) An optimum impedance match has been attained; (C) No power is being transferred to the antenna; (D) A SWR meter never indicates 1:1 unless it is defective.

2D7-2.2 What does a SWR-meter reading of less than 1.5:1 indicate? (A) An unacceptably low reading; (B) An unacceptably high reading; (C) An acceptable impedance match; (D) An antenna gain of 1.5.

2D7-2.3 What does a SWR-meter reading of 4:1 indicate? (A) An unacceptably low reading; (B) An acceptable impedance match; (C) An antenna gain of 4; (D) An impedance mismatch, which is not acceptable; it indicates problems with the antenna system.

2D7-2.4 What does a SWR-meter reading of 5:1 indicate? (A) The antenna will make a 10-watt signal as strong as a 50-watt signal; (B) Maximum power is being delivered to the antenna; (C) An unacceptable mismatch is indicated; (D) A very desirable impedance match has been attained.

2D7-3.1 What kind of SWR-meter reading may indicate poor electrical contact between parts of an antenna system? (A) An erratic reading; (B) An unusually low reading; (C) No reading at all; (D) A negative reading.

2D7-3.2 What does an unusually high SWR-meter reading indicate? (A) That the antenna is not the correct length, or that there is an open or shorted connection somewhere in the feed line; (B) That the signals arriving at the antenna are unusually strong, indicating good radio conditions; (C) That the transmitter is producing more power than normal, probably indicating that the final amplifier tubes or transistors are about to go bad; (D) That there is an unusually large amount of solar white-noise radiation, indicating very poor radio conditions.

2D7-3.3 The SWR-meter reading at the low-frequency end of an Amateur band is 2.5:1, and the SWR-meter reading at the high-frequency end of the same band is 5:1. What does this indicate about your antenna? (A) The antenna is broadbanded; (B) The antenna is too long for operation on this band; (C) The antenna is too short for operation on this band; (D) The antenna has been optimized for operation on this band.

2D7-3.4 The SWR-meter reading at the low-frequency end of an Amateur band is 5:1, and the SWR-meter reading at the high-frequency end of the same band is 2.5:1. What does this indicate about your antenna? (A) The antenna is broadbanded; (B) The antenna is too long for operation on this band; (C) The antenna is too short for operation on this band; (D) The antenna has been optimized for operation on this band.

2D8-1.1 What is meant by receiver overload? (A) Interference caused by transmitter harmonics; (B) Interference caused by overcrowded band conditions; (C) Interference caused by strong signals from a nearby transmitter; (D) Interference caused by turning the receiver volume too high.

2D8-1.2 What is a likely indication that radio-frequency interference to a receiver is caused by front-end overload? (A) A low pass filter at the transmitter reduces interference sharply; (B) The interference is independent of frequency; (C) A high pass filter at the receiver reduces interference little or not at all; (D) Grounding the receiver makes the problem worse.

2D8-1.3 Your neighbor reports interference to his television whenever you are transmitting from your Amateur station. This interference occurs regardless of your transmitter frequency. What is likely to be the cause of the interference? (A) Inadequate transmitter harmonic suppression; (B) Receiver VR tube discharge; (C) Receiver overload; (D) Incorrect antenna length.

2D8-1.4 What type of filter should be installed on a TV receiver as the first step in preventing RF overload from an Amateur HF station transmission? (A) Low pass; (B) High pass; (C) Band pass; (D) Notch.

2D8-2.1 What is meant by harmonic radiation? (A) Transmission of signals at whole number multiples of the fundamental (desired) frequency; (B) Transmission of signals that include a superimposed 60-Hz hum; (C) Transmission of signals caused by sympathetic vibrations from a nearby transmitter; (D) Transmission of signals to produce a stimulated emission in the air to enhance skip propagation.

2D8-2.2 Why is harmonic radiation from an Amateur station undesirable? (A) It will cause interference to other stations and may result in out-of- band signal radiation; (B) It uses large amounts of electric power; (C) It will cause sympathetic vibrations in nearby transmitters; (D) It will produce stimulated emission in the air above the transmitter, thus causing aurora.

2D8-2.3 What type of interference may radiate from a multi-band antenna connected to an improperly tuned transmitter? (A) Harmonic radiation; (B) Auroral distortion; (C) Parasitic excitation; (D) Intermodulation.

2D8-2.4 What is the purpose of shielding in a transmitter? (A) It gives the low pass filter structural stability; (B) It enhances the microphonic tendencies of radiotelephone transmitters; (C) It prevents unwanted RF radiation; (D) It helps maintain a sufficiently high operating temperature in circuit components.

2D8-2.5 Your neighbor reports interference on one or two channels of her television when you are transmitting from your Amateur station. This interference only occurs when you are operating on 15 meters. What is likely to be the cause of the interference? (A) Excessive low-pass filtering on the transmitter; (B) Sporadic-E deionization near your neighbor's TV antenna; (C) TV Receiver front-end overload; (D) Harmonic radiation from your transmitter.

2D8-2.6 What type of filter should be installed on an Amateur transmitter as the first step in reducing harmonic radiation? (A) Key click filter; (B) Low pass filter; (C) High pass filter; (D) CW filter.

2D8-3.1 If you are notified that your Amateur station is causing television interference, what should you do first? (A) Make sure that your Amateur equipment is operating properly, and that it does not cause interference to your own television; (B) Immediately turn off your transmitter and contact the nearest FCC office for assistance; (C) Install a high-pass filter at the transmitter output and a low-pass filter at the antenna-input terminals of the TV; (D) Continue operating normally, since you have no legal obligation to reduce or eliminate the interference.

2D8-3.2 Your neighbor informs you that you are causing television interference, but you are sure your Amateur equipment is operating properly and you cause no interference to your own TV. What should you do? (A) Immediately turn off your transmitter and contact the nearest FCC office for assistance; (B) Work with your neighbor to determine that you are actually the cause of the interference; (C) Install a high-pass filter at the transmitter output and a low-pass filter at the antenna-input terminals of the TV; (D) Continue operating normally, since you have no legal obligation to reduce or eliminate the interference.

SUBELEMENT 3AD (4 questions).

3AD1-1.1 Where should the green wire in an AC line cord be attached in a power supply? (A) To the fuse; (B) To the "hot" side of the power switch; (C) To the chassis; (D) To the meter.

3AD1-1.2 Where should the black (or red) wire in a three-wire line cord be attached in a power supply? (A) To the filter capacitor; (B) To the DC ground; (C) To the chassis; (D) To the fuse.

3AD1-1.3 Where should the white wire in a three-wire line cord be attached in a power supply? (A) To the side of the transformer's primary winding that has a fuse; (B) To the side of the transformer's primary winding without a fuse; (C) To the black wire; (D) To the rectifier junction.

3AD1-1.4 Why is the retaining screw in one terminal of a light socket made of brass while the other one is silver colored? (A) To prevent galvanic action; (B) To indicate correct wiring polarity; (C) To better conduct current; (D) To reduce skin effect.

3AD1-2.1 How much electrical current flowing through the human body is usually fatal? (A) As little as 100 milliamperes may be fatal; (B) Approximately 10 amperes is required to be fatal; (C) More than 20 amperes is needed to kill a human being; (D) No amount of current will harm you. Voltages of over 2000 volts are always fatal, however.

3AD1-2.2 What is the minimum voltage considered to be dangerous to humans? (A) 30 volts; (B) 100 volts; (C) 1000 volts; (D) 2000 volts.

3AD1-2.3 How much electrical current flowing through the human body is usually painful? (A) As little as 50 milliamperes may be painful; (B) Approximately 10 amperes is required to be painful; (C) More than 20 amperes is needed to be painful to a human being; (D) No amount of current will be painful. Voltages of over 2000 volts are always painful, however.

3AD1-3.1 Where should the main power-line switch for a high voltage power supply be situated? (A) Inside the cabinet, to interrupt power when the cabinet is opened; (B) On the rear panel of the high-voltage supply; (C) Where it can be seen and reached easily; (D) This supply should not be switch-operated.

3AD2-1.1 How is a voltmeter typically connected to a circuit under test? (A) In series with the circuit; (B) In parallel with the circuit; (C) In quadrature with the circuit; (D) In phase with the circuit.

3AD2-2.1 How can the range of a voltmeter be extended? (A) By adding resistance in series with the circuit under test; (B) By adding resistance in parallel with the circuit under test; (C) By adding resistance in series with the meter; (D) By adding resistance in parallel with the meter.

3AD3-1.1 How is an ammeter typically connected to a circuit under test? (A) In series with the circuit; (B) In parallel with the circuit; (C) In quadrature with the circuit; (D) In phase with the circuit.

3AD3-2.1 How can the range of an ammeter be extended? (A) By adding resistance in series with the circuit under test; (B) By adding resistance in parallel with the circuit under test; (C) By adding resistance in series with the meter; (D) By adding resistance in parallel with the meter.

3AD4.1 What is a multimeter? (A) An instrument capable of reading SWR and power; (B) An instrument capable of reading resistance, capacitance and inductance; (C) An instrument capable of reading resistance and reactance; (D) An instrument capable of reading voltage, current and resistance.

3AD5-1.1 Where in the antenna transmission line should a peak-reading watt-meter be attached to determine the transmitter output power? (A) At the transmitter output; (B) At the antenna feed point; (C) One-half wavelength from the antenna feed point; (D) One-quarter wavelength from the transmitter output.

3AD5-1.2 For the most accurate readings of transmitter output power, where should the RF watt-meter be inserted? (A) The watt-meter should be inserted and the output measured one-quarter wavelength from the antenna feed point; (B) The watt-meter should be inserted and the output measured one-half wavelength from the antenna feed point; (C) The watt-meter should be inserted and the output power measured at the transmitter antenna jack; (D) The watt-meter should be inserted and the output power measured at the Transmatch output.

3AD5-1.3 At what line impedance are RF watt-meters usually designed to operate? (A) 25 ohms; (B) 50 ohms; (C) 100 ohms; (D) 300 ohms.

3AD5-1.4 What is a directional watt-meter? (A) An instrument that measures forward or reflected power; (B) An instrument that measures the directional pattern of an antenna; (C) An instrument that measures the energy consumed by the transmitter; (D) An instrument that measures thermal heating in a load resistor.

3AD5-2.1 If a directional RF watt-meter indicates 90 watts forward power and 10 watts reflected power, what is the actual transmitter output power? (A) 10 watts; (B) 80 watts; (C) 90 watts; (D) 100 watts.

3AD5-2.2 If a directional RF watt-meter indicates 96 watts forward power and 4 watts reflected power, what is the actual transmitter output power? (A) 80 watts; (B) 88 watts; (C) 92 watts; (D) 100 watts.

3AD6.1 What is a marker generator? (A) A high-stability oscillator that generates a series of reference signals at known frequency intervals; (B) A low-stability oscillator that "sweeps" through a band of frequencies; (C) An oscillator often used in aircraft to determine the craft's location relative to the inner and outer markers at airports; (D) A high-stability oscillator whose output frequency and amplitude can be varied over a wide range.

3AD6.2 What type of circuit is used to inject a frequency calibration signal into a communications receiver? (A) A product detector; (B) A receiver incremental tuning circuit; (C) A balanced modulator; (D) A crystal calibrator.

3AD6.3 How is a marker generator used? (A) To calibrate the tuning dial on a receiver; (B) To calibrate the volume control on a receiver; (C) To test the amplitude linearity of a SSB transmitter; (D) To test the frequency deviation of a FM transmitter.

3AD7.1 What piece of test equipment produces a stable, low-level signal that can be set to a specific frequency? (A) A wave-meter; (B) A reflectometer; (C) A signal generator; (D) A balanced modulator.

3AD7.2 What is an RF signal generator commonly used for? (A) Measuring RF signal amplitude; (B) Aligning receiver tuned circuits; (C) Adjusting the transmitter impedance-matching network; (D) Measuring transmission line impedance.

3AD8-1.1 What is a reflectometer? (A) An instrument used to measure signals reflected from the ionosphere; (B) An instrument used to measure radiation resistance; (C) An instrument used to measure transmission-line impedance; (D) An instrument used to measure standing wave ratio.

3AD8-1.2 What is the device that can indicate an impedance mismatch in an antenna system? (A) A field-strength meter; (B) A set of lecher wires; (C) A wave-meter; (D) A reflectometer.

3AD8-2.1 For best accuracy when adjusting the impedance match between an antenna and feed line, where should the match-indicating device be inserted? (A) At the antenna feed point; (B) At the transmitter; (C) At the midpoint of the feed line; (D) Anywhere along the feed line.

3AD8-2.2 Where should a reflectometer be inserted into a long antenna transmission line in order to obtain the most valid standing wave ratio indication? (A) At any quarter-wavelength interval along the transmission line; (B) At the receiver end; (C) At the antenna end; (D) At any even half-wavelength interval along the transmission line.

3AD9.1 When adjusting a transmitter filter circuit, what device is connected to the transmitter output? (A) A multimeter; (B) A set of Litz wires; (C) A receiver; (D) A dummy antenna.

3AD9.2 What is a dummy antenna? (A) An isotropic radiator; (B) A non-radiating load for a transmitter; (C) An antenna used as a reference for gain measurements; (D) The image of an antenna, located below ground.

3AD9-3 Of what materials may a dummy antenna be made? (A) A wire-wound resistor; (B) A diode and resistor combination; (C) A non-inductive resistor; (D) A coil and capacitor combination.

3AD9.4 What station accessory is used in place of an antenna during transmitter tests so that no signal is radiated? (A) A Transmatch; (B) A dummy antenna; (C) A low-pass filter; (D) A decoupling resistor.

3AD9.5 What is the purpose of a dummy load? (A) To allow off-the-air transmitter testing; (B) To reduce output power for QRP operation; (C) To give comparative signal reports; (D) To allow Transmatch tuning without causing interference.

3AD9.6 How many watts should a dummy load for use with a 100-watt single- sideband phone transmitter be able to dissipate? (A) A minimum of 100 watts continuous; (B) A minimum of 141 watts continuous; (C) A minimum of 175 watts continuous; (D) A minimum of 200 watts continuous.

3AD10.1 What is a S-meter? (A) A meter used to measure sideband suppression; (B) A meter used to measure spurious emissions from a transmitter; (C) A meter used to measure relative signal strength in a receiver; (D) A meter used to measure solar flux.

3AD10.2 A meter that is used to measure relative signal strength in a receiver is known as what? (A) A S-meter; (B) A RST-meter; (C) A signal deviation meter; (D) A SSB meter.

3AD11-1.1 Large amounts of RF energy may cause damage to body tissue, depending on the wavelength of the signal, the energy density of the RF field, and other factors. How does RF energy effect body tissue? (A) It causes radiation poisoning; (B) It heats the tissue; (C) It cools the tissue; (D) It produces genetic changes in the tissue.

3AD11-1.2 Which body organ is most susceptible to damage from the heating effects of radio frequency radiation? (A) Eyes; (B) Hands; (C) Heart; (D) Liver.

3AD11-2.1 Scientists have devoted a great deal of effort to determine safe RF exposure limits. What organization has established an RF protection guide? (A) The Institute of Electrical and Electronics Engineers; (B) The American Radio Relay League; (C) The Environmental Protection Agency; (D) The American National Standards Institute.

3AD11-2.2 What is the purpose of the ANSI RF protection guide? (A) It protects you from unscrupulous radio dealers; (B) It sets RF exposure limits under certain circumstances; (C) It sets transmitter power limits; (D) It sets antenna height requirements.

3AD11-2.3 The American National Standards Institute RF protection guide sets RF exposure limits under certain circumstances. In what frequency range is the maximum exposure level the most stringent (lowest)? (A) 3 to 30 MHz; (B) 30 to 300 MHz; (C) 300 to 3000 MHz; (D) Above 1.5 GHz.

3AD11-2.4 The American National Standards Institute RF protection guide sets RF exposure limits under certain circumstances. Why is the maximum exposure level the most stringent (lowest) in the ranges between 30 MHz and 300 MHz? (A) There are more transmitters operating in this frequency range; (B) There are fewer transmitters operating in this frequency range; (C) Most transmissions in this frequency range are for an extended time; (D) Human body lengths are close to whole-body resonance in that range.

3AD11-2.5 The American National Standards Institute RF protection guide sets RF exposure limits under certain circumstances. What is the maximum safe power output to the antenna terminal of a hand-held VHF or UHF radio, as set by this RF protection guide? (A) 125 milliwatts; (B) 7 watts; (C) 10 watts; (D) 25 watts.

3AD11-3.1 After you make internal tuning adjustments to your VHF power amplifier, what should you do before you turn the amplifier on? (A) Remove all amplifier shielding to ensure maximum cooling; (B) Connect a noise bridge to eliminate any interference; (C) Be certain all amplifier shielding is fastened in place; (D) Be certain no antenna is attached so that you will not cause any interference.

Chapter

Electrical Principles

To be perfectly honest, this is a tough chapter. But look at the bright side. After it's finished, you're halfway through the test preparation! You can probably skip Chapter E and still pass the Technician test or you can simply memorize the correct answers. You will be asked four questions from the section of the Novice test (2E) and 2 questions from the Technician question pool (3AE) related to Electrical Principles. On the other hand, this chapter can provide you with a comprehensive understanding of electronics if you care to study it. The principles described provide the underlying foundation of electronics. I recommend, at a minimum, that you study and understand the paragraphs which end in question numbers in parenthesis.

The World of The Atom

The entire science of electronics is based on the behavior of that minute particle, the **electron.** For any understanding of the electron, what it does and why it does it, we have to observe the electron in its home territory, the world of the **atom.**

The atom is constructed somewhat like our own solar system. It has a central sun (the **nucleus**) and a number of planets (the electrons) revolving or orbiting around it. The nucleus, or core, is comprised of a number of positively charged particles called **protons.**

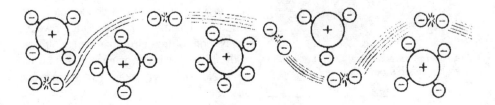

Similarly, the planets revolving around the nucleus are called electrons. They are tiny particles of negative electricity. It should be understood that this explanation is somewhat simplified. Sometimes there are electrons in the nucleus. There are also some other minor types of particles within the atom. However, we are primarily interested in the electrons.

All matter is basically composed of electrons and protons, each carrying an **electric charge**. The difference in characteristics of various substances is dependent on the number and position of the protons and electrons which make up each atom. This is true whether the substance is gold, silver, glass or Coca Cola.

Electrons tend to repel each other with relatively enormous force. Protons react against other protons in the same way. But electrons have a strong attraction for protons, and protons feel the same way about electrons.

This characteristic provides us with one of the basic laws of electricity: *Like charges repel and unlike charges attract*. If this were not so, atoms and molecules would be flying apart in all directions. It is only the attractive force between the positive charge of the nucleus and the negative charge of the planetary electrons which holds them together.

This delicate balance between charges within the atom or molecule may be upset, however. The substance may lose a few electrons from the outermost orbit, or this same orbit may be constantly seeking to add a few more electrons.

If either of these two events occur, the body itself is said to be **charged**. As an example, consider the old trick of running a comb briskly through the hair and then using it to pick up bits of paper by static attraction. In this case, friction has caused the comb to gain of lose some electrons and become charged.

If the comb has lost electrons, the negative charges in the orbit no longer cancel the positive ones in the nucleus, and the substance is said to be positively charged. If the comb has added electrons, their force now exceeds that in each nucleus, and the substance is negatively charged. This leads us to another fundamental electronic law: *A negative charge indicates an excess of electrons, while a positive charge results from an electron deficiency.*

The Ten-Tec receiver has a number of features that make it popular with DX operators.

The reader should understand that we cannot really "make" electricity. We can cause electrons to move from place to place. But whether we use friction to create the movement, or a dynamo or a solar battery, we are simply controlling electrons which are already there. A battery or generator does not create electricity any more than a pump creates water.

Let's get back to our hair and comb experiment. The charge developed between the two bodies can be easily discharged. Simply touch the comb to the hair without the friction which caused the charge and the charge disappears. But note that the bodies themselves do not actually have to touch to cause a discharge.

Suppose instead that one end of a copper wire touches the hair and the comb is touched to the other end of the wire. Now when we try to pick up the bits of paper with the comb, nothing happens. The charge has been equalized or discharged. But how? Obviously electrons must have moved along the wire from the negatively-charged body to the positively-charged one in order to discharge the two objects. There must have been a flow of electron current through the wire.

Anything which causes an electron flow through a conductor is called an **electromotive force** or **e.m.f.** Each excess electron does not flow all the way through the conductor to the point of electron deficiency. It is more like the maneuver in croquet when you try to knock your opponent's ball out. (2E3-1.1)(3AE2.4)

In this case you hold your foot on your own ball so it won't move. But when you smack it with the mallet, the opposing ball which was lying next to it goes flying. You could do the same thing with a whole string of croquet balls in line, if you wanted to. Remember our billiard ball explanation in Chapter C?

Conductors, Resistors and Insulators

This same kind of chain reaction occurs in a **conductor**. An electron near one end strikes another. That in turn, hits still another, and so on until the effect is felt all the way down the line. No one electron moves very far, but the effect of the electron flow is felt at all points along the conductor.

If we connect the ends of a copper wire (a conductor) to the positive and negative terminals of a battery, a fairly sizable **electron current** will flow. If we connect a piece of carbon rod across these same terminals, the current will be much less. If we touch a piece of glass to the terminals, no current will flow at all. Obviously some materials are better conductors than others. (2E2-1.1)(2E3-1.3)

It appears that the better conductors are those, such as gold, silver and aluminum, whose atoms readily give up an electron from its outer shell or orbit. Some materials hold on to their electrons so tightly that it is difficult to free any and cause them to move along in a given direction. Depending upon how strongly the atoms hold on to their outer electrons, the materials are called, **conductors**, **resistors** or **insulators**. (2E4.1)(2E5.1)

Combinations of components are called **circuits**. One of the most basic circuits, the doorbell, is shown in Figure E.1. The button, or switch, opens and closes the circuit. When you press the button, the circuit is closed or completed and the battery forces electrons to

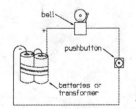

Figure E.1

flow through the bell, which rings. When electrons go rushing through an electronic circuit, they do so because they are being pushed. Something is putting the pressure on them to move. The pressure is the electromotive force (e.m.f.) discussed earlier. This concept is very similar to the water pressure in a pipe. The greater the e.m.f., the more electrons will flow. If you were to short circuit the two battery terminals with a screwdriver, a large number of electrons would also flow. (2E3-1.2)

To get some idea of the fantastic number of electrons which are in motion when even small currents flow, consider this. When the e.m.f. is great enough to send a current of one ampere through a wire, 6,280,000,000,000,000,000 electrons pass a given point every single second! You don't need to memorize this number, by the way. You will not be asked it in a test question.

There are many methods known for generating an e.m.f., but the two most commonly used are **chemical** and **electromagnetic**. The first is the basis of cells and batteries. The second method is the basis of electric generators.

Ohm's Law

Whenever the e.m.f. tends to force electrons through a wire, there will be some opposition to the flow. There is no such thing as a perfect conductor. Every circuit element has some **resistance**. But when it is specifically desired to oppose or limit the current flow to a certain value, a component known as a **resistor** is installed. It is neither a good conductor or a good insulator. The properties of a resistor lie somewhere in between the two extremes depending on the resistance value. (3AE1-1.1)(3AE1-2.1)

Resistors come in all sizes and shapes, and their ability to oppose or limit electron current flow (or resistance) is expressed in a unit called the **ohm**. By international agreement, the ohm is designated as the opposition offered to a steady current by a column of mercury of specified dimensions. (2E6-1.1)(2E6-1.2)(2E6-2.1)(3AD1-2.2)

E.m.f. is described by the term **volts**. The volt is simply that amount of electrical pressure, (or e.m.f.) which will drive a current of one ampere through a resistance of one ohm. From this definition it is obvious that there is a close relationship between volts, ohms and amperes. (2E3-2.1)

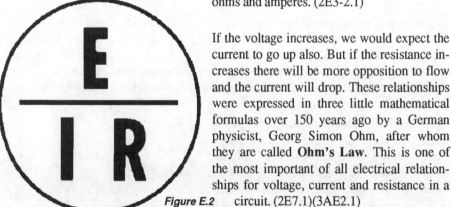

Figure E.2

If the voltage increases, we would expect the current to go up also. But if the resistance increases there will be more opposition to flow and the current will drop. These relationships were expressed in three little mathematical formulas over 150 years ago by a German physicist, Georg Simon Ohm, after whom they are called **Ohm's Law**. This is one of the most important of all electrical relationships for voltage, current and resistance in a circuit. (2E7.1)(3AE2.1)

Figure E.2 shows Mr. Ohm's law in a graphic way. We have adopted the letter symbol (I- intensity) for the current in amperes, (E) for the e.m.f. in volts, and (R) for the resistance in ohms. Ohm's Law tells us that to find the current in amperes in any circuit, we must divide the e.m.f. in volts by the resistance in ohms. Thus the formula becomes (I) equals (E) divided by (R). By the same token we can see that (R) equals (E) divided by (I). Finally, from Figure E.2, we can deduce that (E) equals (I) times (R). (2E2-2.1)(2E2.2)

As an example of how this works, let's find out how much current a light bulb having a filament resistance of 100 ohms will pass when it is connected to a source of e.m.f. of 200 volts. The formula says that current (I) in amperes equals voltage (E) divided by resistance. Thus 200 divided by 100 equals 2 amperes. (2E7.3)(3AE2.2)(3AE2.6) (3AE 2.7)(3AE2.8)(3AE2.9)

The voltage relationship is similar. If a meter connected in series with a 50 ohm resistor shows a current of 2 amperes, how much voltage will develop across the resistor. By multiplying the current (in amperes) by the resistance (E = I times R), the answer is found to be 100 volts. (2E7.2)

Here's the sort of puzzle you might run into everyday as an auto mechanic. Consider this case where the resistance and current are known, and the voltage must be found. Say we have a parking light bulb which has an operating resistance of 4 ohms. When lit to full brilliance it draws a current of 1.5 amperes. Can we use this lamp in a circuit where it will have an e.m.f. of 12 volts placed across it? If we multiply 4 ohms by 1.5 amperes, the answer turns out to be 6 volts. If we insert a 6-volt lamp into the socket, it would quickly burn out with 12 volts impressed across it. Thus the answer is no.

Suppose we want to determine the resistance when the voltage and current is known. For example, what is the resistance of the windings of a 90-volt motor when the current through it is 3 amperes? Resistance (R) equals voltage (E) divided by current (I). Thus we divide 90 volts by 3 amperes for an answer of 30 ohms. (2E 7.4)(3AE2.3)(3AE 2.5)

The way in which the various circuit components are connected is known either as **series** or **parallel**, or some combination called series-parallel. In a series circuit, such as Figure E.3, components are connected so that all of the electron flow passes through all of the resistors. The total resistance is the

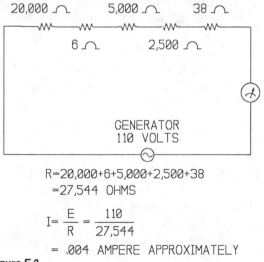

R=20,000+6+5,000+2,500+38
=27,544 OHMS

$$I = \frac{E}{R} = \frac{110}{27,544}$$

= .004 AMPERE APPROXIMATELY

Figure E.3

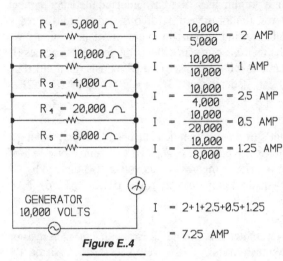

total value of all the resistors in series. (3AE1-3.1) (3AE1-3.2)

$$I = \frac{10,000}{5,000} = 2 \text{ AMP}$$

$$I = \frac{10,000}{10,000} = 1 \text{ AMP}$$

$$I = \frac{10,000}{4,000} = 2.5 \text{ AMP}$$

$$I = \frac{10,000}{20,000} = 0.5 \text{ AMP}$$

$$I = \frac{10,000}{8,000} = 1.25 \text{ AMP}$$

$$I = 2+1+2.5+0.5+1.25$$

$$= 7.25 \text{ AMP}$$

Figure E..4

In the parallel circuit (Figure E.4), all of the resistors are connected directly to the source of e.m.f. The current has a number of paths through which it can pass. An example might be the various headlights, parking and tail lights on an automobile. They are all connected in parallel with the car battery. The total current flowing in and out of the battery is the total of the current through each path. If two resistors of equal value are connected in parallel, the combined resistance will be one-half of either value. (3AE1-4.1)(3AE1-4.2)

To solve Ohm's Law problems, we have to know the total resistance of any given combination of resistors. In the case of series circuits, it's easy. The total resistance is simply the sum of the individual resistances.

As an example, consider Figure E.3 where five resistors are connected in series. The total resistance is the sum of each resistance, as shown. The current is easily calculated in conventional Ohm's Law fashion.

Calculation of equivalent resistance in parallel circuits is a little more complex. Consider Figure E.4 in which we see five resistances connected in parallel across a source e.m.f. of 10,000 volts. If we ignore the resistance of the connecting wire (which is negligible), we see that the same voltage from the 10,000 volt supply appears across each resistor.

The total current from the generator (which also passes through the meter) will split five ways through the resistance network. The amount through any given resistor will depend upon its own ohmic value. Conversely, the branch currents I1 through I5 will add up to (I) total.

To find each of these branch currents, we use Ohm's Law and divide the applied voltage by the individual resistance as shown in Figure E.4.

The resistor is one of the most commonly encountered components in electronic circuits. Its primary use is to convert electrical energy into heat energy. This heat may serve some useful purpose such as for an electric stove. It may be wasted when the purpose of the resistor is simply to provide a needed voltage drop.

The ability to do work is called **energy**. If you chop a pile of wood, you expend energy. When a flashlight is illuminated, it consumes energy. We say the **electrical energy** is converted to heat and light. The rate of energy consumption is called **power**. A high wattage bulb will consume energy faster than a flashlight bulb. In other words it will exhibit a greater power consumption. (2E8.1)(2E8.2)(2E9-1.1)(2E9-1.2)

The rate at which heat is produced when current flows through a resistor is expressed in **watts**. The watt is the basic unit of electrical power. The formula is (W = I squared R), where (W) is the power in watts, (I) is the current in amperes, and (R) is the resistance in ohms. (2E9-2.1)

The watts consumed by a resistor, often called the I-squared-R loss, appear entirely as heat. It is obvious that the larger the surface area of the resistor and the freer the circulation of air around it, the more easily the heat can be dissipated. Resistors are made in a wide variety of sizes, not only in terms of resistance, but also in the amount of power they can safely handle without danger of burn-out.

If there is no current flow between the two terminals of a battery, it is said to be an **open circuit**. If there is an excessively high current between the terminals, it is caused by a **short circuit**. (2E10.1)(2E11.1)

Alternating Current

Up to this point we have discussed direct current (DC) which flows in only one direction in a conductor. However, you should be familiar with **alternating current** (AC). This is an electron flow which periodically reverses itself and flows in both directions. Alternating current appears in power lines, audio and radio frequency (RF) generators. (2E12-1.1)(2E12-2.1)

Current flow is, in many ways, like the flow of water. A hydraulic analogy will help in understanding the basic AC concept. In Figure E.5A we see how a piston, with a back and forth movement, could cause water in a closed circuit to reverse direction.

Figure E.5A

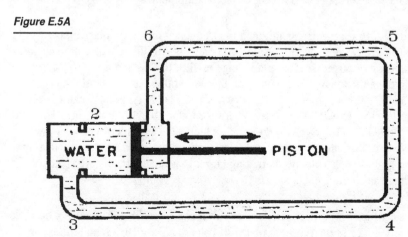

When the piston moves from 1 to 2, water will be pushed ahead of it and will close in behind it. The flow in the circuit will move in the direction 3-4-5-6, which represents the time A-B-C in Figure E.5B. When the piston reaches the end of its travel (position 2 in Figure E.5A and point C in Figure E.5B), it will reverse direction. But note that at the instant of reversal, both the piston motion and the water flow have stopped. Then the piston starts moving from 2 to 1, and the water now flows around 6-5-4-3. This represents C-D-E in Figure E.5.B.

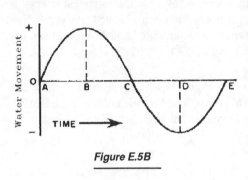

Figure E.5B

Alternating current flow is very similar. Imagine that "water movement" in Figure E.5B is really current flow. The current starts at zero state of flow (A) and gradually increases in strength until it reaches a maximum in one direction (B). Then it gradually decreases until it stops altogether (C). Next, it increases to a maximum in the opposite direction (D), finally decreasing again back to zero (E).

Electricity which behaves in this manner is called **alternating current** or **AC**. This complete series of events is called a **cycle** and the number of these cycles which occur during a period of one second is said to be the **frequency** of AC. As mentioned in Chapter One, we honor Herr Heinrich Hertz by calling this complete sequence a **Hertz**. (2E12-3.1)(2E12-3.2)(2E12-3.3)

Until now we have been talking about rate of current flow. But we already know that any such flow must have a propelling force. The force behind electron flow is called the **voltage**. The way in which an AC voltage changes with time is the same as for current as shown in Figure E.5B. The result of this action is called an **AC sine wave**. This waveform is basic to virtually every piece of radio equipment.

If the time from A to E is 1/60 second, then the frequency this particular voltage would be 60 cycles (or Hertz) per second. Ordinary power lines in this country are standardized at a frequency of 60 Hertz (Hz) at a voltage of 120. In England it is 240 volts at 50 Hz. But what does this mean? We have seen that the voltage is constantly varying. At points A, C and E the voltage is zero, a far cry from 120 volts. At points B and D, as we shall see, the level is actually 170 volts. Where then, does the 120 come in? This 120 volt figure is called the **effective voltage** because that is the amount of DC which would be required to do the same amount of work or produce the same amount of heat in a given resistor as 170 peak volts of alternating current.. Mathematically we speak of the effective voltage as the root-mean-square (RMS) voltage.

An AC voltage which varies between zero and momentary peaks of 170 volts won't get your toaster any hotter in the morning than 120 volts of steady DC. With a little simple arithmetic you can quickly prove that the effective voltage is only 70.7 percent of the peak. From a reciprocal point of view, the peak is 1.414 times as great as the effective voltage. It is important to remember that instrument calibrations, as well as component ratings, are normally given in terms of effective values.

AC Generation

An AC generator consists of a conductor moving through a magnetic field. This movement causes magnetic lines of force to be cut and a voltage is induced within the conductor. In Figure E.6 we see the circular path which would be made by a single conductor rotating between the two poles of a permanent magnet. When the conductor is moving at 90 degrees with respect to the magnet poles, the maximum lines of force are cut and the induced voltage is maximum.

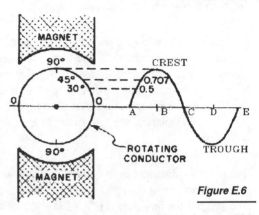

Figure E.6

When the conductor is at A (right angles to the lines of force), the voltage is zero. This is because at right angles no lines of force are being cut by the conductor.

Reactance — The Resistance to AC

We have already noted that the flow of current through a DC circuit is limited by the amount of resistance in the circuit. In AC circuits resistance behavior is the same as with DC. But in addition there are other effects which retard current in addition to the component called a resistor. One is called **reactance**. There are two types of reactance. They are called inductive and capacitive reactance.

Unlike resistance, which is determined mostly by the physical composition of the conductor, reactance is caused by the changing fields of AC. Inductive reactance is due to a property of coiled conductors called **inductance**. This, in turn, results from the fact that every current-carrying conductor has a magnetic field surrounding it. An inductor can store energy in its magnetic field. (3AE3-1.1)

AC current is constantly changing in both intensity and direction, as shown in Figure E.7. The magnetic field around the wire expands and contracts in exactly the same manner. In a straight wire this is not particularly noteworthy. When that wire is twisted into a coil, strange events take place.

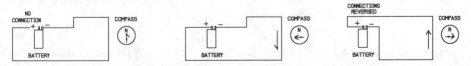

Figure E.7- A flow of current produces a magnetic field around the wire that attracts or repells the point of a compass. This is how a motor works, but on a much larger scale.

The magnetic field consists of "lines of force" similar to those found in the generator mentioned earlier. As they expand and contract around the coil, the lines of force intersect the turns of wire and induce a voltage in them. This induced voltage is called a "**back e.m.f**". Back e.m.f. is always opposite in polarity to the applied voltage and bucks or opposes it. Since current flow is proportional to voltage which drives it, AC current, is therefore less when an inductance is introduced into the circuit. This voltage drop results from the second opposing voltage which subtracts from the source voltage.

Inductors — The inductance of a coil is determined by the number of turns as well as the overall size and shape. If the turns are wound around an iron core (rather than air) the inductance will increase many times, depending upon **permeability** of the core material in an inductor. The permeability of air is taken as 1, while the permeability of core materials may be many thousands of times greater. It is therefore a simple matter to increase the inductance of a coil many times simply by providing it with a high- permeability core.

The unit of inductance is the **Henry**, defined as the inductance of any circuit in which a current changing at the rate of one ampere per second will induce an e.m.f. of one volt. The symbol for inductance is the letter "L." The values of L encountered in electronic work vary from a few microHenries (millionths or 10-6 Henries) up to perhaps several Henries. A milliHenry is equal to 10-3 Henry.

The value of inductors in series is the same as for resistors. Inductors in series will add up in value. If two equal value inductors are connected in parallel, the combined value will be half the value of either inductor. If unequal value inductors are connected in parallel, the combined value will be less than the lowest value inductor. (3AE3-2.1)(3AE3-2.2)(3AE3-2.2)(3AE3-2.3)(3AE3-2.4)(3AE3-3.1)(3AE3-3.2)(3AE3-4.1)(3AE3-4.2)

Capacitors — Still another reactive device often found in electronic circuits is the **capacitor**. Old timers (and a few auto mechanics) call these components "condensers" but these are found in air conditioners and refrigerators. A capacitor is usually an arrangement of two or more metallic plates, separated from one another by air or some other insulating material known as a **dielectric**. Just as an inductor can store energy in a magnetic field, a capacitor can store energy in an electric field. (3AE4-1.1)

When a DC voltage source is connected across the capacitor, electrons will be drawn away from one set of plates toward the positive battery terminal, and they will simultaneously be forced out of the negative terminal and into the opposite set of plates. This action will continue until the capacitor is fully **charged**. The amount of charge it can take is determined by the number, area, and spacing of its plates contributing to its capacitance and the type of dielectric separating the plates.

Since there is no such thing as the perfect insulator there will be some leakage through the dielectric. The excess electrons will try to get back to the opposite plates and fill up the deficiency. But for the most part, the capacitor will remain charged until an external return path is provided for electrons.

This can be proved by the experiment illustrated with a single dry cell battery, an earphone, a capacitor and a double-pole double-throw switch. This is shown in the circuit of Figure E.8. When the switch is thrown to the left, electrons from the negative battery terminal will pile up on plate A of the capacitor while electrons from plate B will drain into the positive terminal of the cell. The capacitor will be quickly charged. When the switch is thrown to the

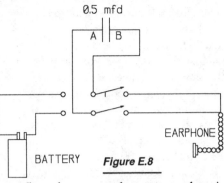

Figure E.8

right, the charge will be equalized (or discharged) as the excess electrons on plate A rush through the earphone circuit and back to plate B. At the same time a distinct "click" will be heard in the earphone. This sound proves there was momentary current flow.

The unit of capacitance is the **Farad**. This is the value a capacitor would have if its voltage were raised one volt by a current of one ampere for one second. Such a capacitor, however, would be physically huge. Thus a Farad is almost never encountered in practice. Electronic circuits use capacitors rated in micro-Farads (10-6 Farads) and in today's miniaturized world, even pico-Farads (10-12 Farads). (3AE4-2.1)(3AE4-2.2)(3AE4-2.3)(3AE4-2.4)

Multiple capacitors connected in a circuit are the mathematical opposite of resistors and inductors. If two equal value capacitors are connected in series. the total value will be half the value of either capacitor. If a number of capacitors are connected in series, the total value will always be less than the smallest value capacitor. By the same token, if two equal value capacitors are connected in parallel, the combined value will be twice the value of either capacitor. If a number of capacitors are connected in parallel, the total value will be the sum of all the capacitor values. (3AE4-3.1)(3AE4-3.2) (3AE4-4.1)(3AE4-4.2)

Current doesn't actually flow through the capacitor but goes around the circuit, back and forth between the plates. Because of this, AC appears to flow through a capacitor while, at the same time, DC is blocked. The alternating current flow through the capacitor is impeded decreasingly as the frequency is increased. This effect is called the **capacitive reactance** to AC. There is also an equivalent with coils (inductors) called **inductive reactance**. An inductor connected in series with a source of AC will increasingly impede the flow of current as the frequency is increased. This is exactly the opposite of the capacitor.

Resonance and Tuned Circuits

There are three electronic components for retarding the flow of current in circuits. They are resistance, inductance and capacitance. Let's see what happens when we use them all in a single circuit.

In Figure E.9, we see each component combined in series with an RF (radio frequency) generator. This AC source is supplying 2 volts at a frequency of 2.5 megaHertz (2.5 million times per second). Under these conditions the inductive reactance of the coil is about 8,000 ohms, and the capacitive reactance of the capacitor is also about 8,000 ohms. With only 2 volts of signal, it would seem that

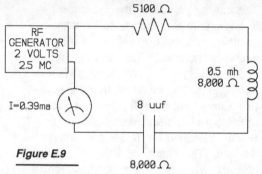

Figure E.9

the current in this circuit should be exceedingly small. But when we measure it, we find the current to be 0.39 milliamperes, or simply the value of current caused by E/R. It seems that the reactances in the circuit are nonexistent and have no effect whatsoever.

There is a reason for this. The reactance of the capacitor and inductors tends to cancel each other. Complete cancellation occurs only at one specific frequency where the reactances are equal. This is known as the **resonant frequency.**

We can understand just what this means simply by shifting the frequency of our generator. Suppose we reduce the generator frequency down to 2.0 megaHertz. The reactance of the capacitor will increase, while the inductive reactance decreases. As a result their reactances no longer completely cancel.

By making the capacitor (C) or inductor (L) variable, the frequency at which the reactances cancel can be moved around. Thus the resonant frequency of the LC combination can be adjusted to a specific frequency. This circuit of an inductor in parallel with a capacitor is said to be **parallel resonant**. The parallel resonant circuit is basic to virtually every piece of radio communications equipment.

Resonant circuits are used in radio and TV receivers, both for the selection of the desired signal and for the rejection of unwanted signals. The relative ability of a receiver to perform these functions is called its **selectivity**. In transmitters, the entire process of generation and amplification of RF energy is dependent upon tuned circuits. Low pass and high pass filters (mentioned in the previous chapter) are simply combinations of capacitors and inductors. These filters oppose certain frequencies, while allowing others to pass.

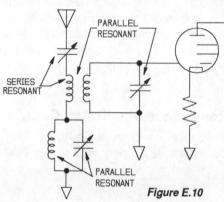

Figure E.10

Not all tuned circuits are parallel resonant. Another type of circuit, called **series resonant**, is encountered somewhat less frequently. A practical application of both types is shown in Figure E.10. The input of a receiver, where the primary of the antenna transformer is tuned to series resonance, while the secondary is made parallel resonant. There is also a parallel resonant trap circuit in the ground leg of the antenna circuit. This trap could be used to get rid of an interfering signal. Each circuit is tunable to resonance by means of a variable capacitor. Both windings of the antenna transformer are tuned for the same purpose. When resonant, the circuits develop maximum voltage at the desired signal frequency.

Amplitude, Wavelength and Frequency

In the last chapter, we made the analogy that radio signals were somewhat akin to the wave action when a pebble was thrown into a quite pool of water. The ripples radiate of from the point of impact (where the pebble hit) in concentric circles.

Let's apply some of the electrical principals you just learned to more clearly visualize the action of the waves we created in the last chapter.

As the first wave reaches the shore, the water level rises. Then as the crest passes the water level drops to its original or normal position. But as the wave continues across the pond, the crest is followed by a trough. This causes the water level to drop below its original position. This action repeats until the wave action runs out of energy and the pond returns to its original still condition. The complete action from normal, crest, normal, valley, normal is our old friend the sine wave.

If we could view the action from the side at a fixed position, the wave action would look exactly like the waveform in Figure E.6. There are three characteristics of a sine wave that you should be aware of. They are the: (1) amplitude, (2) wavelength, and (3) frequency.

The vertical distance between the crest and the trough is the **amplitude** of the wave. The bigger the rock, the larger the amplitude of the wave. If you toss a Volkswagen in the quiet pool, larger waves will be created than for a small pebble.

The distance between any two reference points (for example between two crests or two troughs) is the length of the wave or, more commonly, the **wavelength**. The number of times a crest (or a valley) passes a given point in a specific length of time is called the **frequency**. These repetitive cycles *must* be related to time. The most common unit of time is the second. Thus, frequency is expressed in the number of cycles per second (actually Hertz per second or simply Hz). (2E13.1)(2E13.2)

Remember, the number of sine wave events which occur each second is referred to as the frequency. The distance or length between any two identical and repetitive reference points on a sine wave is called the wavelength

Mathematics and Amateur Radio

By using a water analogy, I may have given you the impression that a cycle was a slow and ponderous event. Nothing could be further from the truth. Sine wave frequencies are usually generated electronically rather than mechanically and the alternations occur very

The Morse Machine from Advanced Electronic Applications is not only a keyer, but it can also send code practice simulations. (AEA Photo)

rapidly. For example, the radio frequencies generated by a cellular telephone alternate more than 800 million times per second (800 megaHertz). Think that's fast? Home satellite receivers operate at frequencies four times as high!

The lowest frequencies hams are involved with are called audio frequencies. This is the range between 20 Hz and 20,000 Hz (20 kHz) that our ears can hear. Above 20,000 Hz, the spectrum is usually referred to as radio frequencies. The various radio frequency sub-definitions were mentioned in Chapter A. (2E12-4.1)(2E12-4.2)(2E12-4.3)(2E12-5.1)(2E12-5.2)

Why is it important to understand mathematics, such as the difference between wavelength and frequency? Let's say a friend makes a schedule to talk with you on 10 meters (wavelength), but your receiver is calibrated in Mhz (frequency). How do you make the conversion?

You also need to understand how to convert metric measurements. What if an antenna drawing specifies a metal tube 400 centimeters long. How big is this in meters or feet? Like it or not, Mathematics is an important part of our hobby.

There are 1,000 Hertz (Hz) in a kiloHertz (kHz). Likewise, there are a million Hertz or a 1,000 kiloHertz in a MegaHertz (MHz). Ten times one hundred kiloHertz is also equals one MHz. The largest unit you will be expected to deal with is the GigaHertz (GHz). There are 1,000 MegaHertz in one GigaHertz. Remember, these are the rates of the alternating radio frequency energy — that's 1,000 million times per second!

Let's say there is a code practice station listed as operating on 1,200 MegaHertz (MHz). But the dial on your radio is calibrated in GigaHertz. Since there are 1,000 MHz in one GHz, you can divide 1,000 into 1,200. The answer is 1.2. The station would be found at 1.2 GigaHertz on your dial. (2E1-1.1) (2E1-2.2)

What if your Helping Ham friend called and said there was a rare DX station on 7,125 kHz. Again, your dial is calibrated in MHz. Where would you find the station? Remember, there are 1,000 kHz in one MHz. But the frequency you are looking for is more than 7,000 kHz. Thus, the answer must be 7.125 MHz. (2E1-2.1)

Using the same analysis, determine what 3.525 Mhz would be in kHz. Or convert 3,725 kHz to Hertz. (The correct answer is 3525 kHz and 3,725,000 Hertz, respectively). (2E1-3.1)(2E1-3.2)

You can use the same technique when converting metric numbers. Remember that "centi" means hundred. Thus, there are four units of 100 in a something that is 400 centimeters long. The four units is the measurement in meters. (2E1-4.1)

If the meter on your transmitter was calibrated in milliamperes, how many amperes would be flowing if the meter indicated 3,000 milliamperes. Remember, "milli" means one thousand. Thus, there are 1,000 milliamperes in one ampere. By dividing 1,000 into 3,000 we arrive at the answer of 3 amperes. (2E1-5.1)

Milli is milli, regardless of how it is used. Another question on metering in the test asks how many volts there are in 3,500 millivolts. There are 1,000 millivolts in a volt so the correct answer is 3.5 volts. (2E1-5.2)

Capacitor values confuse the best of us, even with an Amateur license. We usually wind up with a pencil and paper moving decimal points around with great abandon. The smallest common unit of capacity is the pico-Farad. There are 1,000 pico's in a nano-Farad (1,000 pF equals one nF). There are also 1,000 nano-Farads in a micro-Farad (or a million pico-Farads, at the risk of confusing you further). Finally, there are one-million micro-Farads in a Farad. Thus, 500,000 micro-Farads would be a half-Farad (0.5 F). (2E1-6.1)(2E1-7.1)

Clearly, you are going to have to memorize some of these equivalences. Read and re-read the above material until you are sure you can answer the conversion questions correctly. Once you think you've got it, try answering the following questions.

SUBELEMENT 2E (4 questions)

2E1-1.1 Your receiver dial is calibrated in megaHertz and shows a signal at 1,200 MHz. At what frequency would a dial calibrated in gigaHertz show the signal? (A) 1,200,000 GHz; (B) 12 GHz; (C) 1.2 GHz; (D) 0.0012 GHz.

2E1-2.1 Your receiver dial is calibrated in kiloHertz and shows a signal at 7,125 kHz. At what frequency would a dial calibrated in megaHertz show the signal? (A) 0.007125 MHz; (B) 7.125 MHz; (C) 71.25 MHz; (D) 7,125,000 MHz.

2E1-2.2 Your receiver dial is calibrated in gigaHertz and shows a signal at 1.2 GHz. At what frequency would a dial calibrated in megaHertz show the same signal? (A) 1.2 MHz; (B) 12 MHz; (C) 120 MHz; (D) 1,200 MHz.

2E1-3.1 Your receiver dial is calibrated in megaHertz and shows a signal at 3.525 MHz. At what frequency would a dial calibrated in kiloHertz show the signal? (A) 0.003525 kHz; (B) 3,525 kHz; (C) 35.25 kHz; (D) 3,525,000 kHz.

2E1-3.2 Your receiver dial is calibrated in kiloHertz and shows a signal at 3,725 kHz. At what frequency would a dial calibrated in Hertz show the same signal? (A) 3,725 Hz; (B) 3.725 Hz; (C) 37.25 Hz; (D) 3,725,000 Hz.

2E1-4.1 How long (in meters) is an antenna that is 400 centimeters long? (A) 0.0004 meters; (B) 4 meters; (C) 40 meters; (D) 40,000 meters.

2E1-5.1 What reading will be displayed on a meter calibrated in amperes when it is being used to measure a 3,000-milliampere current? (A) 0.003 amperes; (B) 0.3 amperes; (C) 3 amperes; (D) 3,000,000 amperes.

2E1-5.2 What reading will be displayed on a meter calibrated in volts when it is being used to measure a 3,500-millivolt potential? (A) 350 volts; (B) 35 volts; (C) 3.5 volts; (D) 0.35 volts.

2E1-6.1 How many Farads is 500,000 microFarads? (A) 0.0005 Farads; (B) 0.5 Farads; (C) 500 Farads; (D) 500,000,000 Farads.

2E1-7.1 How many microFarads is 1,000,000 picoFarads? (A) 0.001 microFarads; (B) 1 microFarad; (C) 1,000 microFarads; (D) 1,000,000,000 microFarads.

2E2-1.1 What is the term used to describe the flow of electrons in an electric circuit? (A) Voltage; (B) Resistance; (C) Capacitance; (D) Current.

2E2-2.1 What is the basic unit of electric current? (A) The volt; (B) The watt; (C) The ampere; (D) The ohm.

2E3-1.1 What supplies the force that will cause electrons to flow through a circuit? (A) Electromotive force, or voltage; (B) Magnetomotive force, or inductance; (C) Farad force, or capacitance; (D) Thermodynamic force, or entropy.

2E3-1.2 The pressure in a water pipe is comparable to what force in an electrical circuit? (A) Current; (B) Resistance; (C) Gravitation; (D) Voltage.

2E3-1.3 An electric circuit must connect to two terminals of a voltage source. What are these two terminals called? (A) The north and south poles; (B) The positive and neutral terminals; (C) The positive and negative terminals; (D) The entrance and exit terminals.

2E3-2.1 What is the basic unit of voltage? (A) The volt; (B) The watt; (C) The ampere; (D) The ohm.

2E4.1 List at least three good electrical conductors. (A) Copper, gold, mica; (B) Gold, silver, wood; (C) Gold, silver, aluminum; (D) Copper, aluminum, paper.

2E5.1 List at least four good electrical insulators. (A) Glass, air, plastic, porcelain; (B) Glass, wood, copper, porcelain; (C) Paper, glass, air, aluminum; (D) Plastic, rubber, wood, carbon.

2E6-1.1 There is a limit to the electric current that can pass through any material. What is this current limiting called? (A) Fusing; (B) Reactance; (C) Saturation; (D) Resistance.

2E6-1.2 What is an electrical component called that opposes electron movement through a circuit? (A) A resistor; (B) A reactor; (C) A fuse; (D) An oersted.

2E6-2.1 What is the basic unit of resistance? (A) The volt; (B) The watt; (C) The ampere; (D) The ohm.

2E7.1 What electrical principle relates voltage, current and resistance in an electric circuit? (A) Ampere's Law; (B) Kirchhoff's Law; (C) Ohm's Law; (D) Tesla's Law.

2E7.2 There is a 2-amp current through a 50-ohm resistor. What is the applied voltage? (A) 0.04 volts; (B) 52 volts; (C) 100 volts; (D) 200 volts.

2E7.3 If 200 volts is applied to a 100-ohm resistor, what is the current through the resistor? (A) 0.5 amps; (B) 2 amps; (C) 50 amps; (D) 20000 amps.

2E7.4 There is a 3-amp current through a resistor and we know that the applied voltage is 90 volts. What is the value of the resistor? (A) 0.03 ohms; (B) 10 ohms; (C) 30 ohms; (D) 2700 ohms.

2E8.1 What is the term used to describe the ability to do work? (A) Voltage; (B) Power; (C) Inertia; (D) Energy.

2E8.2 What is converted to heat and light in an electric light bulb? (A) Electrical energy; (B) Electrical voltage; (C) Electrical power; (D) Electrical current.

2E9-1.1 What term is used to describe the rate of energy consumption? (A) Energy; (B) Current; (C) Power; (D) Voltage.

2E9-1.2 You have two lamps with different wattage light bulbs in them. How can you determine which bulb uses electrical energy faster? (A) The bulb that operates from the higher voltage will consume energy faster; (B) The physically larger bulb will consume energy faster; (C) The bulb with the higher wattage rating will consume energy faster; (D) The bulb with the lower wattage rating will consume energy faster.

2E9-2.1 What is the basic unit of electrical power? (A) Ohm; (B) Watt; (C) Volt; (D) Ampere.

2E10.1 What is the term for an electrical circuit in which there can be no current? (A) A closed circuit; (B) A short circuit; (C) An open circuit; (D) A hyper circuit.

2E11.1 What is the term for a failure in an electrical circuit that causes excessively high current? (A) An open circuit; (B) A dead circuit; (C) A closed circuit; (D) A short circuit.

2E12-1.1 What is the term used to describe a current that flows only in one direction? (A) Alternating current; (B) Direct current; (C) Periodic current; (D) Pulsating current.

2E12-2.1 What is the term used to describe a current that flows first in one direction, then in the opposite direction, over and over? (A) Alternating current; (B) Direct current; (C) Negative current; (D) Positive current.

2E12-3.1 What is the term for the number of complete cycles of an alternating waveform that occur in one second? (A) Pulse repetition rate; (B) Hertz; (C) Frequency per wavelength; (D) Frequency.

2E12-3.2 A certain AC signal makes 2000 complete cycles in one second. What property of the signal does this number describe? (A) The frequency of the signal; (B) The pulse repetition rate of the signal; (C) The wavelength of the signal; (D) The Hertz per second of the signal.

2E12-3.3 What is the basic unit of frequency? (A) The Hertz; (B) The cycle; (C) The kiloHertz; (D) The megaHertz.

2E12-4.1 What range of frequencies are usually called audio frequencies? (A) 0 to 20 Hz; (B) 20 to 20,000 Hz; (C) 200 to 200,000 Hz; (D) 10,000 to 30,000 Hz.

2E12-4.2 A signal at 725 Hz is in what frequency range? (A) Audio frequency; (B) Intermediate frequency; (C) Microwave frequency; (D) Radio frequency.

2E12-4.3 Why do we call signals in the range 20 Hz to 20,000 Hz audio frequencies? (A) Because the human ear rejects signals in this frequency range; (B) Because the human ear responds to sounds in this frequency range; (C) Because frequencies in this range are too low for a radio to detect; (D) Because a radio converts signals in this range directly to sounds the human ear responds to.

2E12-5.1 Signals above what frequency are usually called radio-frequency signals? (A) 20 Hz; (B) 2000 Hz; (C) 20,000 Hz; (D) 1,000,000 Hz.

2E12-5.2 A signal at 7,125 kHz is in what frequency range? (A) Audio frequency; (B) Radio frequency; (C) Hyper-frequency; (D) Super-high frequency.

2E13.1 What is the term for the distance an AC signal travels during one complete cycle? (A) Wave velocity; (B) Velocity factor; (C) Wavelength; (D) Wavelength per meter.

2E13.2 In the time it takes a certain radio signal to pass your antenna, the leading edge of the wave travels 12 meters. What property of the signal does this number refer to? (A) The signal frequency; (B) The wave velocity; (C) The velocity factor; (D) The signal wavelength.

SUBELEMENT 3AE (2 questions).

3AE1-1.1 What is meant by the term resistance? (A) The opposition to the flow of current in an electric circuit containing inductance; (B) The opposition to the flow of current in an electric circuit containing capacitance; (C) The opposition to the flow of current in an electric circuit containing reactance; (D) The opposition to the flow of current in an electric circuit that does not contain reactance.

3AE1-2.1 What is an ohm? (A) The basic unit of resistance; (B) The basic unit of capacitance; (C) The basic unit of inductance; (D) The basic unit of admittance.

3AE1-2.2 What is the unit measurement of resistance? (A) Volt; (B) Ampere; (C) Joule; (D) Ohm.

3AE1-3.1 Two equal-value resistors are connected in series. How does the total resistance of this combination compare with the value of either resistor by itself? (A) The total resistance is half the value of either resistor; (B) The total resistance is twice the value of either resistor; (C) The total resistance is the same as the value of either resistor; (D) The total resistance is the square of the value of either resistor.

3AE1-3.2 How does the total resistance of a string of series-connected resistors compare to the values of the individual resistors? (A) The total resistance is the square of the sum of all the individual resistor values; (B) The total resistance is the square root of the sum of the individual resistor values; (C) The total resistance is the sum of the squares of the individual resistor values; (D) The total resistance is the sum of all the individual resistance values.

3AE1-4.1 Two equal-value resistors are connected in parallel. How does the total resistance of this combination compare with the value of either resistor by itself? (A) The total resistance is twice the value of either resistor; (B) The total resistance is half the value of either resistor; (C) The total resistance is the square of the value of either resistor; (D) The total resistance is the same as the value of either resistor.

3AE1-4.2 How does the total resistance of a string of parallel-connected resistors compare to the values of the individual resistors? (A) The total resistance is the square of the sum of the resistor values; (B) The total resistance is more than the highest-value resistor in the combination; (C) The total resistance is less than the smallest-value resistor in the combination; (D) The total resistance is same as the highest-value resistor in the combination.

3AE2.1 What is Ohm's Law? (A) A mathematical relationship between resistance, voltage and power in a circuit; (B) A mathematical relationship between current, resistance and power in a circuit; (C) A mathematical relationship between current, voltage and power in a circuit; (D) A mathematical relationship between resistance, current and applied voltage in a circuit.

3AE2.2 How is the current in a DC circuit calculated when the voltage and resistance are known? (A) I = E / R; (B) P = I x E; (C) I = R x E; (D) I = E x R.

3AE2.3 What is the input resistance of a load when a 12-volt battery supplies 0.25 amperes to it? (A) 0.02 ohms; (B) 3 ohms; (C) 48 ohms; (D) 480 ohms.

3AE2.4 The product of the current and what force gives the electrical power in a circuit? (A) Magnetomotive force; (B) Centripetal force; (C) Electrochemical force; (D) Electromotive force.

3AE2.5 What is the input resistance of a load when a 12-volt battery supplies 0.15 amperes to it? (A) 8 ohms; (B) 80 ohms; (C) 100 ohms; (D) 800 ohms.

3AE2.6 When 120 volts is measured across a 4700-ohm resistor, approximately how much current is flowing through it? (A) 39 amperes; (B) 3.9 amperes; (C) 0.26 ampere; (D) 0.026 ampere.

3AE2.7 When 120 volts is measured across a 47000-ohm resistor, approximately how much current is flowing through it? (A) 392 A; (B) 39.2 A; (C) 26 mA; (D) 2.6 mA.

3AE2.8 When 12 volts is measured across a 4700-ohm resistor, approximately how much current is flowing through it? (A) 2.6 mA; (B) 26 mA; (C) 39.2 A; (D) 392 A.

3AE2.9 When 12 volts is measured across a 47000-ohm resistor, approximately how much current is flowing through it? (A) 255 uA; (B) 255 mA; (C) 3917 mA; (D) 3917 A.

3AE3-1.1 What is the term used to describe the ability of a component to store energy in a magnetic field? (A) Admittance; (B) Capacitance; (C) Inductance; (D) Resistance

3AE3-2.1 What is the basic unit of inductance? (A) Coulomb; (B) Farad; (C) Henry; (D) Ohm.

3AE3-2.2 What is a Henry? (A) The basic unit of admittance; (B) The basic unit of capacitance; (C) The basic unit of inductance; (D) The basic unit of resistance.

3AE3-2.3 What is a microHenry? (A) A basic unit of inductance equal to 10-12 Henrys; (B) A basic unit of inductance equal to 10-6 Henrys; (C) A basic unit of inductance equal to 10-3 Henrys; (D) A basic unit of inductance equal to 10-6 Henrys.

3AE3-2.4 What is a milliHenry? (A) A basic unit of inductance equal to 10-12 Henrys; (B) A basic unit of inductance equal to 10-6 Henrys; (C) A basic unit of inductance equal to 10-3 Henrys; (D) A basic unit of inductance equal to 10-6 Henrys.

3AE3-3.1 Two equal-value inductors are connected in series. How does the total inductance of this combination compare with the value of either inductor by itself? (A) The total inductance is half the value of either inductor; (B) The total inductance is twice the value of either inductor; (C) The total inductance is equal to the value of either inductor; (D) No comparison can be made without knowing the exact inductances.

3AE3-3.2 How does the total inductance of a string of series-connected inductors compare to the values of the individual inductors? (A) The total inductance is equal to the average of all the individual inductances; (B) The total inductance is equal to less than the value of the smallest inductance; (C) The total inductance is equal to the sum of all the individual inductances; (D) No comparison can be made without knowing the exact inductances.

3AE3-4.1 Two equal-value inductors are connected in parallel. How does the total inductance of this combination compare with the value of either inductor by itself? (A) The total inductance is half the value of either inductor; (B) The total inductance is twice the value of either inductor; (C) The total inductance is equal to the square of either inductance; (D) No comparison can be made without knowing the exact inductances.

3AE3-4.2 How does the total inductance of a string of parallel-connected inductors compare to the values of the individual inductors? (A) The total inductance is equal to the sum of the inductances in the combination; (B) The total inductance is less than the smallest inductance value in the combination; (C) The total inductance is equal to the average of the inductances in the combination; (D) No comparison can be made without knowing the exact inductances.

3AE4-1.1 What is the term used to describe the ability of a component to store energy in an electric field? (A) Capacitance; (B) Inductance; (C) Resistance; (D) Tolerance.

3AE4-2.1 What is the basic unit of capacitance? (A) Farad; (B) Ohm; (C) Volt; (D) Ampere.

3AE4-2.2 What is a microFarad? (A) A basic unit of capacitance equal to 10-12 Farads; (B) A basic unit of capacitance equal to 10-6 Farads; (C) A basic unit of capacitance equal to 10-2 Farads; (D) A basic unit of capacitance equal to 10-6 Farads.

3AE4-2.3 What is a picoFarad? (A) A basic unit of capacitance equal to 10-12 Farads; (B) A basic unit of capacitance equal to 10-6 Farads; (C) A basic unit of capacitance equal to 10-2 Farads; (D) A basic unit of capacitance equal to 10-6 Farads.

3AE4-2.4 What is a Farad? (A) The basic unit of resistance; (B) The basic unit of capacitance; (C) The basic unit of inductance; (D) The basic unit of admittance.

3AE4-3.1 Two equal-value capacitors are connected in series. How does the total capacitance of this combination compare with the value of either capacitor by itself? (A) The total capacitance is twice the value of either capacitor; (B) The total capacitance is equal to the value of either capacitor; (C) The total capacitance is half the value of either capacitor; (D) No comparison can be made without knowing the exact capacitances.

3AE4-3.2 How does the total capacitance of a string of series-connected capacitors compare to the values of the individual capacitors? (A) The total capacitance is equal to the sum of the capacitances in the combination; (B) The total capacitance is less than the smallest value of capacitance in the combination; (C) The total capacitance is equal to the average of the capacitances in the combination; (D) No comparison can be made without knowing the exact capacitances.

3AE4-4.1 Two equal-value capacitors are connected in parallel. How does the total capacitance of this combination compare with the value of either capacitor by itself? (A) The total capacitance is twice the value of either capacitor; (B) The total capacitance is half the value of either capacitor; (C) The total capacitance is equal to the value of either capacitor; (D) No comparison can be made without knowing the exact capacitances.

3AE4-4.2 How does the total capacitance of a string of parallel-connected capacitors compare to the values of the individual capacitors? (A) The total capacitance is equal to the sum of the capacitances in the combination; (B) The total capacitance is less than the smallest value of capacitance in the combination; (C) The total capacitance is equal to the average of the capacitances in the combination; (D) No comparison can be made without knowing the exact capacitances.

Chapter

F

Circuit Components

Four of the 55 questions you will be asked on your Technician test come from the Circuit Components Subelements of the Novice (2) and Technician (2) question pools. In this chapter you will be required to associate names with diagram symbols.

Most people have seen the "innards" of an electronic product. Older equipment was a maze of wires and mysterious colorful shapes. Newer electronic devices contain etched circuit boards with more mysterious and colorful objects, but much smaller and aligned in a much more orderly manner. These bits and pieces of electronic trivia are the devices which make the product function. They are called **electronic components**. Their specific names are resistors, capacitors, inductors, connectors and so on.

The collection of components is laced together by copper wires in the handmade product and by copper circuit traces on the etched circuit board in the automated production version. For each piece of electronic equipment, there is a roadmap of where the parts are located and how they are connected together. This guide is called a circuit or **schematic diagram**. It, along with other supporting information, tells the manufacturer exactly how the product should be assembled.

Each of the electronic components has a **schematic symbol** which is a standardized representation of the device. Anyone skilled in electronics can look at the schematic "picture" and say "That's a resistor" or "This end of the capacitor is grounded".

Symbols

The Resistor — In the last chapter, we discussed an electronic component which impeded the flow of electricity. The component was called a resistor. The primary purpose of a resistor is to limit current flow in a circuit. The electronic symbol for a resistor is: (2F1.1) (2F1.3)(3AF1-2.1)(3AF1-5.1)

In addition to their function in limiting current, resistors also convert electrical energy to heat energy. An example is the heating element in a stove or toaster. (3AF1-4.1)

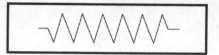

There are four principal types of resistors used in electronics. They are carbon-composition, carbon-film, metal-film and wire-wound. The most common form of resistor is made from carbon. This is very much like the black material that one finds in the center of a pencil. (3AF1-1.1)

Since they do dissipate heat in some cases, it is necessary to observe the wattage rating of resistors. Carbon composition resistors vary in size from 1/8 watt up to 2 watts. Wire-wound resistors use nichrome wire and vary in rating from 1 watt up to several hundred watts. Usually the physical size is proportional to the power dissipation capability for both carbon and wire types. (3AF1-4.2)

Resistors are available in stepped values from 2.7 ohms up to 22 million ohms (22 meg-ohms or 22M). It is difficult to accurately make a value smaller than 2.7 ohms from carbon, where there is very little use for resistors above 22M in electronic equipment.

The numeric value is not printed on the resistor. Rather, a coding scheme employing color bands is used. A typical resistor is shown in the accompanying drawing. The first three color bands are used to indicate the resistance value. The first two value bands are numeric indicators, while the third value band is a multiplier which indicates the number of zeros. Thus, a resistor marked red-red-orange would have a value of 22,000 ohms. For small values, a black band indicates no zeros (values between 2.7 and 99 ohms). A gold band indicates divide by 10 (for values between 2.7 and 9.9 ohms). (3AF1-3.1)(3AF1-3.2)

To determine the accurate value, another factor must be known. A fourth band indicates the tolerance of the resistor. For example if the resistor is 10,000 ohms (brown-black-orange-silver), it has a 10% tolerance as indicated by the silver band. The actual value of the resistor may vary between 9,000 and 11,000 ohms. This is considered a rather poor resistor. Five percent tolerance resistors are almost universal in consumer electronics equipment. Military equipment use 1% resistors. A 1% tolerance resistor has an extra value indicating band. (3AF1-3.3)(3AF1-3.4)

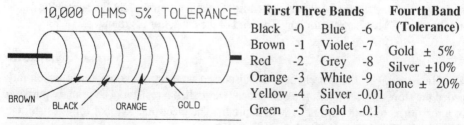

10,000 OHMS 5% TOLERANCE

BROWN BLACK ORANGE GOLD

First Three Bands				Fourth Band (Tolerance)
Black	-0	Blue	-6	
Brown	-1	Violet	-7	Gold ± 5%
Red	-2	Grey	-8	Silver ±10%
Orange	-3	White	-9	none ± 20%
Yellow	-4	Silver	-0.01	
Green	-5	Gold	-0.1	

Occasionally we need a version of resistor which is continuously variable. This variable resistor is called a **potentiometer**. It is simply a resistive element with a sliding contact attached to a shaft. When the shaft position is moved, the resistance is varied. Attached to the shaft is a knob which is used as the resistance value adjustment. The volume control in a radio or television is a good example of a potentiometer. The symbol for a potentiometer is: (2F1.2) (3AF1-2.2)(3AF1-5.2)

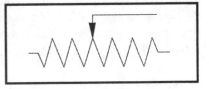

The Inductor- Inductors are a very special component in electronics. Every electronic product contains inductors since every wire has a small amount of inductance.

If a piece of conducting wire is formed into a coil, it's inductance value rises dramatically. It then takes on the property of an **inductor or coil**. The symbol for an inductor or coil is: (3AF2-1.2)(3AF2-1.3)

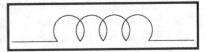

Four parameters will effect the exact value of an inductor, (a) the number of turns in the coil, (b) the diameter of the coil, (c) the spacing between turns and (d) the core the coil is wound on. (3AF2-3.1)

If the number of turns are doubled, the inductance value will increase by four times. The larger the coil, the greater the inductance value. As the spacing between turns is decreased, the inductive value is increased. Finally, the core can have a remarkable effect of the value of an inductor. (3AF2-1.2)

When a current is passed through an inductor, **lines of force** are created. You can demonstrate this by winding some wire on a steel nail. Connect the two wire ends to a flashlight battery and the electromagnet you have just created will attract and hold steel objects like paper clips. The intensity of the field is affected by the same factors that control inductance.

Picking up paperclips is not a unique property. Any magnet will do this. What is unique is the ability of an inductor to store energy in its magnetic field. (3AF2-2.1)

A popular use for inductors is the radio frequency choke from MFJ. It is useful for supressing RF on wires and cables to prevent TV interference.

Another property of inductors is they oppose the flow current but in a very unique manner. When an inductor is connected to a source of DC voltage (a battery, for example), the lines-of-force expand from the coil. But in doing so, the expanding lines cut through the turns of the coil and induce a current flow in them. However, this current flow is exactly opposite from the current caused by the battery. Thus, there is an opposition to current flow.

Eventually, however, the DC current flow does reach maximum, the lines of force stop expanding and no opposition current is created. Thus, the current flow through the circuit is limited only by the DC resistance of the inductor. Thus the magnetic field opposes the increase or decrease in current flow. (3AF2-2.2)

Previously, it was stated that the core can have a significant effect on the value of an inductor. Here's why. The core is defined as the central portion of a coil and may consist of air, iron, brass or other material. So far the discussion has implied a coil of wire wound with an air core. Usually an air core coil is wound on a paper or plastic tube. (3AF2-1.1)

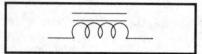

The lines of force in the core area can be aided or opposed if a material other than air is used for the core material. For example, if a core material of **iron** is used, the magnetic lines of force are concentrated by the material and the inductance is **increased**. The symbol used to represent an iron core inductor is shown in the accompanying drawing. (3AF2-3.2)(3AF2-3.3)(3AF2-4.2)

If the core material is **brass** (usually silver plated to reduce loss), the material impedes the lines of force and the inductance is **decreased** below its value with an air core. (3AF2-3.4)

Note that in the case of either iron or brass, some losses will be introduced when used in a RF application. An air core coil will exhibit the least amount of loss. (3AF2-1.4)

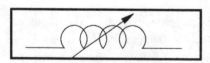

If the iron core can be inserted and removed, the inductor can be made variable. The symbol used to represent an adjustable inductor is shown in the accompanying drawing. (3AF2-4.1)

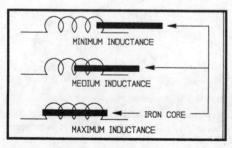

MINIMUM INDUCTANCE

MEDIUM INDUCTANCE

IRON CORE

MAXIMUM INDUCTANCE

Most tunable coils and transformers used in electronics employ cores of powdered iron. A ceramic material called ferrite is also used to greatly increase the inductance of a coil. Virtually every piece of Amateur Radio receiving or transmitting equipment made today uses some form of variable inductor.

Another form of core is a donut cast of powdered iron or ferrite. The turns are wound on the donut and all the lines of force are contained in the core material. There is very little external magnetic energy. This component is called a toroid inductor. The schematic for a toroid is: (3AF2-4.3)

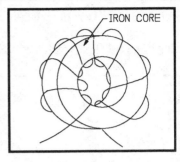

The Capacitor — One of the most useful components in electronics is called a capacitor. A capacitor consists of two or more conducting plates with an insulating material between them. The insulating material can be air, paper (with or without saturating chemicals) and ceramic. The insulating medium is called the dielectric. The symbol for a capacitor is: (3AF3-1.1)(3AF3-1.2)

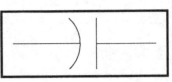

The characteristics of a capacitor are just the opposite of an inductor. There is no electromagnetic field associated with a capacitor. This device stores energy, but in an **electric** or **electrostatic** field. Also, unlike an inductor, capacitors oppose a change in voltage rather than a change in current. (3AF3-2.1)(3AF3-2.2)

Capacitors are specified by the capacitive value and voltage breakdown rating. The area of the conducting plates, the number of plates, the spacing between the plates and the type of dielectric material will determine the value of the capacitor. If the size or number of plates are made larger, the capacitance will increase. If the spacing between the plates in increased, the capacitive value decreases. The spacing between plates and the dielectric determines the breakdown voltage of the capacitor. (3AF3-2.3)(3AF3-2.4)(3AF3-3.1)(3AF3-3.2)(3AF3-3.3)

If the insulator is paper, the device is referred to as a paper capacitor. By the same token, if a chemical is used in the dielectric (to increase its capacitance), the device is referred to an electrolytic capacitor. An electrolytic must be connected in the proper polarity. Thus it's schematic diagram has a symbol indicating the positive terminal. The symbol for an electrolytic capacitor is: (3AF3-1.3)(3AF3-1.4) (3AF3-4.1)

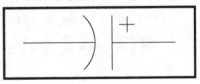

If the spacing between plates is adjustable, the device is called a variable capacitor. The schematic diagram of a variable capacitor is: (3AF3-4.2)

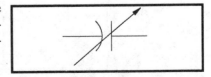

Switches- If you touch the wire from a motor to a battery terminal, you are acting just like a switch. When you touch the wire to the battery and the motor runs, you have *closed* the switch. When you lift the wire and the motor stops, you have *opened* the switch. This is type of switch is called a **single pole, single throw (SPST)** switch. In other words, you are only breaking one wire connection. The symbol for a single-pole, single-throw (SPST) switch is: (2F2.1)(2F2.5)

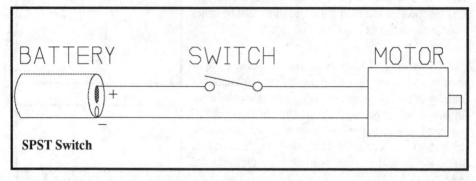

SPST Switch

Let's say you touch the wire first to the negative terminal of battery "A" and then moved the wire to the positive terminal of battery "B". This will control the direction of motor rotation. In doing this, you break only one connection but you are "throwing the switch handle" (the wire you hold) in two positions. This type of switch is called a **single pole, double throw (SPDT)** switch. (2F2.2)

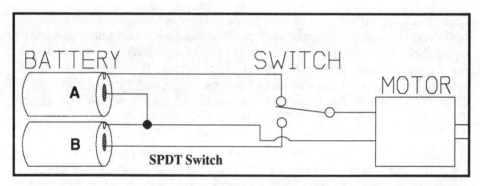

SPDT Switch

In this example, you connected the wire to the positive terminal of one battery and the negative terminal of a second battery. The remaining battery terminals are connected together and are wired to the unswitched terminal of the motor.

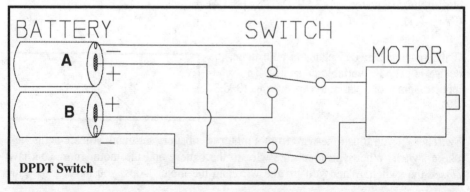

DPDT Switch

What if you want to switch both wires? Let's say you have one in each hand. First you connect the two wires to the positive and negative terminals of battery "A" and the motor runs in one direction. Then you move the two wires over to the minus and plus terminals of battery "B". The motor runs in the opposite direction. In this example you have simulated a **double pole, double throw (DPDT)** switch. (2F2.3)

Switches need not be one way or the other (double throw). Often you will find **rotary switches** in electronic equipment. A common example is the selector on your stereo sys-
tem. The knob on the front can select between AM, FM, phone, compact disk player, tape one, tape two and so on. This type of switch is called a rotary. The symbol for a five position rotary switch (such as might be used in your stereo) is: (2F2.4)

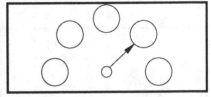

Fuses — Each of us has probably changed a fuse at one time or another. Most pieces of electronic equipment contain these tiny protectors of the electronic kingdom. The symbol for a fuse is #2 in Figure 2F-1 (*see Page 147*). (2F3.1)

Batteries — The symbol for a battery is not a round cylinder with two screw terminals on top as shown in the previous illustrations. This **pictorial** was just a representation to illustrate a familiar object. The voltage of a single cell battery is usually around 1.5
volts. Multiple cell batteries, such as the 9 volt version that Radio Shack gives away with a card, are shown in schematics the following way: (2F4.1)(2F4.2)

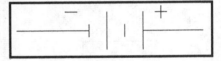

Antenna and Ground — One terminal of the battery (or power source) is usually common to most of the circuits in a piece of electronic equipment. We call this part of a circuit the common point or **common ground**. In older equipment, this common point was usually the metal chassis upon which the circuit was constructed.

Today, few pieces of electronic equipment use a metal chassis for the common ground. The transistor radio for example, uses one or more plastic circuit boards all contained inside a plastic enclosure. Even a large VCR in a metal case confines it's "chassis grounds" to a common length of foil running around each of the many circuit boards inside.

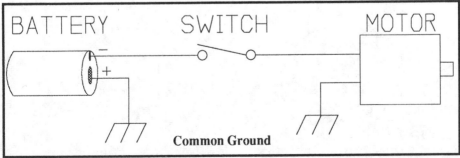

BATTERY   SWITCH   MOTOR

Common Ground

So the term is a little misleading. A common ground simply means the end of the circuit that is common to most of the parts of the circuit. For example, note the battery, motor and SPST switch could have been drawn as shown in the common ground diagram.

The strange looking symbol is called the ground or, for the purposes of the Technician test, the **chassis ground**. Obviously you don't have to go outside and drive three metal stakes into the earth to make the circuit work. We call the common points in a circuit the common ground (chassis ground). (2F5.2)(2F5.3)

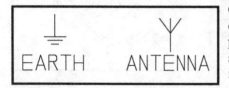

Occasionally we do need to signify an outside **earth ground**, as an example for lightening protection. We do this with a different ground symbol. The symbol denoting earth is shown in the accompanying drawing. (2F5.1) (2F5.4)

One often finds the earth ground symbol in a schematic diagram along with an antenna symbol. The circuit shorthand for an antenna is also shown in the above drawing. (2F6.1)

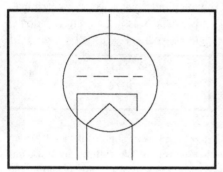

Tubes and Transistors- You won't see them much anymore in schematics but the symbol for a vacuum tube (in this case a triode, or three element "valve") is shown in the accompanying drawing. (2F8.1)

These days, you are much more likely to see a transistor symbol than one for a vacuum tube. Even these are less common with the introduction of the **integrated circuit**. An IC can incorporate thousands of transistors all on a tiny chip of silicon.

There are two principal types of transistors and the difference is a function of the manufacturing process. Impurities added to the silicon determine if the transistor is a negative-positive-negative (**NPN**) or a positive-negative-positive (**PNP**) device. The symbol for each type is shown. The only schematic difference is which way the arrow points on the element known as the emitter. (2F7.1)(2F7.2)(2F7.3)(2F7.4)

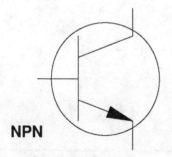

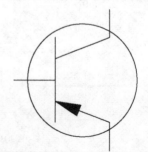

NPN

PNP

Now that you've had a look at some of the symbols used in electronics, let's see how you do with the portion of the test that asks these questions.

SUBELEMENT 2F (2 questions)

2F1.1 What is the symbol used on schematic diagrams to represent a resistor? (Please refer to Diagram 2F-1.1) (A) Symbol A; (B) Symbol B; (C) Symbol C; (D)Symbol D.

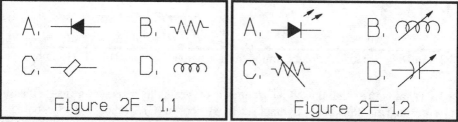

Figure 2F - 1.1   Figure 2F-1.2

2F1.2 What is the symbol used on schematic diagrams to represent a variable resistor or potentiometer? (Please refer to Diagram 2F-1.2) (A) Symbol A; (B) Symbol B; (C) Symbol C; (D)Symbol D.

2F1.3 In Diagram 2F-1, which component is a resistor? (A) 1; (B) 2; (C) 3; (D)4.

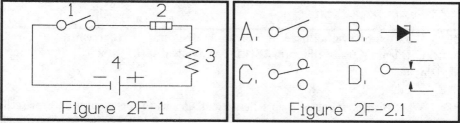

Figure 2F-1   Figure 2F-2.1

2F2.1 What is the symbol used on schematic diagrams to represent a single-pole, single-throw switch? (Please refer to Diagram 2F-2.1) (A) Symbol A; (B) Symbol B; (C) Symbol C; (D)Symbol D.

2F2.2 What is the symbol used on schematic diagrams to represent a single-pole, double-throw switch? (Please refer to Diagram 2F-2.2) (A) Symbol A; (B) Symbol B; (C) Symbol C; (D)Symbol D.

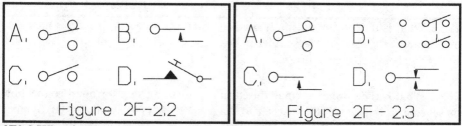

Figure 2F-2.2   Figure 2F - 2.3

2F2.3 What is the symbol used on schematic diagrams to represent a double-pole, double-throw switch? (Please refer to Diagram 2F-2.3) (A) Symbol A; (B) Symbol B; (C) Symbol C; (D)Symbol D.

2F2.4 What is the symbol used on schematic diagrams to represent a single-pole 5-position rotary switch? (Please refer to Diagram 2F-2.4) (A) Symbol A; (B) Symbol B; (C) Symbol C; (D)Symbol D.

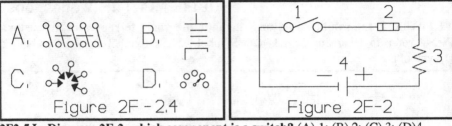

Figure 2F-2.4   Figure 2F-2

2F2.5 In Diagram 2F-2, which component is a switch? (A) 1; (B) 2; (C) 3; (D)4.

2F3.1 What is the symbol used on schematic diagrams to represent a fuse? (Please refer to Diagram 2F-3.1) (A) Symbol A; (B) Symbol B; (C) Symbol C; (D)Symbol D.

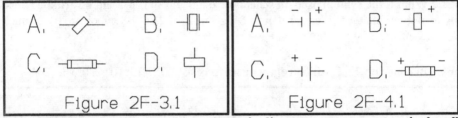

Figure 2F-3.1   Figure 2F-4.1

2F4.1 What is the symbol used on schematic diagrams to represent a single-cell battery? (Please refer to Diagram 2F-4.1) (A) Symbol A; (B) Symbol B; (C) Symbol C; (D)Symbol D.

2F4.2 What is the symbol used on schematic diagrams to represent a multiple-cell battery? (Please refer to Diagram 2F-4.2) (A) Symbol A; (B) Symbol B; (C) Symbol C; (D)Symbol D.

Figure 2F-4.2   Figure 2F-5.1

2F5.1 What is the symbol normally used to represent an earth-ground connection on schematic diagrams? (Please refer to Diagram 2F-5.1) (A) Symbol A; (B) Symbol B; (C) Symbol C; (D)Symbol D.

2F5.2 What is the symbol normally used to represent a chassis-ground connection on schematic diagrams? (Please refer to Diagram 2F-5.2) (A) Symbol A; (B) Symbol B; (C) Symbol C; (D)Symbol D.

2F5.3 In Diagram 2F-5, which symbol represents a chassis ground connection? (A) 1; (B) 2; (C) 3; (D)4.

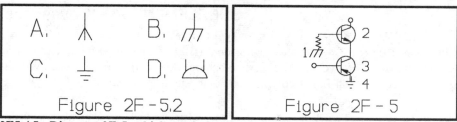

Figure 2F-5.2   Figure 2F-5

2F5.4 In Diagram 2F-5, which symbol represents an earth ground connection? (A) 1; (B) 2; (C) 3; (D)4.

2F6.1 What is the symbol used to represent an antenna on schematic diagrams? (Please refer to Diagram 2F-6.1) (A) Symbol A; (B) Symbol B; (C) Symbol C; (D)Symbol D.

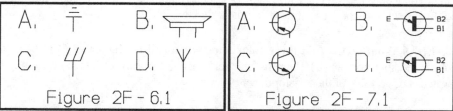

Figure 2F-6.1   Figure 2F-7.1

2F7.1 What is the symbol used to represent an NPN bipolar transistor on schematic diagrams? (Please refer to Diagram 2F-7.1) (A) Symbol A; (B) Symbol B; (C) Symbol C; (D)Symbol D.

2F7.2 What is the symbol used to represent a PNP bipolar transistor on schematic diagrams? (Please refer to Diagram 2F-7.2) (A) Symbol A; (B) Symbol B; (C) Symbol C; (D)Symbol D.

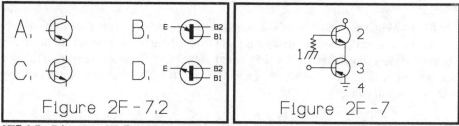

Figure 2F-7.2   Figure 2F-7

2F7.3 In Diagram 2F-7, which symbol represents a PNP bipolar transistor? (A) 1; (B) 2; (C) 3; (D)4.

2F7.4 In Diagram 2F-7, which symbol represents an NPN bipolar transistor? (A) 1; (B) 2; (C) 3; (D)4.

2F8.1 What is the symbol used to represent a triode vacuum tube on schematic diagrams? (Please refer to Diagram 2F-8.1) (A) Symbol A; (B) Symbol B; (C) Symbol C; (D)Symbol D.

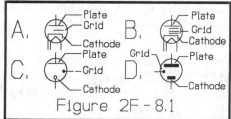

Figure 2F-8.1

SUBELEMENT 3AF (2 questions).

3AF1-1.1 What are the four common types of resistor construction? (A) Carbon-film, metal-film, micro-film and wire-film; (B) Carbon-composition, carbon-film, metal-film and wire-wound; (C) Carbon-composition, carbon-film, electrolytic and metal-film; (D)Carbon-film, ferrite, carbon-composition and metal-film.

3AF1-2.1 What is the primary function of a resistor? (A) To store an electric charge; (B) To store a magnetic field; (C) To match a high-impedance source to a low-impedance load; (D)To limit the current in an electric circuit.

3AF1-2.2 What is a variable resistor? (A) A resistor that changes value when an AC voltage is applied to it; (B) A device that can transform a variable voltage into a constant voltage; (C) A resistor with a slide or contact that makes the resistance adjustable; (D)A resistor that changes value when it is heated.

3AF1-3.1 What do the first three color bands on a resistor indicate? (A) The value of the resistor in ohms; (B) The resistance tolerance in percent; (C) The power rating in watts; (D)The value of the resistor in henrys.

3AF1-3.2 How can a carbon resistor's electrical tolerance rating be found? (A) By using a wavemeter; (B) By using the resistor's color code; (C) By using Thevenin's theorem for resistors; (D)By using the Baudot code.

3AF1-3.3 What does the fourth color band on a resistor indicate? (A) The value of the resistor in ohms; (B) The resistance tolerance in percent; (C) The power rating in watts; (D)The resistor composition.

3AF1-3.4 When the color bands on a group of resistors indicate that they all have the same resistance, what further information about each resistor is needed in order to select those that have nearly equal value? (A) The working voltage rating of each resistor; (B) The composition of each resistor; (C) The tolerance of each resistor; (D)The current rating of each resistor.

3AF1-4.1 Why do resistors generate heat? (A) They convert electrical energy to heat energy; (B) They exhibit reactance; (C) Because of skin effect; (D)To produce thermionic emission.

3AF1-4.2 Why would a large size resistor be substituted for a smaller one of the same resistance? (A) To obtain better response; (B) To obtain a higher current gain; (C) To increase power dissipation capability; (D)To produce a greater parallel impedance.

3AF1-5.1 What is the symbol used to represent a fixed resistor on schematic diagrams? (Please refer to Diagram 3AF1-5.1) (A) Symbol A; (B) Symbol B; (C) Symbol C; (D)Symbol D.

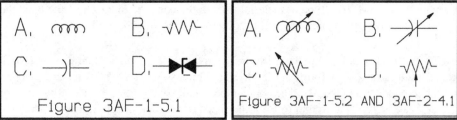

Figure 3AF-1-5.1

Figure 3AF-1-5.2 AND 3AF-2-4.1

3AF1-5.2 What is the symbol used to represent a variable resistor on schematic diagrams. (Please refer to Diagram 3AF1-5.2) (A) Symbol A; (B) Symbol B; (C) Symbol C; (D)Symbol D.

3AF2-1.1 What is an inductor core? (A) The point at which an inductor is tapped to produce resonance; (B) A tight coil of wire used in a transformer; (C) An insulating material placed between the plates of an inductor; (D)The central portion of a coil; may be made from air, iron, brass or other material.

3AF2-1.2 What are the component parts of a coil? (A) The wire in the winding and the core material; (B) Two conductive plates and an insulating material; (C) Two or more layers of silicon material; (D)A donut-shaped iron core and a layer of insulating tape.

3AF2-1.3 Describe an inductor. (A) A semiconductor in a conducting shield; (B) Two parallel conducting plates; (C) A straight wire conductor mounted inside a Faraday shield; (D)A coil of conducting wire.

3AF2-1.4 For radio frequency power applications, which type of inductor has the least amount of loss? (A) Magnetic wire; (B) Iron core; (C) Air core; (D)Slug tuned.

3AF2-2.1 What is an inductor? (A) An electronic component that stores energy in an electric field; (B) An electronic component that converts a high voltage to a lower voltage; (C) An electronic component that opposes DC while allowing AC to pass; (D)An electronic component that stores energy in a magnetic field.

3AF2-2.2 What are the electrical properties of an inductor? (A) An inductor stores a charge electrostatically and opposes a change in voltage; (B) An inductor stores a charge electrochemically and opposes a change in current; (C) An inductor stores a charge electromagnetically and opposes a change in current; (D)An inductor stores a charge electromechanically and opposes a change in voltage.

3AF2-3.1 What factors determine the amount of inductance in a coil? (A) The type of material used in the core, the diameter of the core and whether the coil is mounted horizontally or vertically; (B) The diameter of the core, the number of turns of wire used to wind the coil and the type of metal used in the wire; (C) The type of material used in the core, the number of turns used to wind the core and the frequency of the current through the coil; (D)The type of material used in the core, the diameter of the core, the length of the coil and the number of turns of wire used to wind the coil.

3AF2-3.2 What can be done to raise the inductance of a 5-microhenry air-core coil to a 5-millihenry coil with the same physical dimensions? (A) The coil can be wound on a non-conducting tube; (B) The coil can be wound on an iron core; (C) Both ends of the coil can be brought around to form the shape of a donut, or toroid; (D)The coil can be made of a heavier-gauge wire.

3AF2-3.3 As an iron core is inserted in a coil, what happens to the inductance? (A) It increases; (B) It decreases; (C) It stays the same; (D)It becomes voltage-dependent.

3AF2-3.4 As a brass core is inserted in a coil, what happens to the inductance? (A) It increases; (B) It decreases; (C) It stays the same; (D)It becomes voltage-dependent.

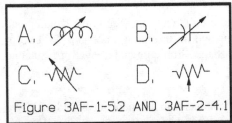

Figure 3AF-1-5.2 AND 3AF-2-4.1

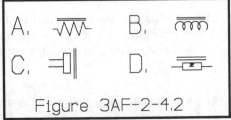

Figure 3AF-2-4.2

3AF2-4.1 What is the symbol used to represent an adjustable inductor on schematic diagrams? (Please refer to Diagram 3AF2-4.1) (A) Symbol A; (B) Symbol B; (C) Symbol C; (D)Symbol D.

3AF2-4.2 What is the symbol used to represent an iron-core inductor on schematic diagrams? (Please refer to Diagram 3AF2-4.2) (A) Symbol A; (B) Symbol B; (C) Symbol C; (D)Symbol D.

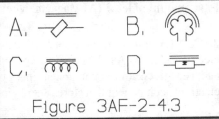

Figure 3AF-2-4.3

3AF2-4.3 What is the symbol used to represent an inductor wound over a toroidal core on schematic diagrams? (Please refer to Diagram 3AF2-4.3) (A) Symbol A; (B) Symbol B; (C) Symbol C; (D)Symbol D.

3AF3-1.1 What is a capacitor dielectric? (A) The insulating material used for the plates; (B) The conducting material used between the plates; (C) The ferrite material that the plates are mounted on; (D)The insulating material between the plates.

3AF3-1.2 What are the component parts of a capacitor? (A) Two or more conductive plates with an insulating material between them; (B) The wire used in the winding and the core material; (C) Two or more layers of silicon material; (D)Two insulating plates with a conductive material between them.

3AF3-1.3 What is an electrolytic capacitor? (A) A capacitor whose plates are formed on a thin ceramic layer; (B) A capacitor whose plates are separated by a thin strip of mica insulation; (C) A capacitor whose dielectric is formed on one set of plates through electrochemical action; (D)A capacitor whose value varies with applied voltage.

3AF3-1.4 What is a paper capacitor? (A) A capacitor whose plates are formed on a thin ceramic layer; (B) A capacitor whose plates are separated by a thin strip of mica insulation; (C) A capacitor whose plates are separated by a layer of paper; (D)A capacitor whose dielectric is formed on one set of plates through electrochemical action.

3AF3-2.1 What is a capacitor? (A) An electronic component that stores energy in a magnetic field; (B) An electronic component that stores energy in an electric field; (C) An electronic component that converts a high voltage to a lower voltage; (D)An electronic component that converts power into heat.

3AF3-2.2 What are the electrical properties of a capacitor? (A) A capacitor stores a charge electrochemically and opposes a change in current; (B) A capacitor stores a charge electromagnetically and opposes a change in current; (C) A capacitor stores a charge electromechanically and opposes a change in voltage; (D)A capacitor stores a charge electrostatically and opposes a change in voltage.

3AF3-2.3 What factors must be considered when selecting a capacitor for a circuit? (A) Type of capacitor, capacitance and voltage rating; (B) Type of capacitor, capacitance and the kilowatt-hour rating; (C) The amount of capacitance, the temperature coefficient and the KVA rating; (D)The type of capacitor, the microscopy coefficient and the temperature coefficient.

3AF3-2.4 How are the characteristics of a capacitor usually specified? (A) In volts and amperes; (B) In microfarads and volts; (C) In ohms and watts; (D)In millihenrys and amperes.

3AF3-3.1 What factors determine the amount of capacitance in a capacitor? (A) The dielectric constant of the material between the plates, the area of one side of one plate, the separation between the plates and the number of plates; (B) The dielectric constant of the material between the plates, the number of plates and the diameter of the leads connected to the plates; (C) The number of plates, the spacing between the plates and whether the dielectric material is N type or P type; (D)The dielectric constant of the material between the plates, the surface area of one side of one plate, the number of plates and the type of material used for the protective coating.

3AF3-3.2 As the plate area of a capacitor is increased, what happens to its capacitance? (A) Decreases; (B) Increases; (C) Stays the same; (D)Becomes voltage dependent.

3AF3-3.3 As the plate spacing of a capacitor is increased, what happens to its capacitance? (A) Increases; (B) Stays the same; (C) Becomes voltage dependent; (D)Decreases.

3AF3-4.1 What is the symbol used to represent an electrolytic capacitor on schematic diagrams? (Please refer to Diagram 3AF3-4.1) (A) Symbol A; (B) Symbol B; (C) Symbol C; (D)Symbol D.

Figure 3AF-3-4.1

Figure 3AF-3-4.2

3AF3-4.2 What is the symbol used to represent a variable capacitor on schematic diagrams? (Please refer to Diagram 3AF3-4.2) (A) Symbol A; (B) Symbol B; (C) Symbol C; (D)Symbol D.

Chapter

Practical Circuits

This chapter tests you on recognition of various elements in a simplified schematic. You will be asked two questions from the Novice pool (2G) and one question from the Technician pool (3AG). In various places, the text references drawings as part of an explanation. These drawings will be found within the 2G and 3AG Subelement questions at the end of the chapter.

In Chapter F you saw how electronic components were connected together to form a **schematic diagram**. It is not always necessary to have such detailed drawings of electronic circuitry to provide useful information, however.

For example, you might want to show how a transmitter, receiver and antenna were related to a power supply. It is not necessary to show every capacitor and resistor in each piece of electronic gear to convey the idea.

Rather, the various circuits which make up a transmitter can be illustrated with a rectangle marked "transmitter". A combination of these boxes and an illustration of the connecting paths is called a **block diagram**.

Block Diagrams

Figure 2G1-1.1 shows a typical block diagram for a basic Amateur station. The power supply energizes the transceiver (transmittter-receiver). The power delivered by the transmitter portion is connected to an unmarked block. This block is an **antenna switch**. Depending on the position of the switch, the power can be delivered to the antenna or to a dummy antenna (load). As we discussed in Operating Procedures (*Chapter B*), tune-up of the transmitter should never be done into an antenna. Tuning should be done into an dummy antenna to avoid interfering with other Amateurs. (2G1-1.1)

If the ham station uses a separate receiver and transmitter, a switch could be connected as shown in Figure 2G1-1.2). The unmarked block infers a **transmitter** since the antenna switch is connected to a block marked receiver. (2G1-1.2)

A similar drawing is shown in Figure 2G1-1.3. In this case, the unmarked block would represent a **receiver**. The block labeled key infers the transmitter is a CW type and this represents a Morse radiotelegraph station. This is also true for the drawing of Figure 2G2.2. The unmarked block in Figure 2G2.2 could also be labeled "electronic keyer." A keyer is a device that delivers timed "dits" and "dahs" and helps one send good Morse code characters. If the "key" block were simply relabeled "microphone," the diagram could infer a voice station. (2G1-1.3)(2G2.1)(2G2.2)(2G2.3)(2G3.1)(2G3.2)

So far, the drawings show the use of a single antenna. Many ham stations, however, use multiple antenna systems even for the same band. A multi-band dipole might be used for local contacts on various frequencies and a beam antenna for chasing DX. A dummy antenna would be included for tune-up, as shown in Figure 2G1-1.4. The unmarked block in this drawing would be a **transceiver** since a transmitter would be of no value without a receiver. (2G1-1.4)

From the preceding chapter, you should recall the symbol for an antenna. It is again shown in Figure 2G-1 as element number 4. (2G1-1.5)

The drawing shown in Figure 2G1-2.1 is similar to the configuration in Figure 2G1-1.4. In this case, the unmarked block is the device that selects the antenna. This device is called an **antenna switch**. (2G1-2.1)

The switch shown in drawing 2G1-2.2 is called a **TR** or **transmit-receive** switch. This device works automatically. When RF output from the transmitter is present, the switch automatically disconnects the receiver and connects the antenna to the transmitter. This is the purpose of the unmarked block in 2G1-2.2. (2G1-2.2)

An Amateur antenna is not always perfect. It may be used on frequencies where it is not dimensionally optimum. As mentioned in Chapter D, this causes standing waves on the transmission line (or feed line as it is called in Figure 2G1-2.3). Standing wave can cause a number of problems.

In this case a device is required for matching the 50 ohm output of the transmitter to the value of the antenna at any given frequency. The solution to standing waves is to employ a device called an **antenna tuner**. This is an impedance matching device which fools the transmitter into thinking it is connected to a perfect antenna. This is the purpose of the unlabeled block in drawing 2G1-2.3. This would also be the purpose of block number 3 in Figure 2G-1. The other unmarked blocks in this drawing are transceiver (1) and SWR meter (2). (2G1-2.3)(2G1-2.4)(2G1-2.5)

The block diagram shown in Figure 3AG4-1.2 illustrates a **CW transmitter**. The operating frequency is controlled by a **variable frequency oscillator**. A similar circuit is shown in Figure 3AF4-1.3. In this case, however, the frequency determining element is a **quartz crystal**. This is called a **crystal controlled transmitter**. (3AG4-1.2)(3AG4-1.3)

The circuit shown in Figure 3AG4-1.4 is for a simple CW-SSB receiver. Signals received by the antenna are selected by the oscillator, then amplified and passed to the unlabeled block. This circuit is a **detector** which converts the received radio frequency energy back to its original audio component. By the way, every receiver incorporates some form of detector. (3AG4-1.1)(3AG4-1.4)

Compare Figure 3AG4-1.4 to Figure 3AG4-2.1 which is the simplified block diagram for a **frequency modulation (FM) receiver**. In this case, the **frequency discriminator** is the detector. (3AG4-2.1)

Similar to Figures 3AG4-1.2 and 3AG4-1.3, the block diagram in Figure 3AG4-1.5 represents a simple CW transmitter. (3AG4-1.5)

A block diagram for a simple FM transmitter is shown in Figure 3AG4-2.2. Audio voltage from the microphone is amplified and passed through a **clipper/filter**. This circuit acts as a **deviation limiter**. This energy is used to change the phase of the frequency determining crystal oscillator. The unmarked circuit which accomplishes this is called a **reactance modulator**. (3AG4-2.2)

Digital Configurations

The earliest "digital" stations were called **radio teletype (RTTY)**. A five-bit code of one's and zero's called Baudot (bah-doe) was used for RTTY. This mode of operation was very popular with Amateurs since anyone could get on RTTY. The **teleprinter** machines (similar to an electronic typewriter) were donated to Amateur groups by Western Union and RCA. All that was required to make the RTTY teleprinter come to life was a **modem (modulator-demodulator)** called a **terminal unit** or **TU**. This is the purpose of the unlabeled block in Figure 2G4.2. (2G4.1)(2G4.2)

In the early part of the '80's, the teleprinters were replaced by computers. With the development of packet radio, the Amateur RTTY station was doomed to obsolescence. Packet permits addressing messages and passing them for long distance through a system of **terminal-node controllers (TNC)** or **digipeaters**. By changing the unmarked block in Figure 2G4.2 or 2G5.2 to TNC, you can bring the block diagram up to date. The TNC, which connects between the computer and the transceiver, is very much like an intelligent modem. For your test remember that modems are used on RTTY and TNC's are used for packet communication. (2G5.1)(2G5.2)(2G5.3)

The "PAKRATT-232" from AEA sends and receives most digital modes, even CW.

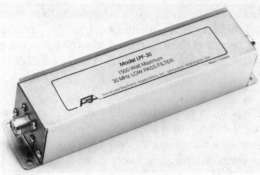

This low pass filter connects to the HF transmitter output and cuts off at 30 MHz. (AEA photo)

Filters

The circuits used to filter unwanted signals makes an interesting illustration of the use and characteristics of inductors and capacitors. This was discussed in Chapter G.

An inductor has increasing opposition to AC as the frequency is increased. Capacitors, on the other hand, have decreasing opposition to AC as the frequency is increased.

If we connect an inductor in series and a capacitor in shunt with the signal path (see Figure G.1), a **low-pass filter** is created. If we feed this with a source of radio frequency energy, it will assume the characteristics shown in the response curve included with Figure G.1. As the frequency of RF is increased, the filter will exhibit increasing opposition (or increasing attenuation). The corner above which the attenuation increases is called the cutoff frequency. The low-pass filter passes energy below this frequency but blocks it above this point. (3AG1-1.1)(3AG1-1.2)

A low-pass filter similar to the circuit shown in G.1 is incorporated in the antenna circuit of virtually every Amateur transmitter. The cutoff frequency would be near the transmitter output frequency. Thus it would attenuate or block the output of any harmonic frequencies. (3AG1-2.1)

The low-pass filter included in the transmitter reduces the level of harmonics below that mandated by the Federal Communications Commission. In some cases even this tiny level can still interfere with a nearby television receiver. In this case it is necessary to add external low-pass filtering to the transmitter to reduce the harmonic level even further. (3AG1-2.2)

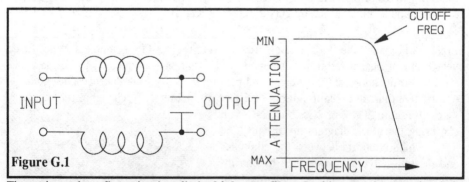

Figure G.1

The reciprocal configuration is called a **high-pass filter**. In this case, the capacitor is in series and the inductor is in shunt with the signal path (see Figure G.2). The capacitor presents decreasing opposition or attenuation to higher frequencies while the inductor

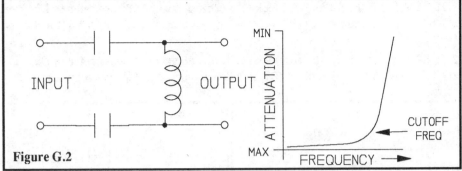

Figure G.2

has decreasing opposition. The high-pass filter also has a reciprocal application. It would be used at the television receiver rather than at the Amateur transmitter. The corner or cutoff frequency is chosen to pass television transmissions but reject low frequency Amateur transmissions. (3AG2-1.1)(3AG2-2.1)(3AG2-2.2)

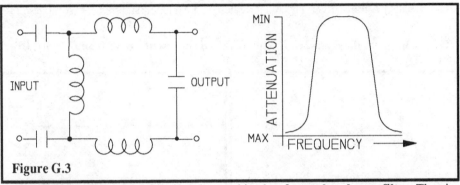

Figure G.3

A low-pass and a high-pass filter can be combined to form a **band-pass filter**. The circuit and characteristics for this configuration is shown in Figure G.3. Note that energy is rejected above and below the frequencies the filter is designed to pass. (3AG3-1.1)(3AG3-1.2)(3AG3-2.1)

Now, let's take a look at the test questions for this chapter, and refer to the block diagrams previously discussed.

SUBELEMENT 2G (2 questions)

2G1-1.1 What is the unlabeled block (?) in this diagram? (Please refer to Diagram 2G-1-1.1) (A) A terminal-node controller; (B) An antenna switch; (C) A telegraph key; (D) A TR switch.

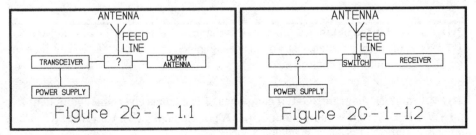

Figure 2G-1-1.1   Figure 2G-1-1.2

2G1-1.2 What is the unlabeled block (?) in this diagram? (Please refer to Diagram 2G-1-1.2) (A) A microphone; (B) A receiver; (C) A transmitter; (D) An SWR meter.

2G1-1.3 What is the unlabeled block (?) in this diagram? (Please refer to Diagram 2G-1-1.3) (A) A key click filter; (B) An antenna tuner; (C) A power supply; (D) A receiver.

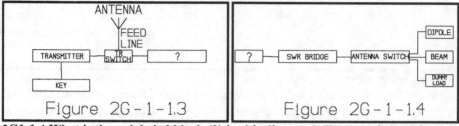

Figure 2G-1-1.3   Figure 2G-1-1.4

2G1-1.4 What is the unlabeled block (?) in this diagram? (Please refer to Diagram 2G-1-1.4) (A) A transceiver; (B) A TR switch; (C) An antenna tuner; (D) A modem.

2G1-1.5 In block diagram 2G-1, which symbol represents an antenna? (A) 1; (B) 2; (C) 3; (D) 4.

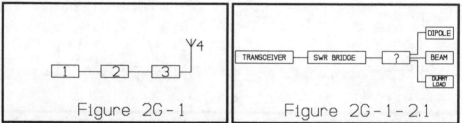

Figure 2G-1   Figure 2G-1-2.1

2G1-2.1 What is the unlabeled block in this diagram? (Please refer to Diagram 2G-1-2.1) (A) A pi network; (B) An antenna switch; (C) A key click filter; (D) A mixer.

2G1-2.2 What is the unlabeled block in this diagram? (Please refer to Diagram 2G-1-2.2) (A) A TR switch; (B) A variable frequency oscillator; (C) A linear amplifier; (D) A microphone.

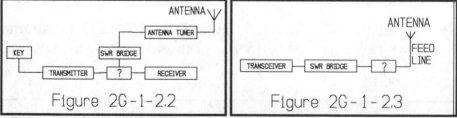

Figure 2G-1-2.2   Figure 2G-1-2.3

2G1-2.3 What is the unlabeled block in this diagram? (Please refer to Diagram 2G-1-2.3) (A) An antenna switch; (B) An impedance-matching network; (C) A key click filter; (D) A terminal-node controller.

2G1-2.4 In block diagram 2G-1, if component 1 is a transceiver and component 2 is an SWR meter, what is component 3? (A) A power supply; (B) A receiver; (C) A microphone; (D) An impedance matching device.

2G1-2.5 In block diagram 2G-1, if component 2 is an SWR meter and component 3 is an impedance matching device, what is component 1? (A) A power supply; (B) An antenna; (C) An antenna switch; (D) A transceiver.

2G2.1 In an Amateur station designed for Morse radiotelegraph operation, what station accessory will you need to go with your transmitter? (A) A terminal-node controller; (B) A telegraph key; (C) An SWR meter; (D) An antenna switch.

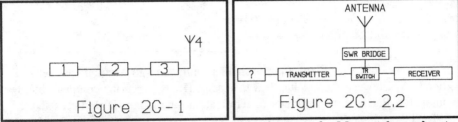

Figure 2G-1   Figure 2G-2.2

2G2.2 What is the unlabeled block (?) in this diagram of a Morse telegraphy station? (Please refer to Diagram 2G-2.2) (A) A sidetone oscillator; (B) A microphone; (C) A telegraph key; (D) A DTMF keypad.

2G2.3 What station accessory do many Amateurs use to help form good Morse code characters? (A) A sidetone oscillator; (B) A key-click filter; (C) An electronic keyer; (D) A DTMF keypad.

2G3.1 In an Amateur station designed for radiotelephone operation, what station accessory will you need to go with your transmitter? (A) A splatter filter; (B) A terminal-voice controller; (C) A receiver audio filter; (D) A microphone.

2G3.2 What is the unlabeled block (?) in this diagram of a radiotelephone station? (Please refer to Diagram 2G-3.2) (A) A splatter filter; (B) A terminal-voice controller; (C) A receiver audio filter; (D) A microphone.

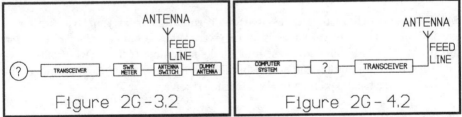

Figure 2G-3.2   Figure 2G-4.2

2G4.1 In an Amateur station designed for radioteletype operation, what station accessories will you need to go with your transmitter? (A) A modem and a teleprinter or computer system; (B) A computer, a printer and a RTTY refresh unit; (C) A terminal-node controller; (D) A modem, a monitor and a DTMF keypad.

2G4.2 What is the unlabeled block (?) in this diagram? (Please refer to Diagram 2G-4.2) (A) An RS-232 interface; (B) SWR bridge; (C) Modem; (D) Terminal-network controller.

2G5.1 In a packet-radio station, what device connects between the radio transceiver and the computer terminal? (A) A terminal-node controller; (B) An RS-232 interface; (C) A terminal refresh unit; (D) A tactical network control system.

2G5.2 What is the unlabeled block (?) in this diagram of a packet-radio station? (Please refer to Diagram 2G-5.2) (A) A terminal-node controller; (B) A RS-232 interface; (C) A terminal refresh unit; (D) A tactical network control system.

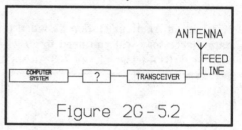

Figure 2G-5.2

2G5.3 Where does a terminal-node controller connect in an Amateur packet-radio station? (A) Between the antenna and the radio; (B) Between the computer and the monitor; (C) Between the computer or terminal and the radio; (D) Between the keyboard and the computer.

SUBELEMENT 3AG (1 question).

3AG1-1.1 Which frequencies are attenuated by a low-pass filter? (A) Those above its cut-off frequency; (B) Those within its cut-off frequency; (C) Those within 50 kHz on either side of its cut-off frequency; (D) Those below its cut-off frequency.

3AG1-1.2 What circuit passes electrical energy below a certain frequency and blocks electrical energy above that frequency? (A) A band-pass filter; (B) A high-pass filter; (C) An input filter; (D) A low-pass filter.

3AG1-2.1 Why does virtually every modern transmitter have a built-in low-pass filter connected to its output? (A) To attenuate frequencies below its cut-off point; (B) To attenuate low frequency interference to other Amateurs; (C) To attenuate excess harmonic radiation; (D) To attenuate excess fundamental radiation.

3AG1-2.2 You believe that excess harmonic radiation from your transmitter is causing interference to your television receiver. What is one possible solution for this problem? (A) Install a low-pass filter on the television receiver; (B) Install a low-pass filter at the transmitter output; (C) Install a high-pass filter on the transmitter output; (D) Install a band-pass filter on the television receiver.

3AG2-1.1 What circuit passes electrical energy above a certain frequency and attenuates electrical energy below that frequency? (A) A band-pass filter; (B) A high-pass filter; (C) An input filter; (D) A low-pass filter.

3AG2-2.1 Where is the proper place to install a high-pass filter? (A) At the antenna terminals of a television receiver; (B) Between a transmitter and a Transmatch; (C) Between a Transmatch and the transmission line; (D) On a transmitting antenna.

3AG2-2.2 Your Amateur Radio transmissions cause interference to your television receiver even though you have installed a low-pass filter at the transmitter output. What is one possible solution for this problem? (A) Install a high-pass filter at the transmitter terminals; (B) Install a high-pass filter at the television antenna terminals; (C) Install a low-pass filter at the television antenna terminals also; (D) Install a band-pass filter at the television antenna terminals.

3AG3-1.1 What circuit attenuates electrical energy above a certain frequency and below a lower frequency? (A) A band-pass filter; (B) A high-pass filter; (C) An input filter; (D) A low-pass filter.

3AG3-1.2 What general range of RF energy does a band-pass filter reject? (A) All frequencies above a specified frequency; (B) All frequencies below a specified frequency; (C) All frequencies above the upper limit of the band in question; (D) All frequencies above a specified frequency and below a lower specified frequency.

3AG3-2.1 The IF stage of a communications receiver uses a filter with a peak response at the intermediate frequency. What term describes this filter response? (A) A band-pass filter; (B) A high-pass filter; (C) An input filter; (D) A low-pass filter.

3AG4-1.1 What circuit is likely to be found in all types of receivers? (A) An audio filter; (B) A beat frequency oscillator; (C) A detector; (D) An RF amplifier.

3AG4-1.2 What type of transmitter does this block diagram represent? (Please refer to Diagram 3AG4-1.2) (A) A simple packet-radio transmitter; (B) A simple crystal-controlled transmitter; (C) A single-sideband transmitter; (D) A VFO-controlled transmitter.

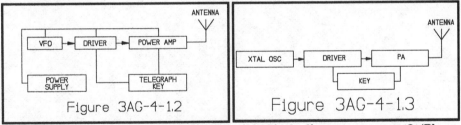

Figure 3AG-4-1.2   Figure 3AG-4-1.3

3AG4-1.3 What type of transmitter does this block diagram represent? (Please refer to Diagram 3AG4-1.3) (A) A simple packet-radio transmitter; (B) A simple crystal-controlled transmitter; (C) A single-sideband transmitter; (D) A VFO-controlled transmitter.

3AG4-1.4 What is the unlabeled block (?) in this diagram? (Please refer to Diagram 3AG4-1.4) (A) An AGC circuit; (B) A detector; (C) A power supply; (D) A VFO circuit.

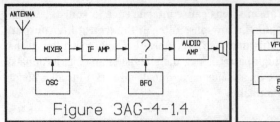

Figure 3AG-4-1.4

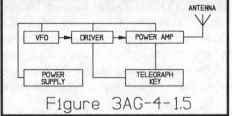

Figure 3AG-4-1.5

3AG4-1.5 What type of device does this block diagram represent? (Please refer to Diagram 3AG4-1.5) (A) A double-conversion receiver; (B) A variable-frequency oscillator; (C) A simple superheterodyne receiver; (D) A simple CW transmitter.

3AG4-2.1 What type of device does this block diagram represent? (Please refer to Diagram 3AG4-2.1) (A) A double-conversion receiver; (B) A variable-frequency oscillator; (C) A simple superheterodyne receiver; (D) A simple FM receiver.

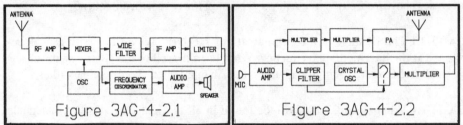

Figure 3AG-4-2.1

Figure 3AG-4-2.2

3AG4-2.2 What is the unlabeled block (?) in this diagram? (Please refer to Diagram 3AG4-2.2) (A) A band-pass filter; (B) A crystal oscillator; (C) A reactance modulator; (D) A rectifier modulator.

Chapter

Signals and Emissions

In order to insure that you understand the concept and characteristics of signals, you will be asked two questions from Subelement 2H and 3AH.

C hapter A mentioned that some of the testing terminology had changed as a result of revisions to Part 97. As you recall, Part 97 is the section of the FCC Rules and Regulations which pertain to Amateurs.

A couple of terms have never changed since the beginning days of our service. The terms are **telegraphy** and **telephony**. Remember telegraphy means telegraph. Picture the old timer, with a transparent green brim shielding his eyes, hunched over the sounder and telegraph key sending messages down the line. To remember that telephony means voice, simply picture the telephone that you talk into each day.

Modulation — Now that you are an expert in understanding kiloHertz, standing waves, Q-signals and so on, you should have no trouble understanding the concept of **modulation**. Modulation is defined as the process of varying the carrier wave in order to convey information. If there is no modulation present on the carrier, the wave is said to be unmodulated. (3AH1.1)(3AH2-1.1)

What is a carrier and where does it come from? Figure H.1 shows the basic ingredients of a typical transmitter. A crystal oscillator generates a radio frequency of high accuracy and stability. The energy is very weak and must be amplified in order to supply useful power to the antenna system. Thus the oscillator is used to drive a

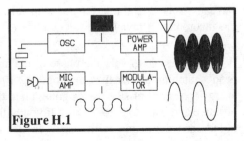

Figure H.1

radio frequency power amplifier to its maximum power rating. This RF energy produced by the power amplifier is referred to as the carrier.

The modulator is an audio frequency amplifier which increases the tiny voltage from the microphone and applies this voice energy to the RF power amplifier. By connecting the modulator in series with the RF power amplifier, the voltage applied to the stage (either a tube or transistor) is made to increase or decrease. In this manner, the amplified carrier energy can be amplitude modulated by the tiny voltage original produced by the microphone.

Figure H.1 shows the result. The carrier provides a continuous "stream" of RF energy which is sent to the antenna. The modulation applied to the RF power amplifier causes the RF output level to increase or decrease in exact proportion to the tiny microphone voltage.

From the drawing, you might conclude that the modulation causes the carrier to increase and decrease. Don't concluded this, however, because you would be 100% wrong. In actual fact, the carrier doesn't move up and down at all! The modulation voltage actually produces additional energy called sidebands. If there is no modulation, no sidebands are created and this is referred to as a test signal. (3AH2-1.2)(3AH3.1)(3AH3.2)

Anything that adds intelligence to the carrier is referred to as modulation. For example, if we turn the carrier on an off with a telegraph key, this is a form of amplitude modulation. Since the signal varies from nothing to maximum, it certainly represents a change in amplitude. By using a standard symbol like Morse code, we add intelligence to the carrier.

It is not necessary to change the amplitude of the carrier to add intelligence. It can be modified in a number of other ways. For example the frequency of the carrier wave can be modified slightly. This is called frequency modulation. Frequency modulated telephony is almost universally used on the VHF bands where Technicians operate. It is the favorite mode since it provides good audio fidelity and a strong signal relative to background noise. (3AH4.1)(3AH2-7.1)(3AH2-7.2)

The amount the frequency varies with modulation is referred to as the deviation of the transmitter. The louder one speaks, the greater the deviation. Obviously if someone gets excited and the amplitude of the audio modulating signal is too high, the excursions or deviation of the carrier frequency can become excessive. When this happens, the signal can cause splatter and interference with adjacent channels. This is why all FM transmitters incorporate a deviation limiter circuit. (3AH7-1.1)(3AH7-2.1)(3AH7-2.2)

It is also possible to vary the phase of the radio frequency energy. It may take a bit of head-scratching to visualize the concept of phase modulation. You will recall that RF energy is a series of sine waves going up to positive, passing through zero and down to negative and back to zero. Picture if you will, the voice being able to vary the position of the sine wave at any given instant. In other words, in phase modulated equipment, the energy can take more or less time to reach a peak depending on the voice information impressed on the carrier by the modulator. This is what phase modulation does and the modulator to accomplish this is called a reactance modulator. Phase modulation is quite similar to frequency modulation and can be detected by the same type of receivers. (3AH2-8.2)(3AH5.1)(3AH5.2)

Bandwidth — From the preceding explanations you can correctly conclude that some emissions take up more spectrum space (bandwidth) than others, A CW transmitter, for example requires the least spectrum of any signal. An RTTY signal requires less space than a voice signal like single sideband. Frequency modulation requires more bandwidth than any of the preceding modes. On the scale of bandwidth, from least to most, you find CW, RTTY, SSB and FM. Since various emissions occupy a wider frequency range (bandwidth) than others, professional communications receivers have selectable filters to optimize reception. Essentially the filter let's though just enough width to hold the particular emission type and chops off the frequencies beyond that. (3AH6.1)(3AH6.2)

Emission Designators

One of the revised areas in Part 97 relates to "Signals and Emissions". If you have study or testing material which refers to A1A, A3J or F1B and so on, they are out-of-date. These symbols are **emission designators** used by the International Telecommunications Union (ITU). They were eliminated from Amateur tests when Part 97 was simplified in 1989.

The FCC no longer uses the ITU emission designations in the Amateur Service. However, there are still two questions relative to these ITU designators in the question pool. The first symbol in the designator describes the type of information to be transmitted, while the second is the nature of the modulating signal. (3AH2-5.2)(3AH2-6.1)

Emission designators are simply a means of identifying what sort of signal you are transmitting. The term A1A was used to identify turning the radio frequency signal from your transmitter on and off with a telegraph key. In the Technician test, it is simply called **CW (continuous wave)** keying. This is considered a form of amplitude modulation since the signal amplitude varies between zero and maximum. CW is the internationally accepted means of sending Morse code telegraphy messages. (2H1-1.1) (2H1-1.2)(3AH2-2.1)(3AH2-2.2)

When FM radiotelephone equipment is used for Morse code work, it is not practical to key the transmitter. Rather, the microphone is replaced by an audio keyer. A tone is turned off and on with a telegraph key. This is called modulated CW or simply the emission designator MCW. (3AH2-4.1)(3AH2-4.2)3AH2-5.1)(3AH2-5.3)

Morse is not the only form of intelligence that can be impressed on a FM transmitter using tones. Many handheld radios incorporate a Touch-Tone pad for controlling repeaters and making telephone calls. RTTY and packet information can be transmitted using two audio tones to represent ones and zeros. (3AH2-6.2)

Radio teletype, or RTTY, was discussed in Chapter B (*see Digital Procedures*). In the Technician test, radio teletype is defined as a **narrow band, direct printing telegraphy** mode. It's a lot easier to simply say "RTTY" and that is also the correct emission designator. (2H1-2.1)

Even though RTTY is considered a form of telegraphy, "signal-no signal" is not used to represent the digital one's and zero's. A scheme like this might work, but it would be prone to error. Noise and static could be received in the no signal period.

Rather than turn the RTTY signal on and off, a keying method involving two alternate frequencies is used. Thus a carrier output is always present. The steady carrier output frequency represents a "one". By shifting the frequency a few hundred Hertz during a zero period, we can send digital information with a continuous carrier. Noise and interference does not create errors since there is never a "no-signal" period. This scheme is called **frequency shift keying** (or **FSK**) and is the standard method of transmitting digital information (either RTTY or packet) via radio. (2H1-2.2)(3AH2-3.1)(3AH2-3.2)

On the VHF bands it is not so easy to detect the change of a few hundred Hz. Above 30 MHz, voice emissions are usually frequency modulation (and the emission designator is FM phone), one-zero data is transmitted by using two audio tones rather than two radio frequencies. This scheme is called **audio frequency shift keying (AFSK)**. (2H1-3.1)

Another popular emission is called **single sideband**, suppressed carrier. This is a voice mode and is usually abbreviated as **SSB**. If you operate voice on 10 meters, after receiving your Novice license or "Tech-Plus" CSCE, you will use SSB equipment. A technical explanation of sideband is beyond the scope of this book but will be the subject of a future NARA publication. (2H1-4.1)

Purity of Emissions

Sometimes one hears rather "raunchy" signals on the Amateur bands. Using the RST scale, they might be graded as 5-9-0. In other words, the tone of the CW signal is terrible.

Key clicks don't count in the tone scale but they can be a problem, particularly with "home-brew" transmitters. Key clicks are caused by the sudden application or removal of power when the telegraph key is pressed and released. This creates RF emissions with an excessively square wave. In other words, the rise and fall times of the keying waveform are extremely fast. (2H2.1)

Key clicks can be completely eliminated by inserting a key click filter in the telegraph key circuitry *(see Chapter G - Filters)*. This is nothing more than a low pass filter. Remember, a low pass filter opposes a change in current. Thus it slows the rise and fall of the RF waveform. This eliminates the energy that causes spurious key clicks. (2H2.2)

Modern transmitters and transceivers all have built in keying filters to shape and soften the transmitted signal. Today key clicks are seldom heard except from the occasional "home-brewed" transmitter where the designer has forgotten to add a suitable filter.

Another keying problem, which is still heard, is called a **chirp**. This happens when an unwanted frequency shift occurs while sending Morse. If the transmitter frequency changes even a few Hz during the "dit" or "dah", it is heard at the receiving end as a "tweet" and not a pure tone.

This usually occurs due to an inadequately rated power supply. For example, let's say the transceiver draws 20 amperes during key-down periods. If the power supply can only deliver 15 amperes, the output voltage will sag during the period the key is held down. This reduced or unregulated voltage may affect the frequency determining circuit. If so, the transmitter may shift frequency slightly and the received signal will have a chirping sound to it. The cure is to have an adequately rated regulated voltage power supply connected to the transmitter. (2H3.1)(2H3.2)

Power supplies can cause another problem on both the CW and voice modes. If the power supply has a defective or inadequate electrolytic filter capacitor, it may cause a hum or buzzing sound to be superimposed on the transmitted signal. In this case the cure is to either repair or replace the power supply. (2H4.1)(2H4.2)

Spurious Emissions

Spurious emissions are created when a transmitter radiates signals outside the Amateur band during transmissions. One form of spurious signal is the harmonic. (2H7.2)

Harmonics — What is a harmonic? It is defined as the multiple of a fundamental frequency. The harmonic is considered to be a spurious or unwanted emission. The fourth harmonic of an emission at 7160 KHz is 28,640 KHz. The second harmonic of a 222 MHz signal is 444 MHz. (2H5.1)

At one time, all the high frequency (HF) Amateur bands were harmonically related. The bands were 1.8, 3.5, 7, 14, 21 and 28 MHz. Thus, if your 7 Mhz transmitter radiated a strong second harmonic signal, it would still fall in a ham band and not cause trouble to other services. Harmonic radiation was quite common with vacuum tube powered equipment since manual tuning adjustments were used to "tweak" the amplifier circuits. It was not at all unusual to have the amplifier misadjusted to a harmonic, rather than correctly tuned to the fundamental frequency.

Modern solid-state equipment does not have this problem since there are no adjustments. Harmonics are eliminated by **low pass filters** as described in Chapter G.

On the other hand, harmonic emission is more serious today with the various classes of operation in use. For example, let's say a Novice or "Tech-Plus" station operating on 7,125 KHz radiates an excessive third harmonic on 21,375 KHz. The Novice is legally permitted to operate on the 7 Mhz frequency, but not in that portion of the 21 MHz band. The excessive harmonic signals will be noticed by an FCC monitoring station and a citation will result. (2H5.2)

Parasitics — Spurious emissions are not always harmonic multiples of the fundamental. Transmitter circuits which are supposed to only amplify can become unstable and oscillate. This can cause spurious signals, called **parasitics**, at numerous unrelated frequencies. Parasitics can be a problem in vacuum tube linear power amplifiers. If the shielding is poor and the circuits were not properly **neutralized**, parasitics can occur. Improper neutralization means the high power output energy can reach the sensitive input circuitry. This can cause parasitic oscillations that create significant radiated spurious emissions. (2H7.1)

Incidentally, spurious emissions don't always radiate from your antenna system. If you were to operate a transmitter or high power linear amplifier with the covers and shields removed, the internal circuitry can directly radiate spurious emissions which interfere with nearby television sets. The direct radiation energy bypasses and avoids the spurious emission elimination filters. (2H7.3)

Splatter — Turning up the microphone gain on a transmitter can cause a problem called **overmodulation**. Overmodulation can cause a transmitted voice to spread out or **splatter** and interfere with stations operating on nearby frequencies. The same effect can occur if you turn on speech processing circuits when the microphone volume is too high. (2H7.4)(2H7.5)(2H7.6)

Safety

You will recall that you were admonished in Chapter D to be cautious regarding the effects and dangers of radio frequency energy. You may be asked a question or two on safety in this part of the Technician test.

Spealking of safety, be sure to wear your helmet when operating bicycle mobile." Meet Steve Roberts, KV8OVA, and his Winnebiko II. Steve describs himself and a "high-tech nomad."

Remember the microwave oven example. Radio frequency energy can elevate temperatures sufficiently to cook meat (your meat!) so never allow yourself (or anyone else) to be exposed to concentrated radio energy fields near antennas of all types. (2H6.1)

Never stand in front of a parabolic dish microwave antenna. The RF energy radiated by the antenna is focused by the shape of the dish. If you are near the focal point of the energy it can also cause bodily harm. If it is necessary to make adjustments to any antenna, make sure the transmitter power is off and cannot be accidentally activated. (2H6.2)

To follow this warning when installing a mobile antenna, where is the best place for whip antenna on the car body? In the middle of the roof, of course. The high intensity radio energy from the mobile transmitter would not penetrate the roof nor enter the windows from this location. (2H6.3)

You have been reminded, in various sections of this book, that a strong electrical field exists around a transmitting antenna. There is also a significant voltage on the antenna conductor itself. If you doubt this, take a standard 40 watt fluorescent lamp and touch one of the two end-pins to the tip of your mobile or base station antenna. Suprise! It lights brightly near the antenna. Remember this if you ever mount an antenna in the attic of your home. It should be well insulated to prevent a fire and to keep anyone from touching it. (3AH2-8.1)

With this background, see how you do answering the following questions.

SUBELEMENT 2H (2 questions)

2H1-1.1 What keying method is used to transmit CW? (A) Frequency-shift keying of a radio-frequency signal; (B) On/off keying of a radio-frequency signal; (C) Audio-frequency-shift keying of an oscillator tone; (D) On/off keying of an audio-frequency signal.

2H1-1.2 What emission type describes international Morse code telegraphy messages? (A) RTTY; (B) Image; (C) CW; (D) Phone.

2H1-2.1 What emission type describes narrow-band direct-printing telegraphy emissions? (A) RTTY; (B) Image; (C) CW; (D) Phone.

2H1-2.2 What keying method is used to transmit RTTY messages? (A) Frequency-shift keying of a radio-frequency signal; (B) On/off keying of a radio-frequency signal; (C) Digital pulse-code keying of an unmodulated carrier; (D) On/off keying of an audio-frequency signal.

2H1-3.1 What emission type describes frequency-modulated voice transmissions? (A) FM phone; (B) Image; (C) CW; (D) Single sideband phone.

2H1-4.1 What emission type describes single sideband suppressed-carrier (SSB) voice transmissions? (A) FM phone; (B) Image; (C) CW; (D) Sideband phone.

2H2.1 What does the term key click mean? (A) The mechanical noise caused by closing a straight key too hard; (B) The clicking noise from an excessively square CW keyed waveform; (C) The sound produced in a receiver from a CW signal faster than 20 WPM; (D) The sound of a CW signal being copied on an AM receiver.

2H2.2 How can key clicks be eliminated? (A) By reducing your keying speed to less than 20 WPM; (B) By increasing power to the maximum allowable level; (C) By using a power supply with better regulation; (D) By using a key-click filter.

2H3.1 What does the term chirp mean? (A) A distortion in the receiver audio circuits; (B) A high-pitched audio tone transmitted with a CW signal; (C) A slight shift in oscillator frequency each time a CW transmitter is keyed; (D) A slow change in transmitter frequency as the circuit warms up.

2H3.2 What can be done to the power supply of a CW transmitter to avoid chirp? (A) Resonate the power supply filters; (B) Regulate the power supply output voltages; (C) Use a buffer amplifier between the transmitter output and the feed line; (D) Hold the power supply current to a fixed value.

2H4.1 What is a common cause of superimposed hum? (A) Using a non-resonant random-wire antenna; (B) Sympathetic vibrations from a nearby transmitter; (C) Improper neutralization of the transmitter output stage; (D) A defective filter capacitor in the power supply.

2H4.2 What type of problem can a bad power-supply filter capacitor cause in a transmitter or receiver? (A) Sympathetic vibrations in nearby receivers; (B) A superimposed hum or buzzing sound; (C) Extreme changes in antenna resonance; (D) Imbalance in the mixers.

2H5.1 What is the 4th harmonic of a 7,160 kHz signal? (A) 28,640 kHz; (B) 35,800 kHz; (C) 28,160 kHz; (D) 1,790 kHz.

2H5.2 You receive an FCC Notice of Violation stating that your station was heard on 21,375 kHz. At the time listed on the notice, you were operating on 7,125 kHz. What is a possible cause of this violation? (A) Your transmitter has a defective power-supply filter capacitor; (B) Your CW keying speed was excessively fast; (C) Your transmitter was radiating excess harmonic signals; (D) Your transmitter has a defective power-supply filter choke.

2H6.1 What may happen to body tissues that are exposed to large amounts of UHF or microwave RF energy? (A) The tissue may be damaged because of the heat produced; (B) The tissue may suddenly be frozen; (C) The tissue may be immediately destroyed because of the Maxwell Effect; (D) The tissue may become less resistant to cosmic radiation.

2H6.2 What precaution should you take before working near a high-gain UHF or microwave antenna (such as a parabolic, or dish antenna)? (A) Be certain the antenna is FCC type accepted; (B) Be certain the antenna and transmitter are properly grounded; (C) Be certain the transmitter cannot be operated; (D) Be certain the antenna safety interlocks are in place.

2H6.3 You are installing a VHF or UHF mobile radio in your vehicle. What is the best location to mount the antenna on the vehicle to minimize any danger from RF exposure to the driver or passengers? (A) In the middle of the roof; (B) Along the top of the windshield; (C) On either front fender; (D) On the trunk lid.

2H7.1 You discover that your tube-type transmitter power amplifier is radiating spurious emissions. What is the most likely cause of this problem? (A) Excessively fast keying speed; (B) Undermodulation; (C) Improper neutralization; (D) Tank-circuit current dip at resonance.

2H7.2 Your transmitter radiates signals outside the Amateur band where you are transmitting. What term describes this radiation? (A) Off-frequency emissions; (B) Transmitter chirp; (C) Incidental radiation; (D) Spurious emissions.

2H7.3 What problem can occur if you operate your transmitter without the cover and other shielding in place? (A) Your transmitter can radiate spurious emissions; (B) Your transmitter may radiate a "chirpy" signal; (C) The final amplifier efficiency of your transmitter may decrease; (D) You may cause splatter interference to other stations operating on nearby frequencies.

2H7.4 What type of interference will you cause if you operate your SSB transmitter with the microphone gain adjusted too high? (A) You may cause digital interference to computer equipment in your neighborhood; (B) You may cause splatter interference to other stations operating on nearby frequencies; (C) You may cause atmospheric interference in the air around your antenna; (D) You may cause processor interference to the microprocessor in your rig.

2H7.5 What may happen if you adjust the microphone gain or deviation control on your FM transmitter too high? (A) You may cause digital interference to computer equipment in your neighborhood; (B) You may cause interference to other stations operating on nearby frequencies; (C) You may cause atmospheric interference in the air around your antenna; (D) You may cause processor interference to the microprocessor in your rig.

2H7.6 What type of interference can excessive amounts of speech processing in your SSB transmitter cause? (A) You may cause digital interference to computer equipment in your neighborhood; (B) You may cause splatter interference to other stations operating on nearby frequencies; (C) You may cause atmospheric interference in the air around your antenna; (D) You may cause processor interference to the microprocessor in your rig.

SUBELEMENT 3AH (2 questions).

3AH1.1 What is the meaning of the term modulation? (A) The process of varying some characteristic of a carrier wave for the purpose of conveying information; (B) The process of recovering audio information from a received signal; (C) The process of increasing the average power of a single sideband transmission; (D) The process of suppressing the carrier in a single sideband transmitter.

3AH2-1.1 If the modulator circuit of your FM transmitter fails, what emission type would likely result? (A) An unmodulated carrier wave; (B) A phase modulated carrier wave; (C) An amplitude modulated carrier wave; (D) A frequency modulated carrier wave.

3AH2-1.2 What emission does not have sidebands resulting from modulation? (A) AM phone; (B) Test; (C) FM phone; (D) RTTY.

3AH2-2.1 What is the FCC emission designator for a Morse code telegraphy signal produced by switching the transmitter output on and off? (A) Test; (B) AM phone; (C) CW; (D) RTTY.

3AH2-2.2 What is CW? (A) Morse code telegraphy using amplitude modulation; (B) Morse code telegraphy using frequency modulation; (C) Morse code telegraphy using phase modulation; (D) Morse code telegraphy using pulse modulation.

3AH2-3.1 What is RTTY? (A) Amplitude-keyed telegraphy; (B) Frequency- shift-keyed telegraphy; (C) Frequency-modulated telephony; (D) Phase-modulated telephony.

3AH2-3.2 What is the emission designation for telegraphy by frequency shift keying without the use of a modulating tone? (A) RTTY; (B) MCW; (C) CW; (D) Single sideband phone.

3AH2-4.1 What emission type results when an on/off keyed audio tone is applied to the microphone input of an FM transmitter? (A) RTTY; (B) MCW; (C) CW; (D) Single sideband phone.

3AH2-4.2 What is tone-modulated international Morse code telegraphy? (A) Telephony produced by audio fed into a FM transmitter; (B) Telegraphy produced by on/off keyed audio tone fed into a CW transmitter; (C) Telegraphy produced by on/off keying of the carrier amplitude; (D) Telegraphy produced by an on/off keyed audio tone fed into a FM transmitter.

3AH2-5.1 What is the emission designated as "MCW"? (A) Frequency-modulated telegraphy using audio tones; (B) Frequency-modulated telephony; (C) Frequency-modulated facsimile using audio tones; (D) Phase-modulated television.

3AH2-5.2 In an ITU emission designator like A1A, what does the first symbol describe? (A) The nature of the signal modulating the main carrier; (B) The type of the information to be transmitted; (C) The speed of a radiotelegraph transmission; (D) The type of modulation of the main carrier.

3AH2-5.3 What emission type results when an AF shift keyer is connected to the microphone jack of an FM phone transmitter? (A) SS; (B) RTTY; (C) MCW; (D) Image.

3AH2-6.1 In an ITU emission designator like F3B, what does the second symbol describe? (A) The nature of the signal modulating the main carrier; (B) The type of modulation of the main carrier; (C) The type of information to be transmitted; (D) The frequency modulation index of a carrier.

3AH2-6.2 How would you transmit packet using an FM 2-meter transceiver? (A) Use your telegraph key to interrupt the carrier wave; (B) Modulate your FM transmitter with audio tones from a terminal node controller; (C) Use your microphone for telephony; (D) Use your touch-tone (DTMF) key pad to signal in Morse code.

3AH2-7.1 What type of emission results when speaking into the microphone of a 2-meter FM handheld transceiver? (A) Amplitude modulated phone; (B) Code telegraphy; (C) An unmodulated carrier wave; (D) Frequency modulated phone.

3AH2-7.2 What emission type do most 2-meter FM transmitters transmit? (A) Interrupted pure carrier wave; (B) Frequency modulated phone; (C) Single sideband voice emissions; (D) Amplitude modulated carrier waves.

3AH2-8.1 What is the most important consideration when installing a 10-meter dipole inside an attic? (A) It will exhibit a low angle of radiation; (B) The dipole must always be run horizontally polarized; (C) It will be covered by an insulation to prevent fire and high enough to prevent being accidentally touched during transmission; (D) Dipoles usually don't work in attics.

3AH2-8.2 Which type of transmitter will produce a frequency modulated carrier wave? (A) A CW transmitter; (B) An amplitude modulated transmitter; (C) A single-sideband transmitter; (D) A phase modulated transmitter.

3AH3.1 What is the term used to describe a constant-amplitude radio-frequency signal? (A) An RF carrier; (B) An AF carrier; (C) A sideband carrier; (D) A subcarrier.

3AH3.2 What is another name for an unmodulated radio-frequency signal? (A) An AF carrier; (B) An RF carrier; (C) A sideband carrier; (D) A subcarrier.

3AH4.1 What characteristic makes FM telephony especially well-suited for local VHF/UHF radio communications? (A) Good audio fidelity and intelligibility under weak-signal conditions; (B) Better rejection of multipath distortion than the AM modes; (C) Good audio fidelity and high signal-to-noise ratio above a certain signal amplitude threshold; (D) Better carrier frequency stability than the AM modes.

3AH5.1 What emission is produced by a transmitter using a reactance modulator? (A) CW; (B) Unmodulated carrier; (C) Single sideband, suppressed-carrier phone; (D) Phase modulated phone.

3AH5.2 What other emission does phase modulation most resemble? (A) Amplitude modulation; (B) Pulse modulation; (C) Frequency modulation; (D) Single sideband modulation.

3AH6.1 Many communications receivers have several IF filters that can be selected by the operator. Why do these filters have different bandwidths? (A) Because some ham bands are wider than others; (B) Because different bandwidths help increase the receiver sensitivity; (C) Because different bandwidths improve S-meter readings; (D) Because some emission types occupy a wider frequency range than others.

3AH6.2 List the following signals in order of increasing bandwidth (narrowest signal first): CW, FM voice, RTTY, SSB voice. (A) RTTY, CW, SSB voice, FM voice; (B) CW, FM voice, RTTY, SSB voice; (C) CW, RTTY, SSB voice, FM voice; (D) CW, SSB voice, RTTY, FM voice.

3AH7-1.1 To what is the deviation of a FM transmission proportional? (A) Only the frequency of the audio modulating signal; (B) The frequency and the amplitude of the audio modulating signal; (C) The duty cycle of the audio modulating signal; (D) Only the amplitude of the audio modulating signal.

3AH7-2.1 What is the result of overdeviation in a FM transmitter? (A) Increased transmitter power consumption; (B) Out-of-channel emissions (splatter); (C) Increased transmitter range; (D) Inadequate carrier suppression.

3AH7-2.2 What is splatter? (A) Interference to adjacent signals caused by excessive transmitter keying speeds; (B) Interference to adjacent signals caused by improper transmitter neutralization; (C) Interference to adjacent signals caused by overmodulation of a transmitter; (D) Interference to adjacent signals caused by parasitic oscillations at the antenna.

Chapter

I

Antennas and Feedlines

This final section of the Technician test will present three questions each from Subelement 2I and 3AI.

A ntennas are one of the most fascinating subjects in the field of Amateur radio. Amateurs have many opinions as to the relative merits of various types of antenna. Some claim the **beam** is better while others swear by the **cubical quad.** Some rugged individualists insist that a single **vertical** is best of all for working distant stations.

An Amateur antenna need not be complicated. It can be as simple as stringing up a random length of wire such as that shown in Figure I.1. For transmitting, a random length antenna must be used with an impedance matching device. More about that later.

Antennas come in all shapes and sizes. A number of years ago, it was popular to design vertical antennas using soda cans soldered together. The operating frequency was de-

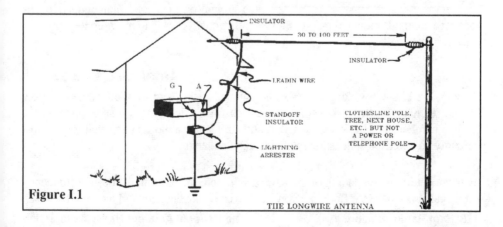

Figure I.1

THE LONGWIRE ANTENNA

signed by varying the number of cans used in order to make the correct length. Unfortunately, with aluminum cans, this is no longer a practical way to make a vertical antenna.

Resonant Frequency

The correct length? Yes — the length of an antenna is crucially important to its' performance. As you might expect, reducing the length reduces the antenna performance. Surprisingly, the same thing happens if you increase the length of the antenna! There is a critical length where the antenna works the best. Maximum voltage is induced in the antenna when the length of the antenna is the same as the wavelength of the radio signal reaching it. This is called the **resonant frequency** of the antenna.

The simplest and best performing antenna is called the **half wave dipole**. The length, from tip-to-tip is exactly one-half the wavelength of a specific frequency. Imagine for a moment that you could tape measure the distance between the peaks and valley's of the signal. If you measured from one positive peak to an adjacent positive peak, the distance would be the wavelength for that frequency. The distance from a positive peak to a negative peak (or the other way around) would be the half wavelength.

Antenna Directivity

The dipole has a directive characteristic. Figure I.2 shows the radiation (and reception sensitivity) characteristics of a dipole antenna looking down on it from above. Note that the signal (and reception sensitivity) is maximum broadside to the dipole element. There is a very deep null off the ends of the antenna. This, by the way, is the basis for direction finding equipment. The dipole is rotated until the null is indicated. The end of the dipole points in the direction of the station you are trying to locate by direction finding.

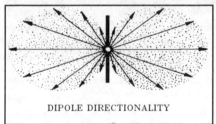

DIPOLE DIRECTIONALITY

Figure I.2- A dipole is directional broadside to its length, with very low pickup from the ends. Arrows indicate sensitivity in given directions.

You can also see that if the dipole is positioned vertically it will radiate equally well in the vertical plane. There will still be a null above the antenna. The null below the antenna doesn't matter since a vertical antenna is usually a quarter wave and is mounted on the ground or a car top. The conductive surface the antenna is mounted on provides the other quarter wave to make up the optimum quarter wavelength.

Antenna Calculations

How do we know how long to make the antenna for a specific frequency? We use a "magic number" called a **constant**. In the case of a half wave dipole antenna, the "magic number" is **468**. Remember that number — it's important and you will almost certainly be asked a test question related to antenna length.

You can determine the length of the half wave dipole by dividing the desired frequency (in megaHertz) into 468. Let's say you want to calculate the length of a dipole for 3,725 kHz in the 80 meter Novice band. First, we must convert kiloHertz to megaHertz. As I'm sure you remember from Chapter E, 3,725 kHz is the same as 3.725 MHz. You can round off this off to 3.7 and divide that number into 468. The answer is that a dipole for 3.7 MHz is 126.5 feet or 126 feet, six inches. (2I1.1)(2I1.2)(2I1.3)(2I1.4)(2I1.5)

Incidentally, determining the answer to this sort of test question will be much easier if you have a calculator. You are permitted to bring a calculator to your testing session.

How do you calculate the length of a quarter wave antenna such as a vertical that you might install on your car? Easy. Simply calculate it as a half wave dipole as shown above and then divide by two. Thus, if you were making a quarter wave vertical for 3,725 kHz out of soda cans, how tall would it be? Divide the number you calculated above and the answer is 63 feet, 3 inches. Now, if you like, you can measure a soda can and see how many if will require to make the antenna. This question is not on your test, however! But, always read a test question carefully to see if the length for a quarter or half wave antenna is required and if the frequency is in kHz or MHz. The formula, once again is 468 divided by the frequency in MHz. (2I2.1)(2I2.2)(2I2.3)(2I2.4)

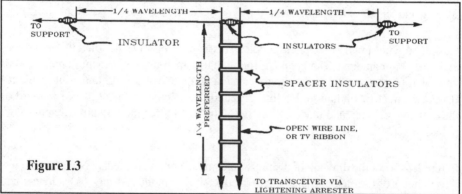

Figure I.3

From the formula you can see that as the frequency is lowered, the antenna becomes longer. By the same token, if an antenna length is shortened, its' resonant frequency increases. If the antenna is lengthened or shortened, the resonant frequency is decreased or increased respectively. (2I2.5)

So far we have spoken of half and quarter wave antenna. With special designs, it is possible to make antennas which are resonant and radiate properly but are not a multiple of a quarter wavelength. A 5/8 wave antenna radiates a stronger signal than a 1/4 wave and is said to have somewhat more gain over a quarter wave reference. This type of antenna is also favored because it has a lower angle of radiation. In other words, like the vertical antenna discussed above, the 5/8 wavelength antenna radiates equally in all compass directions with most of the radiation going close to the horizon. For this reason, the 5/8 wavelength antenna is very popular for mobile installations. (2I3.1)(2I3.2)

This may be confusing since it was stated earlier that an antenna works best when it is a multiple of a quarter wave. By using special networks at the base of the antenna, it is possible to make an antenna other than a quarter or half wavelength extremely efficient.

The Beam Antenna

The radiation pattern of an antenna can be modified by placing other element(s) near the radiator. This technique has been used for years in broadcasting to squirt the radio station's signal in a given direction. For example, consider a radio station broadcasting in Santa Barbara, California. The major listening audience is not to the west of the station. That's the Pacific Ocean. By adding additional elements to their antenna system, the "wasted" energy to the west can be redirected toward the land.

Strictly speaking an antenna which redirects the beam of a normally non-directional radiator is called a **beam antenna**. It produces a radiation pattern with most of the transmitted signal concentrated in a particular direction an attenuated in other directions. (2I4-1.1)(3AI1-1.1)(3AI1-1.2)

When the term "beam" is mentioned, an Amateur usually thinks of a series of rods fastened to a central support called a boom. In actual fact, this describes beam antenna for concentrating radiation in one direction, called a **Yagi**. The Yagi is actually a series of formulas, developed by a Japanese engineer, Dr. Yagi, which describes the optimum spacing and length of the elements of this type of beam antenna. (2I4-1.2)(3AI1-1.3)

He started with a half wavelength dipole. This is referred to as the directly driven element in a Yagi antenna. The good Dr. found that if an undriven element (a metal rod or wire) was placed parallel to the driven element and made about 5% longer, it would reflect or redirect the radiation. He further found that another element placed forward of the radiating element and made 5% shorter, would reinforce the forward strength of the radiation. (2I4-1.3)(3AI1-1.4)(3AI1-1.5)(3AI1-1.6)

Figure I.4 shows the drawing of a simple parasitic beam Yagi antenna. Note that the relative lengths of the elements are exaggerated to show that the reflector (A) is longer and the director (C) is shorter than the radiating element (B). If you imagine that it is an arrow head, the direction of maximum radiation is from the "point" at the left side of the drawing. (2I4-2.1)(2I4-2.2)(2I4-2.3)(2I4-2.4)(3AI1-1.7)

As more and more directors are added to the Yagi antenna, the radiation that is normally lost to the side of the antenna is redirected to the forward radiation **lobe.** As directors are added, the antenna is said to be more **directive.**

If the beam or Yagi antenna is mounted with its elements parallel to the earth, the antenna is said to be horizontally polarized. If the antenna is perpendicular with respect to the ground, it radiates a vertically polarized wave. (2I10-1.1)(2I11-1.1)

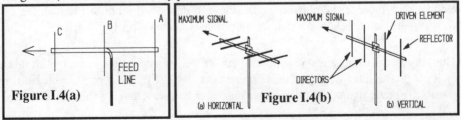

Figure I.4(a)

Figure I.4(b)

The Cubical Quad — One of the favorite antennas among Amateurs is the **cubical quad**. You can easily recognize one when driving through a neighborhood. The antenna uses two or more x-shaped spreaders with a wire stretched between the four tips in a cube shape. Each side of the wire cube is approximately one quarter wavelength long. Thus the total wire length of each loop is one wavelength at the design frequency. (3AI1-2.1)(3AI1-2.3)(3AI1-2.4)

The driven array is mounted at one end of a boom. At the other end is a similar looking structure. This is the parasitic element which usually functions like the reflector in the Yagi type antenna. There may be more parasitic elements on a huge quad but the majority employ a driven element and a reflector. Some quads have as many as three wire loops on each array. These are quads which operate on more than one band. (3AI1-2.2)

The Delta Loop — An antenna similar to the quad, but with only three sides like a triangle, is the delta loop. Each side of the triangle is a quarter wavelength. A special matching network is required to feed the delta loop with coax. In theory the antenna should not perform as well as the quad but it has a number of supporters of its performance. (3AI1-3.1)

Polarization — Antenna polarization was discussed in Chapter B - Propagation. You may wish to review the comments and theory before proceeding. At the risk of confusing you, some comments on the cubical quad are in order. Many fans of the cubical quad antenna believe it radiates electromagnetic wave with both vertical and horizontal components. However, don't pick a fight with your Volunteer Examiner over this point. Just remember the following explains the accepted answers.

How an antenna is mounted determines on which plane its radiated energy will travel. If the elements of the dipole are mounted horizontally, the electric lines of force it emits will travel parallel to the earth's surface. This is also true for a cubical quad if the fed point is at the center or corner of a horizontal element. The radiation will be horizontally polarized. This is true even if the array is rotated 45 degrees so the corners are at the top and bottom of the antenna. (3AI2-1.1)(3AI2-1.2)(3AI2-1.3)

If the feed point is at the center or corner of a vertical wire of the quad, the electromagnetic waves will be vertically polarized with respect to the earth's surface. (3AI2-2.4)(3AI12-2.5)

If a dipole is mounted so that it is perpendicular to the earth's surface, the antenna will radiate electromagnetic waves that are vertically polarized, that is, perpendicular to the earth's surface. This is the polarity most commonly used in VHF work since many of the stations are mobile. Automobiles do not lend themselves to the installation of horizontally polarized antenna systems. This is somewhat unfortunate since most man-made electrical noise and interference is also vertically polarized. There would be some interference rejection on VHF if it were of the opposite polarization. (3AI2-2.1)(3AI2-2.2)(3AI2-2.3)

Transmission Lines

With the exception of hand-helds, antennas are seldom located near the Amateur radio station equipment. It is necessary to route the radio frequency from the transmitter to the antenna and the energy intercepted by the antenna to the receiver. The medium to accomplish this is called the **transmission line**.

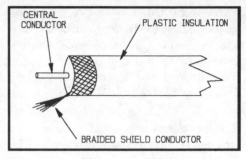

The most popular form of transmission line is called **coaxial cable.** It is characterized as round and is usually covered with black plastic weatherproof insulation, as shown in the accompanying drawing. Since it is weatherproof, it can be buried in the ground. It's 50 ohm impedance rating matches that of Amateur receiving and transmitting equipment.

Inside the coax cable, there is a central conductor, either solid or stranded. This is surrounded by a high quality, high frequency insulation, usually polystyrene. On top of this is a braided shield of copper or tin plated copper wire. (2I6.1)(2I6.2)(2I6.3)(2I6.4)

Physically coax is like a wooden pencil. The lead is the central conductor, the wood is the insulation and the yellow paint is the shield braid and the outer insulation. By maintaining a constant wire size and spacing, the coaxial cable exhibits a characteristic impedance, usually 50 or 75 ohms. The 50 ohm type is the most common for Amateur radio work since most receivers and transmitter are designed to match this impedance. Seventy five ohm cable is used for cable television systems and other applications requiring a higher impedance. The advantage of coaxial cable is that all the radiation is carried inside the shielded "pipe." It is unaffected by nearby metallic objects and the cable closely matches the impedance of most common amateur antennas. (2I6.5)

Balanced Feeds — So far we have discussed only unbalanced systems using coaxial cable. Unbalanced means a transmission line with one conductor carrying the RF energy and the other connected to ground. (3AI4-1.2)

Twin lead transmission lines are popular when used with an antenna coupler or other devices intended to match the 50 ohm impedance of the transmitter/receiver to the unknown impedance of an antenna. Twin lead or parallel conductor transmission line has two wires held apart a specific distance by an insulating material. The insulator can be continuous like the chocolate brown television wire or it can utilize individual insulator or spreaders spaced along the length of the line. This type of transmission line is sometimes called ladder line because of the similarity in appearance to that of a ladder (see Figure I.3). (2I7.1)(2I7.5)

A mismatch situation might occur if one tried to use a 40 meter antenna on the 15 or 20 meter band. It would not be the right length and would exhibit a high **SWR (standing wave ratio)**. An antenna that is not resonant (the wrong length) simply won't work with a coaxial cable transmission line. The open wire lead can be used, however, since it will withstand a much higher SWR than coaxial cable. The antenna coupler can be used to match the high impedance of the antenna to the fixed 50 ohm output impedance of the transmitter and receiver. (2I7.2)(2I7.3)(2I7.4)(3AI3-3.2)

A typical open wire transmission line such as TV twin-lead, is used with the antenna in Figure I.3. This type of transmission line is characterized as two parallel wires held apart at constant spacing by an insulating material (usually polystyrene).

There are disadvantages to this type of transmission line. It must be spaced well away from nearby metal object or they can absorb some of the transmitter power. For example, if the open wire transmission line is run near the telephone wires coming into your home, you might actually hear your voice. It can be strong enough to interfere with the telephone conversation. Another disadvantage is open wire transmission line must be used with an antenna coupler.

SWR — Once again the subject of standing waves rears it electromagnetic head in our discussions. The subject has been previously discussed. You may wish to review this material before proceeding.

Standing waves on a transmission line results when there is an impedance mismatch, usually between the antenna and the line. The term ratio describes the level of the maximum to minimum voltage on the transmission line. (3AI3-1.1)(3AI3-1.2)

Let's see if we can acutally visualize what happens. I'm going to feed one watt of RF to a piece of 50 ohm coax. At the other end I've connected a 50 ohm, 2 watt carbon composition resistor. If we could put a meter on the center conductor of the coax, we would find it measures 7 volts at any point. This shows there are no standing waves.

Now, if I replace the resistor with one measuring 100 ohms, the voltage will now measure above and below 7 volts at various points along the cable. This indicates the presence of standing waves.

The standing waves will confuse the reading of a directional wattmeter. This instrument measures the power in the forward and reverse or reflected direction. The standing waves also cause power to be lost. The loss will increase with increasing SWR. This lost power is dissipated as heat in the coax cable, transmitter and even the antenna.(3AI3-2.1)(3AI3-2.2)(3AI3-3.1)(3AI3-3.3)

Impedance Matching

Figure I.5 shows the schematic diagram for a simple antenna coupler. It is suitable for matching the antenna system in Figure I.1. Capacitor C1 and C2 are 140 pF variables and SW is a five-position rotary switch. Coil L is 100 turns of #26 enamel wire closewound on a 1.25 inch cardboard tube, tapped at 5, 12, 36 and 50 turns.

An antenna coupler is a great matching device when located near the transmitter/receiver. But what about the case where you want to provide a match between a 35 ohm antenna and the 50 ohm transmission line. An impedance matching device is required at the antenna. (2I8.1)(2I8.2)

Some intelligent, computer controlled couplers like the SGC, Inc. "Smartuner" can be mounted right at the dipole feed-point. It uses a CPU to calculate the correct tuning adjustments and can retune itself in a fraction of a second.

The Balun — There is another device that provides a limited amount of impedance matching capability. More important, it can also be used to connect the unbalanced coaxial cable to the balanced feed-point of the dipole antenna. The device is called a **balun**. This stands for balanced-to-unbalanced. (2I9.1)(2I9.3)(3AI4-3.1)(3AI4-3.2)

Let's say you want to feed your balanced dipole with unbalanced 50 ohm coaxial cable. You could make a perfect match, by connecting a balun at the antenna.

The balun can also be used at the transmitter/receiver end of the transmission line. Consider the case where you want to connect an open wire 200 ohm parallel conductor line to your transmitter receiver. It can be connected between the parallel wire transmission line an the 50 ohm unbalanced output of your equipment. (2I9.2)

The dipole and quad mentioned earlier are balanced antenna systems. This means the antenna (or driven element in a beam) is balanced or equal on each side of the feed point. (3AI4-2.1)

A whip antenna on the roof of an automobile is certainly not balanced. The wire whip is one-half of the dipole, while the metal roof replaces the other half. This is an unbalanced antenna and is always fed with coax An unbalanced antenna (or driven element in an array) is not symmetrical or identical on each side of the feed point. (3AI4-2.2)

A balanced line is one in which neither conductor is connected to ground. An example of a balanced line is the television cable mentioned earlier. (3AI4-1.1)

Some claim that the signal pattern of an antenna is skewed to one side when an unbalanced coax is used to drive a balanced antenna. A balun can be used to correct the situation, if desired.

Figure I.5- This antenna coupler can match almost any length antenna and feedline on ham bands between 3 and 30 MHz.

Cable Loss — As we know all too well, nothing is perfect in this world. The adage certainly holds true for transmission lines carrying radio frequency energy. If we drive one end of a coax with one watt of RF, something less than one watt will emerge from the other end due to inherent loss in any transmission line.

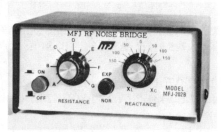

The MFJ Noise Bridge can be used to adjust an antenna for optimum performance.

Open wire line will have less loss than coaxial cable below 30 MHz. As a general rule, cable loss is proportional to size. RG-8 is about 5/8" in diameter and some of the special foam dielectric versions have exceptionally low loss. RG-58 is about the diameter of a pencil and has noticeably more loss per 100 feet. The smallest common coax is RG-174 (about the size of a soda straw) has even more loss. Thus, on a scale of loss, you would list (least to most) parallel, RG-8, RG-58 and RG-174. (3AI5-1.1)

From the preceding explanation you can see that for feeding long runs to VHF antenna, you would select RG-8 coax for the lowest loss characteristic. (3AI5-1.2)

Cable loss is proportional to length and frequency. The longer the run and the higher the frequency, the greater the loss. To minimize loss, you should cut off any excess cable after it had been routed from the antenna to the ham station. (3AI5-2.1)(3AI5-2.2)(3AI5-3.1)(3AI5-3.2)(3AI5-3.3)

Antenna Radiation and Safety

Even though it was mentioned in previous chapters, it is not repetitious to mention that radio frequency radiation can be harmful particularly if it is prolonged and/or a high intensity. Remember, when using a hand-held radio, position the antenna away from your head as far as possible. (2I5.1)

If you purchase or upgrade a hand-held radio, you have the choice of antenna styles. It is generally believed that a 1/2 wavelength whip antenna causes the least amount of radiation near the head. The short, helically wound, flexible antenna's are the worst since the energy is concentrated just a few inches above the top of the hand-held. (2I5.3)

The precaution is also valid for an antenna that you erect. It should be high and out-of-reach. This will prevent anyone from touching the antenna and getting an RF burn or receiving excessive exposure to RF radiation. Observe the same precaution with parallel transmission lines since they also have dangerously high RF voltage on the exposed open wires.(2I5.2)(3AI6-1.1)(3AI6-2.1)

Now let's tackle the questions on antenna's and transmission lines associated with this final chapter.

SUBELEMENT 2I (3 questions)

2I1.1 What is the approximate length (in feet) of a half wavelength dipole antenna for 3,725 kHz? (A) 126 ft; (B) 81 ft; (C) 63 ft; (D) 40 ft.

2I1.2 What is the approximate length (in feet) of a half wavelength dipole antenna for 7,125 kHz? (A) 84 ft; (B) 42 ft; (C) 33 ft; (D) 66 ft.

2I1.3 What is the approximate length (in feet) of a half wavelength dipole antenna for 21,125 kHz? (A) 44 ft; (B) 28 ft; (C) 22 ft; (D) 14 ft.

2I1.4 What is the approximate length (in feet) of a half wavelength dipole antenna for 28,150 kHz? (A) 22 ft; (B) 11 ft; (C) 17 ft; (D) 34 ft.

2I1.5 How is the approximate length (in feet) of a half wavelength dipole antenna calculated? (A) By substituting the desired operating frequency for f in the formula: 150 / f (in MHz); (B) By substituting the desired operating frequency for f in the formula: 234 / f (in MHz); (C) By substituting the desired operating frequency for f in the formula: 300 / f (in MHz); (D) By substituting the desired operating frequency for f in the formula: 468 / f (in MHz).

2I2.1 What is the approximate length (in feet) of a quarter wavelength vertical antenna for 3,725 kHz? (A) 20 ft; (B) 32 ft; (C) 40 ft; (D) 63 ft.

2I2.2 What is the approximate length (in feet) of a quarter wavelength vertical antenna for 7,125 kHz? (A) 11 ft; (B) 16 ft; (C) 21 ft; (D) 33 ft.

2I2.3 What is the approximate length (in feet) of a quarter wavelength vertical antenna for 21,125 kHz? (A) 7 ft; (B) 11 ft; (C) 14 ft; (D) 22 ft.

2I2.4 What is the approximate length (in feet) of a quarter wavelength vertical antenna for 28,150 kHz? (A) 5 ft; (B) 8 ft; (C) 11 ft; (D) 17 ft.

2I2.5 When a vertical antenna is lengthened, what happens to its resonant frequency? (A) It decreases; (B) It increases; (C) It stays the same; (D) It doubles.

2I3.1 Why do many Amateurs use a 5/8 wavelength vertical antenna rather than a 1/4 wavelength vertical antenna for their VHF or UHF mobile stations? (A) A 5/8 wavelength antenna can handle more power than a 1/4 wavelength antenna; (B) A 5/8 wavelength antenna has more gain than a 1/4 wavelength antenna; (C) A 5/8 wavelength antenna exhibits less corona loss than a 1/4 wavelength antenna; (D) A 5/8 wavelength antenna looks more like a CB antenna, so it does not attract as much attention as a 1/4-wavelength antenna.

2I3.2 What type of radiation pattern is produced by a 5/8 wavelength vertical antenna? (A) A pattern with most of the transmitted signal concentrated in two opposite directions; (B) A pattern with the transmitted signal going equally in all compass directions, with most of the radiation going high above the horizon; (C) A pattern with the transmitted signal going equally in all compass directions, with most of the radiation going close to the horizon; (D) A pattern with more of the transmitted signal concentrated in one direction than in other directions.

2I4-1.1 What type of antenna produces a radiation pattern with more of the transmitted signal concentrated in a particular direction than in other directions? (A) A dipole antenna; (B) A vertical antenna; (C) An isotropic antenna; (D) A beam antenna.

2I4-1.2 What type of radiation pattern is produced by a Yagi antenna? (A) A pattern with the transmitted signal spread out equally in all compass directions; (B) A pattern with more of the transmitted signal concentrated in one direction than in other directions; (C) A pattern with most of the transmitted signal concentrated in two opposite directions; (D) A pattern with most of the transmitted signal concentrated at high radiation angles.

2I4-1.3 Approximately how long (in wavelengths) is the driven element of a Yagi antenna? (A) 1/4 wavelength; (B) 1/3 wavelength; (C) 1/2 wavelength; (D) 1 wavelength. *(See Figure 2I.4 on page 180)*

2I4-2.1 On the Yagi antenna shown in Figure 2I-4, what is the name of section B? (A) Director; (B) Reflector; (C) Boom; (D) Driven element.

2I4-2.2 On the Yagi antenna shown in Figure 2I-4, what is the name of section C? (A) Director; (B) Reflector; (C) Boom; (D) Driven element.

2I4-2.3 On the Yagi antenna shown in Figure 2I-4, what is the name of section A? (A) Director; (B) Reflector; (C) Boom; (D) Driven element.

2I4-2.4 What are the names of the elements in a 3-element Yagi antenna? (A) Reflector, driven element and director; (B) Boom, mast and reflector; (C) Reflector, base and radiator; (D) Driven element, trap and feed line.

2I5.1 How should the antenna on a hand-held transceiver be positioned while you are transmitting? (A) Away from your head and away from others standing nearby; (B) Pointed in the general direction of the repeater or other station you are transmitting to; (C) Pointed in a general direction 90 degrees away from the repeater or other station you are transmitting to; (D) With the top of the antenna angled down slightly to take the most advantage of ground reflections.

2I5.2 Why should you always locate your antennas so that no one can come in contact with them while you are transmitting? (A) Such contact can detune the antenna, causing television interference; (B) To prevent RF burns and excessive exposure to RF energy; (C) The antenna is more likely to radiate harmonics when it is touched; (D) Such contact may reflect the transmitted signal back to the transmitter, damaging the final amplifier.

2I5.3 You are going to purchase a new antenna for your VHF or UHF hand-held radio. Which type of antenna is the best choice to produce a radiation pattern that will be least hazardous to your face and eyes? (A) A 1/8 wavelength whip; (B) A 7/8 wavelength whip; (C) A 1/2 wavelength whip; (D) A short, helically wound, flexible antenna.

2I6.1 What is a coaxial cable? (A) Two parallel conductors encased along the edges of a flat plastic ribbon; (B) Two parallel conductors held at a fixed distance from each other by insulating rods; (C) Two conductors twisted around each other in a double spiral; (D) A center conductor encased in insulating material which is covered by a conducting sleeve or shield.

2I6.2 What kind of antenna feed line is constructed of a center conductor encased in insulation which is then covered by an outer conducting shield and weatherproof jacket? (A) Twin lead; (B) Coaxial cable; (C) Open-wire feed line; (D) Wave guide.

2I6.3 What are some advantages of using coaxial cable as an antenna feed line? (A) It is easy to make at home, and it has a characteristic impedance in the range of most common Amateur antennas; (B) It is weatherproof, and it has a characteristic impedance in the range of most common Amateur antennas; (C) It can be operated at a higher SWR than twin lead, and it is weatherproof; (D) It is unaffected by nearby metallic objects, and has a characteristic impedance that is higher than twin lead.

2I6.4 What commonly available antenna feed line can be buried directly in the ground for some distance without adverse effects? (A) Twin lead; (B) Coaxial cable; (C) Parallel conductor; (D) Twisted pair.

2I6.5 When an antenna feed line must be located near grounded metal objects, which commonly available feed line should be used? (A) Twisted pair; (B) Twin lead; (C) Coaxial cable; (D) Ladder-line.

2I7.1 What is parallel-conductor feed line? (A) Two conductors twisted around each other in a double spiral; (B) Two parallel conductors held a uniform distance apart by insulating material; (C) A conductor encased in insulating material which is then covered by a conducting shield and a weatherproof jacket; (D) A metallic pipe whose diameter is equal to or slightly greater than the wavelength of the signal being carried.

2I7.2 How can TV-type twin lead be used as a feed line? (A) By carefully running the feed line parallel to a metal post to ensure self resonance; (B) TV-type twin lead cannot be used in an Amateur station; (C) By installing an impedance-matching network between the transmitter and feed line; (D) By using a high-power amplifier and installing a power attenuator between the transmitter and feed line.

2I7.3 What are some advantages of using parallel-conductor feed line? (A) It has a lower characteristic impedance than coaxial cable, and will operate at a higher SWR than coaxial cable; (B) It will operate at a higher SWR than coaxial cable, and it is unaffected by nearby metal objects; (C) It has a lower characteristic impedance than coaxial cable, and has less loss than coaxial cable; (D) It will operate at higher SWR than coaxial cable and it has less loss than coaxial cable.

2I7.4 What are some disadvantages of using parallel-conductor feed line? (A) It is affected by nearby metallic objects, and it has a characteristic impedance that is too high for direct connection to most Amateur transmitters; (B) It is more difficult to make at home than coaxial cable and it cannot be operated at a high SWR; (C) It is affected by nearby metallic objects, and it cannot handle the power output of a typical Amateur transmitter; (D) It has a characteristic impedance that is too high for direct connection to most Amateur transmitters, and it will operate at a high SWR.

2I7.5 What kind of antenna feed line is constructed of two conductors maintained a uniform distance apart by insulated spreaders? (A) Coaxial cable; (B) Ladder-line open conductor line; (C) Twin lead in a plastic ribbon; (D) Twisted pair.

2I8.1 A certain antenna has a feed-point impedance of 35 ohms. You want to use a 50-ohm-impedance coaxial cable to feed this antenna. What type of device will you need to connect between the antenna and the feed line? (A) A balun; (B) A SWR bridge; (C) An impedance matching device; (D) A low-pass filter.

2I8.2 A certain antenna system has an impedance of 1,000 ohms on one band. What must you use to connect this antenna system to the 50 ohm output on your transmitter? (A) A balun; (B) A SWR bridge; (C) An impedance matching device; (D) A low-pass filter.

2I9.1 The word balun is a contraction for what phrase? (A) Balanced-antenna-lobe use network; (B) Broadband-amplifier linearly unregulated; (C) Balanced unmodulator; (D) Balanced to unbalanced.

2I9.2 Where would you install a balun if you wanted to feed your dipole antenna with 450 ohm parallel-conductor feed line? (A) At the transmitter end of the feed line; (B) At the antenna feed point; (C) In only one conductor of the feed line; (D) From one conductor of the feed line to ground.

2I9.3 Where might you install a balun if you wanted to feed your dipole antenna with 50 ohm coaxial cable? (A) You might install a balun at the antenna feed point; (B) You might install a balun at the transmitter output; (C) You might install a balun 1/2 wavelength from the transmitter; (D) You might install baluns in the middle of each side of the dipole.

2I10-1.1 A four-element Yagi antenna is mounted with its elements parallel to the ground. A signal produced by this antenna will have what type of polarization? (A) Broadside polarization; (B) Circular polarization; (C) Horizontal polarization; (D) Vertical polarization.

2I11-1.1 A four-element Yagi antenna is mounted with its elements perpendicular to the ground. A signal produced by this antenna will have what type of polarization? (A) Broadside polarization; (B) Circular polarization; (C) Horizontal polarization; (D) Vertical polarization.

SUBELEMENT 3AI (3 questions).

3AI1-1.1 What antenna type best strengthens signals from a particular direction while attenuating those from other directions? (A) A beam antenna; (B) An isotropic antenna; (C) A monopole antenna; (D) A vertical antenna.

3AI1-1.2 What is a directional antenna? (A) An antenna whose parasitic elements are all constructed to be directors; (B) An antenna that radiates in direct line-of-sight propagation, but not skywave or skip propagation; (C) An antenna permanently mounted so as to radiate in only one direction; (D) An antenna that radiates more strongly in some directions than others.

3AI1-1.3 What is a Yagi antenna? (A) Half wavelength elements stacked vertically and excited in phase; (B) Quarter wavelength elements arranged horizontally and excited out of phase; (C) Half wavelength linear driven element(s) with parasitically excited parallel linear elements; (D) Quarter wavelength, triangular loop elements.

3AI1-1.4 What is the general configuration of the radiating elements of a horizontally polarized Yagi? (A) Two or more straight, parallel elements arranged in the same horizontal plane; (B) Vertically stacked square or circular loops arranged in parallel horizontal planes; (C) Two or more wire loops arranged in parallel vertical planes; (D) A vertical radiator arranged in the center of an effective RF ground plane.

3AI1-1.5 What type of parasitic beam antenna uses two or more straight metal-tubing elements arranged physically parallel to each other? (A) A delta loop antenna; (B) A quad antenna; (C) A Yagi antenna; (D) A Zepp antenna.

3AI1-1.6 How many directly driven elements does a Yagi antenna have? (A) None; they are all parasitic; (B) One; (C) Two; (D) All elements are directly driven.

3AI1-1.7 What is a parasitic beam antenna? (A) An antenna where the director and reflector elements receive their RF excitation by induction or radiation from the driven element; (B) An antenna where wave traps are used to assure magnetic coupling among the elements; (C) An antenna where all elements are driven by direct connection to the feed line; (D) An antenna where the driven element receives its RF excitation by induction or radiation from the directors.

3AI1-2.1 What is a cubical quad antenna? (A) Four parallel metal tubes, each approximately 1/2 electrical wavelength long; (B) Two or more parallel four-sided wire loops, each approximately one electrical wavelength long; (C) A vertical conductor 1/4 electrical wavelength high, fed at the bottom; (D) A center-fed wire 1/2 electrical wavelength long.

3AI1-2.2 What kind of antenna array is composed of a square full wave closed loop driven element with parallel parasitic element(s)? (A) Delta loop; (B) Cubical quad; (C) Dual rhombic; (D) Stacked Yagi.

3AI1-2.3 Approximately how long is one side of the driven element of a cubical quad antenna? (A) 2 electrical wavelengths; (B) 1 electrical wavelength; (C) 1/2 electrical wavelength; (D) 1/4 electrical wavelength.

3AI1-2.4 Approximately how long is the wire in the driven element of a cubical quad antenna? (A) 1/4 electrical wavelength; (B) 1/2 electrical wavelength; (C) 1 electrical wavelength; (D) 2 electrical wavelengths.

3AI1-3.1 What is a delta loop antenna? (A) A variation of the cubical quad antenna, with triangular elements; (B) A large copper ring, used in direction finding; (C) An antenna system composed of three vertical antennas, arranged in a triangular shape; (D) An antenna made from several coils of wire on an insulating form.

3AI2-1.1 To what does the term horizontal as applied to wave polarization refer? (A) The magnetic lines of force in the radio wave are parallel to the earth's surface; (B) The electric lines of force in the radio wave are parallel to the earth's surface; (C) The electric lines of force in the radio wave are perpendicular to the earth's surface; (D) The radio wave will leave the antenna and radiate horizontally to the destination.

3AI2-1.2 What electromagnetic wave polarization does a cubical quad antenna have when the feed point is in the center of a horizontal side? (A) Circular; (B) Helical; (C) Horizontal; (D) Vertical.

3AI2-1.3 What electromagnetic wave polarization does a cubical quad antenna have when all sides are at 45 degrees to the earth's surface and the feed point is at the bottom corner? (A) Circular; (B) Helical; (C) Horizontal; (D) Vertical.

3AI2-2.1 What is the polarization of electromagnetic waves radiated from a half-wavelength antenna perpendicular to the earth's surface? (A) Circularly polarized waves; (B) Horizontally polarized waves; (C) Parabolically polarized waves; (D) Vertically polarized waves.

3AI2-2.2 What is the electromagnetic wave polarization of most man-made electrical noise radiation in the HF-VHF spectrum? (A) Horizontal; (B) Left-hand circular; (C) Right-hand circular; (D) Vertical.

3AI2-2.3 To what does the term vertical as applied to wave polarization refer? (A) The electric lines of force in the radio wave are parallel to the earth's surface; (B) The magnetic lines of force in the radio wave are perpendicular to the earth's surface; (C) The electric lines of force in the radio wave are perpendicular to the earth's surface; (D) The radio wave will leave the antenna and radiate vertically into the ionosphere.

3AI2-2.4 What electromagnetic wave polarization does a cubical quad antenna have when the feed point is in the center of a vertical side? (A) Circular; (B) Helical; (C) Horizontal; (D) Vertical.

3AI2-2.5 What electromagnetic wave polarization does a cubical quad antenna have when all sides are at 45 degrees to the earth's surface and the feed point is at a side corner? (A) Circular; (B) Helical; (C) Horizontal; (D) Vertical.

3AI3-1.1 What is meant by the term standing wave ratio? (A) The ratio of maximum to minimum inductances on a feed line; (B) The ratio of maximum to minimum resistances on a feed line; (C) The ratio of maximum to minimum impedances on a feed line; (D) The ratio of maximum to minimum voltages on a feed line.

3AI3-1.2 What is standing wave ratio a measure of? (A) The ratio of maximum to minimum voltage on a feed line; (B) The ratio of maximum to minimum reactance on a feed line; (C) The ratio of maximum to minimum resistance on a feed line; (D) The ratio of maximum to minimum sidebands on a feed line.

3AI3-2.1 What is meant by the term forward power? (A) The power traveling from the transmitter to the antenna; (B) The power radiated from the front of a directional antenna; (C) The power produced during the positive half of the RF cycle; (D) The power used to drive a linear amplifier.

3AI3-2.2 What is meant by the term reflected power? (A) The power radiated from the back of a directional antenna; (B) The power returned to the transmitter from the antenna; (C) The power produced during the negative half of the RF cycle; (D) Power reflected to the transmitter site by buildings and trees.

3AI3-3.1 What happens to the power loss in an unbalanced feed line as the standing wave ratio increases? (A) It is unpredictable; (B) It becomes nonexistent; (C) It decreases; (D) It increases.

3AI3-3.2 What type of feed line is best suited to operating at a high standing wave ratio? (A) Coaxial cable; (B) Flat ribbon "twin lead"; (C) Parallel open-wire line; (D) Twisted pair.

3AI3-3.3 What happens to RF energy not delivered to the antenna by a lossy coaxial cable? (A) It is radiated by the feed line; (B) It is returned to the transmitter's chassis ground; (C) Some of it is dissipated as heat in the conductors and dielectric; (D) It is canceled because of the voltage ratio of forward power to reflected power in the feed line.

3AI4-1.1 What is a balanced line? (A) Feed line with one conductor connected to ground; (B) Feed line with both conductors connected to ground to balance out harmonics; (C) Feed line with the outer conductor connected to ground at even intervals; (D) Feed line with neither conductor connected to ground.

3AI4-1.2 What is an unbalanced line? (A) Feed line with neither conductor connected to ground; (B) Feed line with both conductors connected to ground to suppress harmonics; (C) Feed line with one conductor connected to ground; (D) Feed line with the outer conductor connected to ground at uneven intervals.

3AI4-2.1 What is a balanced antenna? (A) A symmetrical antenna with one side of the feed point connected to ground; (B) An antenna (or a driven element in an array) that is symmetrical about the feed point; (C) A symmetrical antenna with both sides of the feed point connected to ground, to balance out harmonics; (D) An antenna designed to be mounted in the center.

3AI4-2.2 What is an unbalanced antenna? (A) An antenna (or a driven element in an array) that is not symmetrical about the feed point; (B) A symmetrical antenna, having neither half connected to ground; (C) An antenna (or a driven element in an array) that is symmetrical about the feed point; (D) A symmetrical antenna with both halves coupled to ground at uneven intervals.

3AI4-3.1 What device can be installed on a balanced antenna so that it can be fed through a coaxial cable? (A) A balun; (B) A loading coil; (C) A triaxial transformer; (D) A wavetrap.

3AI4-3.2 What is a balun? (A) A device that can be used to convert an antenna designed to be fed at the center so that it may be fed at one end; (B) A device that may be installed on a balanced antenna so that it may be fed with unbalanced feed line; (C) A device that can be installed on an antenna to produce horizontally polarized or vertically polarized waves; (D) A device used to allow an antenna to operate on more than one band.

3AI5-1.1 List the following types of feed line in order of increasing attenuation per 100 feet of line (list the line with the lowest attenuation first): RG-8, RG-58, RG-174 and open-wire line. (A) RG-174, RG-58, RG-8, open-wire line; (B) RG-8, open-wire line, RG-58, RG-174; (C) Open-wire line, RG-8, RG-58, RG-174; (D) Open-wire line, RG-174, RG-58, RG-8.

3AI5-1.2 You have installed a tower 150 feet from your radio shack, and have a 6-meter Yagi antenna on top. Which of the following feed lines should you choose to feed this antenna: RG-8, RG-58, RG-59 or RG-174? (A) RG-8; (B) RG-58; (C) RG-59; (D) RG-174.

3AI5-2.1 You have a 200-foot coil of RG-58 coaxial cable attached to your antenna, but the antenna is only 50 feet from your radio. To minimize feed-line loss, what should you do with the excess cable? (A) Cut off the excess cable to an even number of wavelengths long; (B) Cut off the excess cable to an odd number of wavelengths long; (C) Cut off the excess cable; (D) Roll the excess cable into a coil a tenth of a wavelength in diameter.

3AI5-2.2 How does feed line length affect signal loss? (A) The length has no effect on signal loss; (B) As length increases, signal loss increases; (C) As length decreases, signal loss increases; (D) The length is inversely proportional to signal loss.

3AI5-3.1 What is the general relationship between frequencies passing through a feed line and the losses in the feed line? (A) Loss is independent of frequency; (B) Loss increases with increasing frequency; (C) Loss decreases with increasing frequency; (D) There is no predictable relationship.

3AI5-3.2 As the operating frequency decreases, what happens to conductor losses in a feed line? (A) The losses decrease; (B) The losses increase; (C) The losses remain the same; (D) The losses become infinite.

3AI5-3.3 As the operating frequency increases, what happens to conductor losses in a feed line? (A) The losses decrease; (B) The losses increase; (C) The losses remain the same; (D) The losses decrease to zero.

3AI6-1.1 You are using open-wire feed line in your Amateur station. Why should you ensure that no one can come in contact with the feed line while you are transmitting? (A) Because contact with the feed line while transmitting will cause a short circuit, probably damaging your transmitter; (B) Because the wire is so small they may break it; (C) Because contact with the feed line while transmitting will cause parasitic radiation; (D) Because high RF voltages can be present on open-wire feed line.

3AI6-2.1 How can you minimize exposure to radio frequency energy from your transmitting antennas? (A) Use vertical polarization; (B) Use horizontal polarization; (C) Mount the antennas where no one can come near them; (D) Mount the antenna close to the ground.

Answers

2A-1.1	(A)	2A-15.3	(A)	2A-24.1	(B)	2A-40.3	(D)	2B-4-1.1	(B)
2A-1.2	(D)	2A-15.4	(B)	2A-25.1	(C)	**2B-1-1.1**	**(A)**	2B-4-2.1	(B)
2A-1.3	(D)	2A-15.5	(D)	2A-26.1	(D)	2B-1-1.2	(C)	2B-5-1.1	(C)
2A-1.4	(B)	2A-16.1	(A)	2A-27.1	(C)	2B-1-1.2	(C)	2B-5-1.2	(D)
2A-2.1	(C)	2A-17.1	(A)	2A-27.2	(B)	2B-1-2.1	(D)	2B-5-2.1	(A)
2A-2.2	(A)	2A-17.2	(A)	2A-27.3	(B)	2B-2-1.1	(A)	2B-5-2.2	(B)
2A-3.1	(A)	2A-17.3	(A)	2A-27.4	(A)	2B-2-1.2	(B)	2B-6-1.1	(C)
2A-3.2	(D)	2A-17.4	(A)	2A-27.5	(B)	2B-2-2.1	(C)	2B-6-2.1	(D)
2A-4.1	(B)	2A-17.5	(D)	2A-27.6	(C)	2B-2-3.1	(C)	2B-6-3.1	(A)
2A-4.2	(D)	2A-17.6	(D)	2A-27.7	(B)	2B-2-3.2	(D)	2B-6-4.1	(B)
2A-5.1	(C)	2A-17.7	(D)	2A-28.1	(D)	2B-2-3.3...	(A)	2B-6-5.1	(C)
2A-5.2	(B)	2A-17.8	(C)	2A-28.2	(C)	2B-2-3.4	(B)	2B-6-5.2	(D)
2A-6.1	(B)	2A-17.9	(C)	2A-29.1	(B)	2B-2-3.5	(C)	**2C-1.1**	**(A)**
2A-6.2	(C)	2A-17.10	(D)	2A-29.2	(D)	2B-2-4.1	(D)	2C-1.2	(B)
2A-7.1	(D)	2A-17.11	(D)	2A-30.1	(A)	2B-2-4.2	(A)	2C-2.1	(D)
2A-8.1	(A)	2A-17.12	(D)	2A-30.2	(B)	2B-2-4.3	(A)	2C-2.2	(B)
2A-8.2	(D)	2A-17.13	(C)	2A-30.3	(D)	2B-2-5.1	(D)	2C-2.3	(B)
2A-9.1	(D)	2A-18.1	(D)	2A-31.3	(D)	2B-2-5.2	(B)	2C-2.4	(A)
2A-9.3	(B)	2A-18.2	(C)	2A-32.1	(A)	2B-2-5.3	(A)	2C-3.1	(A)
2A-10.2	(C)	2A-18.3	(C)	2A-32.2	(D)	2B-2-6.1	(B)	2C-3.2	(B)
2A-10.3	(A)	2A018.4	(C)	2A-33.1	(A)	2B-2-6.2	(C)	2C-3.3	(D)
2A-10.4	(C)	2A-18.5	(C)	2A-34.1	(A)	2B-2-6.3	(D)	2C-3.4	(A)
2A-10.5	(B)	2A-19.1	(C)	2A-34.2	(B)	2B-2-6.4	(A)	2C-3.5	(C)
2A-10.6	(C)	2A-19.2	(B)	2A-34.3	(D)	2B-2-6.5	(B)	2C-3.6	(D)
2A-10.7	(A)	2A-19.3	(C)	2A-35.1	(A)	2B-3-1.1	(C)	2C-4.1	(C)
2A-10.8	(B)	2A-19.4	(D)	2A-36.1	(C)	2B-3-1.2	(D)	2C-4.2	(D)
2A-10.9	(C)	2A-19.5	(B)	2A-36.2	(D)	2B-3-2.1	(A)	2C-5.1	(A)
2A-10.10	(D)	2A-20.1	(C)	2A-37.1	(A)	2B-3-2.2	(C)	2C-5.2	(B)
2A-11.1	(A	2A-20.2	(C)	2A-37.2	(C)	2B-3-2.3	(A)	2C-6.1	(C)
2A-11.2	(B)	2A-20.3	(D)	2A-38.1	(C)	2B-3-2.4	(D)	2C-6.2	(C)
2A-12.1	(C)	2A-21.1	(C)	2A-38.2	(D)	2B-3-2.5	(A)	**2D-1.1**	**(B)**
2A-12.2	(A)	2A-21.2	(A)	2A-38.3	(A)	2B-3-2.6	(C)	2D-1.2	(A)
2A-12.3	(D)	2A-21.3	(D)	2A-39.1	(C)	2B-3-2.7	(A)	2D-2.1	(D)
2A-13.1	(A)	2A-21.4	(B)	2A-39.2	(B)	2B-3-2.8	(D)	2D-2.2	(C)
2A-14.1	(B)	2A-22.1	(C)	2A-39.3	(B)	2B-3-2.9	(B)	2D-2.3	(D)
2A-15.1	(C)	2A-22.2	(A)	2A-40.1	(C)	2B-3-2.10	(A)	2D-2.4	(B)
2A-15.2	(D)	2A-23.1	(B)	2A-40.2	(D)	2B-3-2.11	(C)	2D-3.1	(A)

2D-3.2 (C)	2D-8-3.2 (B)	2E-12-3.3 (A)	2G-1-2.4 (D)	2I-1.3 (C)
2D-3.3 (B)	**2E-1-1.1 (C)**	2E-12-4.1 (B)	2G-1-2.5 (D)	2I-1.4 (C)
2D-3.4 (C)	2E-1-2.1 (B)	2E-12-4.2 (A)	2G-2.1 (B)	2I-1.5 (D)
2D-4.1 (B)	2E-1-2.2 (D)	2E-12-4.3 (B)	2G-2.2 (C)	2I-2.1 (D)
2D-4.2 (A)	2E-1-3.1 (B)	2E-12-5.1 (C)	2G-2.3 (C)	2I-2.2 (D)
2D-4.3 (C)	2E-1-3.2 (D)	2E-12-5.2 (B)	2G-3.1 (D)	2I-2.3 (B)
2D-4.4 (A)	2E-1-4.1 (B)	23-13.1 (C)	2G-3.2 (D)	2I-2.4 (B)
2D-4.5 (B)	2E-1-5.1 (C)	2E-13.1 (D)	2G-4.1 (A)	2I-2.5 (A)
2D-4.6 (B)	2E-1-5.2 (C)	**2F-1.1 (B)**	2G-4.2 (C)	2I-3.1 (B)
2D-5.1 (D)	2E-1-6.1 (B)	2F-1.2 (C)	2G-5.1 (A)	2I-3.2 (C)
2D-5.2 (A)	2E-1-7.1 (B)	2F-1.3 (C)	2G-5.2 (A)	2I-4-1.1 (D)
2D-6.1 (D)	2E-2-1.1 (D)	2F-2.1 (A)	2G-5.3 (C)	2I-4-1.2 (B)
2D-6.2 (D)	2E-2-2.1 (C)	2F-2.2 (A)	2H-1-1.1 (B)	2I-4-1.2 (C)
2D-6.3 (A)	2E-3-1.1 (A)	2F-2.3 (B)	2G-1-1.2 (C)	2I-4-2.1 (D)
2D-6.4 (D)	2E-3-1.2 (D)	2F-2.4 (D)	2H-1-2.1 (A)	2I-4-2.2 (A)
2D-6.5 (A)	2E-3-1.3 (C)	2F-2.5 (A)	2G-1-2.2 (A)	2I-4-2.3 (B)
2D-7-1.1 (C)	2E-3-2.1 (A)	2F-3.1 (C)	2H-1-3.1 (A)	2I-4-2.4 (A)
2D-7-1.2 (D)	2E-4.1 (C)	2F-4.1 (A)	2G-1-4.1 (D)	2I-5.1 (A)
2D-7-2.1 (B)	2E-5.1 (A)	2F-4.2 (B)	2G-2.1 (B)	2I-5.2 (B)
2D-7-2.2 (C)	2E-6-1.1 (D)	2F-5.1 (D)	**2H-2.2 (D)**	2I-5.3 (C)
2D-7-2.3 (D)	2E-6-1.2 (A)	2F-5.2 (B)	2H-3.1 (C)	2I-6.1 (D)
2D-7-2.4 (C)	2E-6-2.1 (D)	2F-5.3 (A)	2H-3.2 (B)	2I-6.2 (B)
2D-7-3.1 (A)	2E-7.1 (C)	2F-5.4 (D)	2H-4.1 (D)	2I-6.3 (B)
2D-7-3.2 (A)	2E-7.2 (C)	2G-6.1 (D)	2H-4.2 (B)	2I-6.4 (B)
2D-7-3.3 (B)	2E-7.3 (B)	2F-7.1 (C)	2H-5.1 (A)	2I-6.5 (C)
2D-7-3.4 (C)	2E-7.4 (C)	2F-7.2 (A)	2H-5.2 (C)	2I-7.1 (B)
2D-8-1.1 (C)	2E-8.1 (D)	2F-7.3 (C)	2H-6.1 (A)	2I-7.2 (C)
2D-8-1.2 (B)	2E-8.2 (A)	2F-7.4 (B)	2H-6.2 (C)	2I-7.3 (D)
2D-8-1.3 (C)	2E-9-1.1 (C)	2F-8.1 (A)	2H-6.3 (A)	2I-7.4 (A)
2D-8-1.4 (B)	2E-9-1.2 (C)	**2G-1-1.2 (B)**	2H-7.1 (C)	2I-7.5 (B)
2D-8-2.1 (A)	2E-9-2.1 (B)	2G-1-1.2 (C)	2H-7.2 (D)	2I-8.1 (C)
2D-8-2.2 (A)	2E-10.1 (C)	2G-1-1.3 (D)	2H-7.3 (A)	2I-8.2 (C)
2D-8-2.3 (A)	2E-11.1 (D)	2G-1-1.4 (A)	2H-7.4 (B)	2I-9.1 (D)
2D-8-2.4 (C)	2E-12-1.1 (B)	2G-1-1.5 (D)	2H-7.5 (B)	2I-9.2 (A)
2D-8-2.5 (D)	2E-12-2.1 (A)	2G-1-2.1 (B)	2H-7.6 (B)	2I-9.3 (A)
2D-8-2.6 (B)	2E-12-3.1 (D)	2G-1-2.2 (A)	**2I-1.1 (A)**	2I-10-1.1 (C)
2D-8-3.1 (A)	2E-12-3.2 (A)	2G-1-2.3 (B)	2I-1.2 (D)	2I-11-1.1 (D)

3AA-1.1 (A)	3AA-12.4 (D)	3AB-6-3.2 (C)	3AD-5-1.3 (B)	3AE-3-2.1 (C)
3AA-1.2 (B)	3AA-12.5 (C)	**3AC-1-1.1 (A)**	3AD-5-1.4 (A)	3AE-3-2.2 (C)
3AA-2.2 (C)	3AA-13.1 (B)	3AC-1-1.2 (D)	3AD-5-2.1 (B)	3AE-3-2.3 (B)
3AA-2.3 (B)	3AA-13.2 (D)	3AC-1-1.3 (C)	3AD-5-2.2 (C)	3AE-3-2.4 (C)
3AA-2.4 (A)	3AA-13.3 (D)	3AC-1-2.1 (A)	3AD-6.1 (A)	3AE-3-3.1 (B)
3AA-2.5 (B)	3AA-13.4 (C)	3AC-1-2.2 (B)	3AD-6.2 (D)	3AE-3-3.2 (C)
3AA-3.1 (A)	3AA-14.1 (D)	3AC-1-3.1 (B)	3AD-6.3 (A)	3AE-3-4.1 (A)
3AA-3.2 (A)	3AA-14.2 (C)	3AC-1-4.1 (D)	3AD-7.1 (C)	3AE-3-4.2 (B)
3AA-3.3 (A)	3AA-14.3 (D)	3AC-1-4.2 (B)	3AD-7.2 (B)	3AE-4-1.1 (A)
3AA-4.1 (B)	3AA-15.1 (A)	3AC-1-4.3 (C)	3AD-8-1.1 (D)	3AE-4-2.1 (A)
3AA-4.2 (A)	3AA-15.2 (C)	3AC-2.1 (D)	3AD-8-1.2 (D)	3AE-4-2.2 (B)
3AA-4.3 (A)	3AA-15.3 (D)	3AC-2.2 (B)	3AD-8-2.1 (A)	3AE-4-2.3 (A)
3AA-5.1 (D)	3AA-15.4 (B)	3AC-2.3 (A)	3AD-8-2.2 (C)	3AE-4-2.4 (B)
3AA-5.2 (C)	3AA-16.1 (B)	3AC-2.4 (B)	3AD-9.1 (D)	3AE-4-3.1 (C)
3AA-6-1.1 (C)	3AA-16.2 (D)	3AC-3.1 (D)	3AD-9.2 (B)	3AE-4-3.2 (B)
3AA-6-1.2 (D)	3AA-16.3 (C)	3AC-3.2 (C)	3AD-9.3 (C)	3AE-4-4.1 (A)
3AA-6-2.1 (C)	3AA-17.1 (A)	3AC-3.3 (A)	3AD-9.4 (B)	3AE-4-4.2 (A)
3AA-6-3.1 (D)	**3AB-1.1 (A)**	3AC-3.4 (B)	3AD-9.5 (A)	**3AF-1-1.1 (B)**
3AA-6-4.1 (B)	3AB-1.2 (C)	3AC-4.1 (D)	3AD-9.6 (A)	3AF-1-2.1 (D)
3AA-7-1.1 (C)	3AB-1.3 (D)	3AC-4.2 (C)	3AD-10.1 (C)	3AF-1-2.2 (C)
3AA-7-1.2 (B)	3AB-2-1.1 (B)	3AC-4.3 (A)	3AD-10.2 (A)	3AF-1-3.1 (A)
3AA-7-1.3 (D)	3AB-2-1.2 (C)	3AC-5.1 (C)	3AD-11-1.1 (B)	3AF-1-3.2 (B)
3AA-7-2.1 (C)	3AB-2-1.3 (A)	3AC-5.2 (C)	3AD-11-1.2 (A)	3AF-1-3.3 (B)
3AA-7-2.2 (C)	3AB-2-1.4 (D)	3AC-6.1 (A)	3AD-11-2.1 (D)	3AF-1-3.4 (C)
3AA-7-3.1 (A)	3AB-2-1.5 (B)	3AC-6.2 (B)	3AD-11-2.2 (B)	3AF-1-4.1 (A)
3AA-7-3.2 (D)	3AB-2-1.6 (B)	3AC-7.1 (C)	3AD-11-2.3 (B)	3AF-1-4.2 (C)
3AA-7-3.3 (D)	3AB-2-1.7 (D)	3AC-7.2 (A)	3AD-11-2.4 (D)	3AF-1-5.1 (B)
3AA-8-1.1 (B)	3AB-2-2.1 (C)	3AC-7.3 (D)	3AD-11-2.5 (B)	3AF-1-5.2 (C)
3AA-8-2.1 (B)	3AB-2-2.2 (C)	3AC-7.4 (A)	3AD-11-3.1 (C)	3AF-2-1.1 (D)
3AA-8-3.1 (C)	3AB-2-3.1 (D)	3AC-7.5 (B)	**3AE-1-1.1 (D)**	3AF-2-1.2 (A)
3AA-9-1.1 (A)	3AB-2-3.2 (B)	3AC-7.6 (D)	3AE-1-2.1 (A)	3AF-2-1.3 (D)
3AA-9-2.1 (A)	3AB-2-3.3 (A)	**3AD-1-1.1 (C)**	3AE-1-2.2 (D)	3AF-2-1.4 (C)
3AA-10.1 (A)	3AB-2-3.4 (C)	3AD-1-1.2 (D)	3AE-1-3.1 (B)	3AF-2-2.1 (D)
3AA-10.2 (C)	3AB-2-4.1 (D)	3AD-1-1.3 (B)	3AE-1-3.2 (D)	3AF-2-2.2 (C)
3AA-10.3 (D)	3AB-3.1 (A)	3AD-1-1.4 (B)	3AE-1-4.1 (B)	3AF-2-3.1 (D)
3AA-10.4 (B)	3AB-3.2 (B)	3AD-1-2.1 (A)	3AE-1-4.2 (C)	3AF-2-3.2 (B)
3AA-11-1.1 (A)	3AB-3.3 (C)	3AD-1-2.2 (A)	3AE-2.1 (D)	3AF-2-3.3 (A)
3AA-11-1.2 (B)	3AB-4.1 (A)	3AD-1-2.3 (A)	3AE-2.2 (A)	3AF-2-3.4 (B)
3AA-11-1.3 (A)	3AB-4.2 (D)	3AD-1-3.1 (C)	3AE-2.3 (C)	3AF-2-4.1 (A)
3AA-11-2.1 (D)	3AB-5-1.1 (C)	3AD-2-1.1 (B)	3AE-2.4 (D)	3AF-2-4.2 (B)
3AA-11-2.2 (A)	3AB-5-1.2 (B)	3AD-2-2.1 (C)	3AE-2.5 (B)	3AF-2-4.3 (C)
3AA-11-2.3 (C)	3AB-5-2.1 (D)	3AD-3-1.1 (A)	3AE-2.6 (D)	3AF-3-1.1 (D)
3AA-11-2.4 (A)	3AB-6-1.1 (A)	3AD-3-2.1 (D)	3AE-2.7 (D)	3AF-3-1.2 (A)
3AA-12.1 (A)	3AB-6-1.2 (B)	3AD-4.1 (D)	3AE-2.8 (A)	3AF-3-1.3 (C)
3AA-12.2 (C)	3AB-6-2.1 (D)	3AD-5-1.1 (A)	3AE-2.9 (A)	3AF-3-1.4 (C)
3AA-12.3 (B)	3AB-6-3.1 (B)	3AD-5-1.2 (C)	3AE-3-1.1 (C)	3AF-3-2.1 (B)

3AF-3-2.2 (D)	3AG-4-1.2 (D)	3AH-2-6.2 (B)	3AI-1-1.5 (C)	3AI-3-2.2 (B)
3AF-3-2.3 (A)	3AG-4-1.3 (B)	3AH-2-7.1 (D)	3AI-1-1.6 (B)	3AI-3-3.1 (D)
3AF-3-2.4 (B)	3AG-4-1.4 (B)	3AH-2-7.2 (B)	3AI-1-1.7 (A)	3AI-3-3.2 (C)
3AF-3-3.1 (A)	3AG-4-1.5 (D)	3AH-2-8.1 (C)	3AI-1-2.1 (B)	3AI-3-3.3 (C)
3AF-3-3.2 (B)	3AG-4-2.1 (D)	3AH-2-8.2 (D)	3AI-1-2.2 (B)	3AI-4-1.1 (D)
3AF-3-3.3 (D)	3AG-4-2.2 (C)	3AH-3.1 (A)	3AI-1-2.3 (D)	3AI-4-1.2 (C)
3AF-3-4.1 (D)	**3AH-1.1 (A)**	3AH-3.2 (B)	3AI-1-2.4 (C)	3AI-4-2.1 (B)
3AF-3-4.2 (A)	3AH-2-1.1 (A)	3AH-4.1 (C)	3AI-1-3.1 (A)	3AI-4-2.2 (A)
3AG-1-1.1 (A)	3AH-2-1.2 (B)	3AH-5.1 (D)	3AI-2-1.1 (B)	3AI-4-3.1 (A)
3AG-1-1.2 (D)	3AH-2-2.1 (C)	3AH-5.2 (C)	3AI-2-1.2 (C)	3AI-4-3.2 (B)
3AG-1-2.1 (C)	3AH-2-2.2 (A)	3AH-6.1 (D)	3AI-2-1.3 (C)	3AI-5-1.1 (C)
3AG-1-2.2 (B)	3AH-2-3.1 (B)	3AH-6-1.2 (C)	3AI-2-2.1 (D)	3AI-5-1.2 (A)
3AG-2-1.1 (B)	3AH-2-3.2 (A)	3AH-7-1.1 (D)	3AI-2-2.2 (D)	3AI-5-2.1 (C)
3AG-2-2.1 (A)	3AH-2-4.1 (B)	3AH-7-2.1 (B)	3AI-2-2.3 (C)	3AI-5-2.2 (B)
3AG-2-2.2 (B)	3AH-2-4.2 (D)	3AH-7-2.2 (C)	3AI-2-2.4 (D)	3AI-5-3.1 (B)
3AG-3-1.1 (A)	3AH-2-5.1 (A)	**3AI-1-1.1 (A)**	3AI-2-2.5 (D)	3AI-5-3.2 (A)
3AG-3-1.2 (D)	3AH-2-5.2 (D)	3AI-1-1.2 (D)	3AI-3-1.1 (D)	3AI-5-3.3 (B)
3AG-3-2.1 (A)	3AH-2-5.3 (C)	3AI-1-1.3 (C)	3AI-3-1.2 (A)	3AI-6-1.1 (D)
3AG-4-1.1 (C)	3AH-2-6.1 (A)	3AI-1-1.4 (A)	3AI-3-2.1 (A)	3AI-6-2.1 (C)

Don't Miss An Issue!

NARA has an ambitious program to introduce people to Amateur Radio - The King Of Hobbies.

Thinking about becoming a ham? Even if you are not yet licensed, you should be a member of this fast growing, prestigious organization.

Your financial support will allow NARA to produce The Amateur Radio Communicator each month. There are no advertisements in the journal to support costs. However, not accepting advertising allows us incredible freedom to tell you the truth.

With no advertising revenue, our only support comes from your memberships and donations. You alone will determine the future of our organization and how effective we are in promoting our hobby.

Memberships will pay for a Washington presence. If we are to have a positive influence on The Federal Communications Commission,

NARA must be represented by a communications attorney. As in most other things, you get what you pay for and experienced counsel is not inexpensive.

The educational programs of The National Amateur Radio Association must be expanded. Your memberships will help us to exhibit at educational conferences such as those held by The National Science Teachers Association.

Few people realize the awesome power for change that they hold in their fingertips. NARA intends to show you how to unleash this power and use it as a positive force for the betterment of our fraternity.

Your membership will help us accomplish all these things!

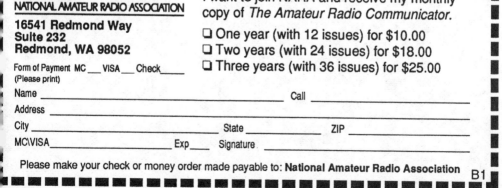

If it is more convenient and you have a credit card, simply call the National Amateur Radio Association and join right over the telephone. The toll-free number is 1-800-GOT-2-HAM. Depending on the time, you'll either reach a friendly operator or an impersonal machine. You can give either one your name, address, credit card type and number and the expiration date. In a couple of weeks, you'll receive your first issue of *The Amateur Radio Communicator*.

Even if you are not yet ready to part with the $10.00 membership fee, you can wait until inflation and the high cost of success result in an increase. We still want to hear from you. Call the NARA number and announce that you would like to be an Associate Member. We'll send you a FREE sample copy of *The Amateur Radio Communicator* and occasional mailings on items of interest to Amateurs. Don't forget to give us your mailing address.

Most important, when you have read this book and are ready to take your test, call and let us know. We'll send you a listing of Helping Hams so you can select the one who lives nearest you. He or she may not be able to assist you directly, but they will know who is conducting the testing sessions in your area and when and where they are held. If you call after normal business hours, simply leave your name and address and tell the "silicon secretary" that you want the list of Helping Hams. It will be forwarded to you promptly.

Careful readers will note that this is the second printing of The Ham Radio Handbook. The response in the marketplace has been awesome. The first printing sold out in about two months and the phone at NARA has not quit ringing with calls from new members.

Thanks for buying the book, good luck to you and welcome to Amateur Radio- The King of Hobbies.

Don Stoner, W6TNS

73, DE Don Stoner, W6TNS

Index

AC sine wave, 124
Advanced Class hams, 26
Allen, Dr. Van, 89
Alternating current, 123
AM, 6, 20-21, 89
Amateur license, 24
Amateur radio, 1-2, 27, 31, 42
American Radio
  Relay League, 11, 18, 51
Amateur Radio Service, 1-2, 23, 41
Amateur Satellite Corp.
  (AMSTAT), 12, 22
Amateur Television
  Transmissions (ATV), 31
Ambassadors, 4
Antenna
      beam, 180
      directivity, 178
      polarization, 86
      radiation, 185
      switch, 155, 156
      tuner, 156
Amplification, 19
Amplitude, 129
AR, 65
Armstrong, Major Edwin, 20
Atom, 117
Audion, 19
Autopatch, 70

Back e.m.f., 126
Band propagation, 65
Bands, 29-33, 65
Bandwidth emission, 38, 166
Batteries, 145
Baud rate, 68
Beacon station, 34, 40

Block diagram, 156
Broadcasting, 35
Business communications, 36

Call letters, 19, 25
Capacitor, 143
Circuits, 156
Chassis ground, 146
Citizen's band, 6
Class licenses, 7-10, 24, 26
Communications
      business, 36
      emergency, 34, 37
Computer communication
  emissions, 48
Computers, 27
Conductor, 119
Continuous wave (CW), 33
Control operator, 34-35
Control point, 34
CQ, 64
Critical frequency, 88
Crystal controlled transmitter, 157

DE, 64
Deceptive signals, 38
DeForest, Dr. Lee, 19
Dielectric, 126
Digipeater, 68
Digital procedures, 68
Digital radio transmissions, 38
DN, 65
Double pole, double throw, 145
Dummy antenna,
  dummy load, 65, 106

D-layer, 89
DX, 2, 91

E-layer, 85
Effective voltage, 124
Electric charge, 118
Electric current, 119
Electrical energy, 123
Electrical shock, 98-99
Electromagnetic
    waves, 15-16, 20, 120
Electronic ambassadors, 4
Electronic mirror, 85
Electronics, 118
Electrostatic, 143
Emergency
    communications, 34, 37, 71
Emission, 26, 38
Emission bandwidth, 38
Emission designators, 167

F-layer, 85
Farad, 127
FCC, 23-24, 37, 40, 70
Fessenden, Aubrey, 17
Filters, 104, 158-159
Fleming, Sir Ambrose, 19
FM, 5, 20, 38
Frequency, 29-33, 70, 129
Frequency discrimination, 157

General Class hams, 26
Generators, 105

Godly, Paul F., 19
Griswold, Butch, 20

Ham radio, 1, 11
Harmonic radiation, 104
Harmonics, 169
Health and welfare traffic, 71
Hertz, Heinrich, 15, 124, 130
High Frequency (HF), 33, 69, 83

Inductive reactance, 127
Inductors, 126, 140
Integrated circuit, 146
Interference, 40, 63-64, 111
Interlock, 98
International Telecommunications
    Union (ITV), 33, 40
Ionization, 83, 88
Ionosphere, 84-89

Key clicks, 168
KN, 65

LeMay, Curtis, 20
License
        amateur, 24, 63
        novice, 7
        operator, 24
        station, 24
        technician, 7-8, 24-26, 82
Lid, 69

Lightning, 99
Line-of-sight band, 65, 83
Lines of force, 141

Marconi, Guglielmo, 16
Maxim, Hiram Percy, 6, 18
Maximum usable frequency, 88
MAYDAY, 53, 38, 71
megaHertz, 28, 70
Mercado, Dr. John, 22
Meter bands, 31
Meters, 66
Mobile operation, 3
Modem, 157
Modulation, 165
Morse, 7, 10, 16

National Amateur
  Radio Association, 11, 21

Obscene language, 39
Official Notice of Violation, 40
Ohm's Law, 120
OM, 66
Open circuit, 123
Operator license, 24
OSCAR, 21

Pacitive reactance, 127
Packet radio, 22
Parallel resonant, 128
Parasitics, 170
Peak envelope power, 31, 39

Phonetic alphabet, 67
Potentiometer, 141
Powell, Cecil, 6
Power output, 39
Procedural signals, 65

Q signals, 66
QRM, 64
QRS, 64
QSLR's, 4

R-S-T reporting system, 65
RACES, 71
Radio control, 30
Radio signals, 82
Radio teletype, 68
Radiotelephone
  transmission, 17
Rag chewing, 2
Reactance, 124-127
Receiver, 156
Receiver overload, 104
Reciprocal license
  agreements, 38
Relative power, 103
Repeaters, 5, 40, 69
Resistance, 82, 139
Resonant frequency, 128

Safety belt, 97
Scatter, 90
Schematic diagram, 139, 156
Schematic symbol, 139
Selectivity, 128

Series resonant, 128
Short circuit, 123
Simplex frequency, 69
Single pole, single throw, 144
Single sideband (SSB), 20-21, 89
SK, 65
Skip transmissions, 85
Skip zone, 85
Skywave communications, 84
Splatter, 170
Sporadic-E, 85, 90
Station
       identification, 25
       license, 24
       location, 38
Sunspots, 86-87
Super Morse, 10, 13
Superheterodyne receiver, 20
Switches, 143-144
SWR meter, 102

UHF, 9, 82

Variable frequency oscillator, 157
VHF, 9, 20, 29, 82, 91
Volunteer Examiner (VE), 7-8

Watts, 123
Wavelength, 129
Wireless Act of 1912, 18

YL's, 5

Tactical communications, 71
Tech Plus operators, 9, 26, 33, 34, 40
Telecommand, 48
Telegraphy, 165
Telephony, 165
Teletype, 27
Terminal Node Controller, 22, 68
Third party, 36, 52
Time-out device, 70
Traffic, 71
Transceiver, 156
Transistor, 146
Transmission line, 81, 182
Transmitter, 156
Transmitting power, 47, 82
TRF receivers, 20
Tropospheric propagation, 91